Using Speech Recognition

Judith A. Markowitz

For book and bookstore information

http://www.prenhall.com

Prentice Hall PTR
Upper Saddle River, New Jersey 07458

Library of Congress Cataloging-in-Publication Data

Markowitz, Judith A.
    Using speech recognition / Judith A. Markowitz.
      p.   cm.
    Includes bibliographical references and index.
    ISBN 0-13-186321-5
    1. Speech processing systems. 2. Automatic speech recognition.
  I. Title.
    TK7895.S65M37   1996
    006.4'54—dc20   95-33724
                                                                   CIP

Editorial/production supervision: *Progressive Publishing Alternatives*
Cover design director: *Jerry Votta*
Cover design: *Design Source*
Manufacturing manager: *Alexis Heydt*
Acquisitions editor: *Karen Gettman*

©1996 by Prentice Hall PTR
Prentice-Hall, Inc.
A Simon & Schuster Company
Upper Saddle River, New Jersey 07458

The publisher offers discounts on this book when offered in bulk quantities.
For more information contact.

      Corporate Sales Department
      Prentice Hall PTR
      One Lake Street
      Upper Saddle River, NJ 07458
      Phone: 800-382-3419 Fax: 201-236-7141
      E-mail: corpsales@prenhall.com

Printed in the United States of America
10 9 8 7 6 5 4 3 2 1

ISBN 0-13-186321-5

Prentice-Hall International (UK) Limited, *London*
Prentice-Hall of Australia Pty. Limited, *Sydney*
Prentice-Hall Canada Inc., *Toronto*
Prentice-Hall Hispanoamericana, S.A., *Mexico*
Prentice-Hall of India Private Limited, *New Delhi*
Prentice-Hall of Japan, Inc., *Tokyo*
Simon & Schuster Asia Pte. Ltd., *Singapore*
Editors Prentice-Hall do Brasil, Ltda., *Rio de Janeiro*

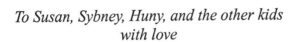

*To Susan, Sybney, Huny, and the other kids
with love*

Contents

Chapter 3 — Representing the Vocabulary   54

Chapter 10—What Lies Ahead?   251

List of Figures

List of Trademark Names

The following is a list of the known trademarks mentioned in this book. Omission of a trademark from the list is inadvertent and has not been done with any intension to infringe.

ActionLine is a trademark of National Westminster Bank

Alice's Interactive Wonderland is a trademark of Walt Disney Company

Alpha is a trademark of Digital Equipment Corporation

AT is a trademark of IBM

AudioNav is a trademark of Amerigon

AutoCAD is a trademark of Autodesk, Inc.

Automated Alternate Billing Services is a trademark of Bell-Northern Research Ltd.

Bug Voice Interface is a trademark of Command Corp. Inc.

Busytown is a trademark of Richard Soarry

Busytown Talker is a trademark of Tomy

ChartWell Patient Tracking System is a trademark of KorTeam International, Inc.

Compton's Interactive Encyclopedia is a trademark of Compton's NewMedia

Conversant is a trademark of AT&T

Deciper is a trademark of SRI International

Dragon Systems is a trademark of Dragon Systems, Inc.

DragonDictate is a trademark of Dragon Systems, Inc.

DragonScribe is a trademark of Dragon Systems, Inc.

Enhancemate is a trademark of Hill-Rom, Inc.

Excel is a trademark of Microsoft Corporation

Flexword is a trademark of AT&T

GoodListener is a trademark of Voice Control Systems, Inc.

Gorzak is a trademark of TYCO

Home Assisted Nursing Care (HANC) is a trademark of HealthTech Services Corporation

HARK is a trademark of Bolt Beranek and Newman, Inc.

IBM is a trademark of International Business Machines (IBM)

IBM Continuous Speech System is a trademark of IBM

IBM Personal Dictation System is a trademark of IBM

IN³ Voice Command is a trademark of Command Corp. Inc.

IN CUBE Pro is a trademark of Command Corp. Inc.

InfoWorks is a trademark of AT&T

InterActive Communicator is a trademark of InterActive Inc.

IntroVoice is a trademark of The Voice Connection Inc.

Keystone is a trademark of ApTech Limited

LawTalk is a trademark of Kolvox Communications Inc.

Lexis is a trademark of Mead Data Central

Listen for Windows is a trademark of Verbex Voice Systems

Lotus 123 is a trademark of Lotus Development Corporation

Macintosh is a trademark of Apple Computer, Inc.

META 3250 is a trademark of International Meta Systems, Inc.

Microsoft Word is a trademark of Microsoft Corporation

Mobile Assistant is a trademark of Computer Products and Services, Inc.

Mwave is a trademark of IBM

OLE is a trademark of Microsoft Corporation

Orbitor is a trademark of Bell-Northern Research Ltd.

PE100 is a trademark of Speech Systems, Inc.

Pentium is a trademark of Intel Corporation

PowerPC is a joint trademark of Apple Computer, IBM, and Motorola

Robby Rabbit Rhyme Reason-n-Remember is a trademark of Intertainment

SAVR is a trademark of Mimic, Inc.

Say&See is a trademark of Natural Speech Technologies

Signal Computing System Architecture (SCSA) is a trademark of Dialogic Corporation

SimplyVoice for DOS is a trademark of Interactive Products, Inc.

Sound Blaster is a trademark of Creative Labs, Inc.

SoundXchange is a trademark of InterActive Inc.

Speak2Directions is a trademark of Pure Speech, Inc.

Speech Secretary is a trademark of Applications Express

SpeechMagic is a trademark of Philips Dictation Systems, Inc.

Sporting News Pro Football Guide is a trademark of Compton's NewMedia

Star Trek: 25th Anniversary is a trademark of Interplay Productions

StockTalk is a trademark of Bell-Northern Research Ltd.

Tangora is a trademark of IBM

Tmap is a trademark of Northern Telecom

Trade$tar is a trademark of International Trading Institute

UNIX is a trademark of UNIX System Laboratories, Inc.

VCR Voice is a trademark of Voice Powered Technology International, Inc.

VIP 100 is a trademark of Threshold Technology, Inc.

Voice Across America is a trademark of Texas Instruments Incorporated

Voice Activated Robotic Retrofit System is a trademark of Montefiori Hospital

Voice Bot is a trademark of Toy Biz

Voice Calling is a trademark of Ameritech, Inc.

Voice FONCARD is a trademark of Sprint

VOICE MESSAGEPAD is a trademark of Voice Powered Technology International, Inc.

Voice Nagivator is a trademark of Articulate Systems, Inc.

Voice Organizer is a trademark of Voice Powered Technology International, Inc.

Voice Pilot is a trademark of Microsoft Corporation

Voice Recognition Call Processing is a trademark of AT&T

VoiceMed is a trademark of Kurzweil Applied Intelligence Inc.

VoiceRad is a trademark of Kurzweil Applied Intelligence Inc.

VoiceTrader is a trademark of Verbex Voice Systems, Inc.

VoiceType is a trademark of IBM

Voice Assist is a trademark of Creative Labs, Inc.

WESTLAW is a trademark of West Publishing Corporation

WESTLAW is Natural is a trademark of West Publishing Corporation

Wildfire Electronic Assistant is a trademark of Wildfire Communications, Inc.

WIN is a trademark of West Publishing Corporation

Windows is a trademark of Microsoft Corporation

Windows 95 is a trademark of Microsoft Corporation

Windsurfer is a trademark of IBM

WordPerfect is a trademark of WordPerfect The Novell Applications Group

Preface

T he growing commercial success of speech recognition has stimulated increased curiosity among computer application developers, consumer product designers, researchers, and the public. In my work as a consultant I am often asked:

Does speech recognition add value?

Does it work?

How can an application developer use it?

Will people like it?

The simple and easy answer to these questions is "Yes." A more responsible reply is the question "What do you want to do with it?" Since I cannot sit down with each reader to discuss the answer to that question, I hope this book can offer some of the needed assistance.

Although the title page has only one author's name on it, this book was written with the help and counseling of many people. As with all my publications, I consulted the companies whose products, technology, and research are described in this book. In every case, they were asked to examine those descriptions for accuracy. I want to thank them for their assistance.

There is another group of people to whom I owe an even greater debt. Some of them reviewed chapters of my manuscript and others gave me access to equipment, information, or reading material. They include: Dr. Chester Anderson, Mr. David Basore, Mr. Dave Brown, Mr. Robert Perdue, Mr. Bill Porter, Dr. Judith Tschrgi, Dr. Jim Webb and Mr. Chris Welsh of AT&T; Mr. Robert Bossemeyer and Ms. Eileen Schwab of Ameritech; Mr. Chuck Bunting formerly of Kurzweil Applied Intelligence; Professor Thomas Carrell of Northwestern University; Ms. Patricia Flynn-McKenzie and Mr. Brian Kinkade of Dragon Systems; Dr. Gabriel

Groner of Insight Solutions; Professor John H.L. Hansen of Duke University; Mr. Jeff Hill of Voice Processing Corp.; Ms. Jeannette Lawrence of California Scientific Software; Mr. Leon Lerman of the American Voice Input/Output Society (AVIOS); Dr. Martha Lindeman of Users First, Ltd.; Ms. Paula Messamer of U S West; Mr. Matt Miller and Mr. Eric Nahm of Verbex Voice Systems; Mr. David Pallett of the National Institute of Standards and Technology (NIST); Ms. Lisa Poulson of Burson-Marsteller; Dr. Jack Sherman of Motorola and the Motorola library staff; Mr. Elton Sherwin formerly of IBM; Mr. Graeme Smith of Bolt Beranek and Newman; Dr. Herman J.M. Steeneken of the TNO-Institute of Perception, The Netherlands; and Mr. Ed Tagg formerly of Voice Control Systems.

Special thanks to Mr. Bruce Balentine of Voice Control Systems; Ms. Susan Franz of FFP, Ltd.; Professor Stephanie Haas of the University of North Carolina at Chapel Hill; and Professor Beatrice Oshika of Portland State University for their careful examination of drafts of the entire book.

The information contained in this book is derived from personal experience, from the advice and assistance of people listed above, and from data extracted from other sources believed to be reliable. Any errors are mine. Furthermore, the rapid changes occurring in the speech recognition industry will produce alterations in the products, technology, research activities, and opinions found in this book. Readers are advised to use the material in the following chapters as the basis of their understanding of the industry and to apply the analyses and evaluation techniques (also described in this book) to update their knowledge.

1

WHAT IS SPEECH RECOGNITION?

INTRODUCTION

Speech is the ultimate, ubiquitous interface. It is how we should be able to interact with computers. The question is when should it begin supplementing the keyboard and mouse? We think the time is now. (Bruce Armstrong, Manager of the Speech Technologies Group, WordPerfect, The Novell Applications Group, personal communication, 1994)

A growing number of people agree with Bruce Armstrong, but they do not limit speech recognition to control of computers.

AT&T introduced its Voice Recognition Call Processing system in 1992. The system places long-distance collect, third-party, and credit card calls. By mid-1993 it was handling nearly 50 million calls a month.

By 1995, voice-activated dialing services were being offered by most major cellular telephone service providers, and industry analysts estimated that more than 19 million voice-activated dialing systems would be in operation by 1999. (*ASR News*, January 1995, p. 1)

By the mid-1990's, speech recognition had gained a foothold in the healthcare industry. More than five hundred hospital emergency departments were using voice-driven systems to generate clinical reports; Blue Cross and Blue Shield of New Jersey had deployed a medical reporting system in ten healthcare centers throughout the state; and medical report-generation systems had been developed for radiology, pathology, orthopaedic surgeons, emergency medicine, cardiology, nephrology, and family medicine.

Asserting that queries to *WESTLAW* "just lend themselves to speech" (personal communication, 1994), West Publishing began offering a speech recognition interface for all 4,800 on-line databases of its *WESTLAW* legal research system. *WESTLAW* is widely used by attorneys and legal researchers throughout the United States and Canada.

In 1995, Visa Interactive, the remote-banking subsidiary of Visa International, announced a voice-driven bill payment service.

At the 1995 annual convention of the National Association of Home Builders, the Whirlpool Corporation demonstrated the *KitchenAid Voice Command* prototypes: a line of voice-activated home-appliances. The product line includes a wall oven, dishwasher, and refrigerator.

PC hardware and software manufacturers are incorporating speech recognition into their products: Microsoft Corporation is offering built-in operations to create "voice-command objects" under *Windows 95;* Creative Laboratories bundles speech recognition with most of its *Sound Blaster* sound cards; Compaq Computer Corporation and PureSpeech Inc. are jointly developing speech recognition technology that Compaq plans to implement in many of its systems; and Seagate Technology purchased 25 percent equity in Dragon Systems, a leading developer of speech-recognition products.

The American public has also taken notice of speech recognition as a viable tool. Television commercials showing actress Candice Bergen instructing her telephone to "Call Mom," articles on speech recognition in *The Wall Street Journal* and other prestigious business publications, and comic strips with voice-controlled computers have spawned growing curiosity and a marketplace for voice-activated systems.

1.1 WHY SPEECH RECOGNITION?

1.1.1 The Allure

There are many reasons why companies are choosing to use and develop systems with speech recognition interfaces. Among the most frequently cited are the following benefits:

1. Increased productivity

In most instances, productivity is defined in terms of the ability to get more work done with comparable or better accuracy than can be achieved using existing methods.

In the brokerage industry, for example, saving seconds in a trader's ability to respond to breaking market news translates directly into greater profit or reduced loss. Any tool that increases the speed of operations without impairing accuracy is considered a form of competitive advantage. According to Michael Poser, first vice president of technology at Lehman Brothers in 1993, productivity at their two "voicified" trading desks rose 50 to 75 percent and trading volume grew by 250 percent. Their Central Funding desk reported an average 100 percent increase in the number of trades executed in a day by using voice control and the accuracy rate for order entry rose from 75 to 98 percent (Yraslorza, 1993).

The healthcare industry has always placed a premium on accuracy, but regulatory requirements and cash-flow pressures have heightened the need for greater speed in the completion of documents and reports. Using speech recognition to generate reports

> . . . actually takes less of the doctor's time, requires no transcription, and is available immediately. So that if the patient gets wheeled into the operating room the report is there rather than two weeks later. (Ray Kurzweil, founder and chairman of Kurzweil Applied Intelligence Inc., Leader's Panel, "Money-making opportunities in speech recognition," *Advanced Speech Applications and Technology Conference '95*, April 5, 1995)

Because document-generation using speech is structured, it also fosters more complete documentation than is often found in handwritten notes. Better documentation facilitates rapid bill payment by both Medicare and third-party payers and provides greater protection from malpractice lawsuits.

In manufacturing, the number of "red tags" and "rejects" that must be fixed and the ability to rapidly identify and correct the sources of defects determines the productivity of an entire plant. The time available to find and record information about defects is limited by the movement of the assembly line.

> Because data entry [by speech] is less cumbersome, the operator can collect much more comprehensive data on each defect found . . . At Delco, voice recognition systems have allowed manufacturing engineering . . . to reduce the solder machine parts per million reject levels by an order of magnitude. (Lee Pfarrer, Project Engineer, Delco Electronics, "Using voice recognition for data collection in a factory environment," 1989, p. 154)

For people with physical disabilities affecting the use of their hands, productivity is far more personal. Speech recognition can enable some people to perform daily living tasks without assistance. For others, such as the growing number of professionals afflicted with Repetitive Stress Syndrome (RSI), speech recognition represents a means of getting or keeping employment.

2. Rapid return on investment

> We recently equipped a major package handler with input devices for moving packages through a brand-new hub. That customer spent about $1.8M to deploy ASR systems and will receive a payback on that investment in about 9 months. (Larry Dooling, President and CEO of Verbex Voice Systems, Leader's Panel, "Money-making opportunities in speech recognition," *Advanced Speech Applications and Technology Conference '95*, April 5, 1995)

Return on investment (ROI) is an evaluation metric applied by many organizations. Sometimes ROI for speech recognition is a by-product of reducing the cost of correcting errors. In the late 1980's Shearson invested in a voice-activated trading system. Steven Gott, executive vice president of Shearson Trade Services Group in 1989, reported that increased productivity and reduced errors resulting from the use of the system produced a payback ratio of between five and ten dollars for each dollar spent.

ROI may be defined in terms of reducing staffing costs. The New York City Teachers' Retirement System provides information to its members via 24-hour telephone access. Through the use of speech recognition they have made this 24-hour access available to members with rotary-dial telephones without adding to their staff. Other organizations report comparable results when they used speech recognition to replace off-hour operators and receptionists. One of the most striking examples is the ROI for AT&T's long-distance calling system:

> Fifty million people a month use the collect calling system. This is what you call "ubiquitous" and AT&T is saving a bundle of money. (Chester Anderson, Manager, Center for Excellence in Audio and Speech Processing, AT&T, panel discussion at *Advanced Speech Applications and Technologies Conference '94*)

Speech recognition services can also produce a rapid ROI. Anthony Bladen, vice president of the Telephony Business Unit of Voice Processing Corp., estimates that voice-activated dialing on telephone networks can bring a ROI within three months if only 7 percent of the telephone subscribers elect to use the service.

3. Access to new markets

Speech recognition can be used to facilitate entry into new markets or to solidify existing markets. These objectives can be accomplished by making speech input over the telephone available to customers who do not have touch-tone telephones. Local banks and other businesses are implementing speech recognition as a service for customers using rotary-dial technology.

A growing number of businesses use speech recognition to extend 24-hour and weekend telephone service to markets outside of the United States where touch-tone telephone technology is uncommon. Many of these systems incorporate speech recognition for multiple languages.

4. Environment control

Speech recognition is giving people with severe disabilities more control over their personal environments:

> Speech recognition is being used to give some severely disabled people a means of remote control of their environments—a way to choose independently among several activities such as watching television and listening to the radio, for example. (Judith Harkins, Director, Technology Assessment Program, Gallaudet University, "Voice processing and disabled people," 1989, p. 10)

5. Naturalness

Speaking is the most natural and universal method of communication between people. The aim of speech recognition is to extend that communication modality to interaction with machines, such as computers.

Speech recognition is being programmed into computer software to provide a more natural interface for populations of computer-naive users, including busy professionals who cannot take the time to learn complex keyboard commands. It reduces training time while increasing ease-of-use.

Worker's compensation professionals at Navistar International were initially intimidated by the prospect of using a new artificial intelligence system to do their work. The incorporation of speech recognition was an important source of user acceptance of that system:

> It not only reduced their fears, it made using the system fun. One of them even reported he did not want to use the system without the speech . . . [without speech recognition] they probably would have required more training and hand-holding from the developers. (Judith Markowitz, President, J. Markowitz, Consultants, "Next Steps: Navistar's Compensation Reserve Expert System Advisor," 1989, p. 782)

An additional benefit experienced by service organizations is discovering their customers simply like speech recognition. Usually, this was not the original objective, but it is seen as a decided plus. According to The New York City Teachers' Retirement System:

> About 46 percent of our callers use the speech recognition feature to access information from the system . . . It was surprising to all of us to learn that the speech recognition usage was so high . . . Apparently people with touch-tone phones prefer to use voice because they are allowed to use the phone for what it was designed—speaking. (George Rose, Voice Response Administrator, New York City Teachers' Retirement System, "Speech recognition/IVR combo a hit with agency members," 1991, p. 49)

6. Company or product differentiation

When companies recognize that consumers are having difficulty distinguishing them from their competitors they may turn to speech recognition as a way to differentiate themselves or their products from the competition. This rationale for using speech can enhance the image of a company, service, or product, but it is often temporary because competitors soon follow with comparable speech features.

In the early 1990's, telephone companies began to use voice-activated dialing services to help differentiate themselves from competitors. The spread of voice-controlled services was so rapid, particularly among cellular service providers, that the uniqueness quickly dissipated.

West Publishing is one of the leading suppliers of on-line resources for legal research. In 1994, West distinguished itself from its competition by offering *LawTalk for WESTLAW,* a speech-driven interface to its database query systems. *LawTalk for WESTLAW* enables attorneys and paralegals to search *WESTLAW's* on-line databases using speech and to create *WordPerfect* documents from the information they have gathered. Interest in West's speech system was so strong that one year later Lexis-Nexis, West Publishing's principal competitor, began offering a comparable speech front-end. Both companies are now expanding the functionality of their speech interfaces.

1.1.2 The Challenge

The successes described in the preceding sections resulted from forty years of work that has produced technology capable of accurately processing spoken input containing sizable vocabularies. Despite those impressive achievements, speech recognition still has not reached its goal to develop systems capable of understanding virtually anything anyone says on any topic when they are speaking in a natural, free-flowing style of speech and situated in almost any speaking environment, no matter how noisy, that is, to understand spoken language as well as humans can. This shortcoming may be surprising since, for humans, understanding what other people say may seem to be a simple task. In fact, it is extremely complex and difficult. Here are a few reasons why:

1. The voluminous data in the speech sound wave

Although it may seem as if we speak using a single tone, the quantity of data in the sound wave is overwhelming. Within the range of human hearing, speech sounds can span more than 20,000 frequencies. The time required to capture, digitize, and recognize frequency patterns for every nanosecond of speech would overwhelm any PC on the market (and most other computer systems). In order to recognize speech at a speed that is acceptable to users, the amount of data in the signal must be dramatically reduced.

As we shall see in chapter 2, it is not necessary to manipulate all the data from the entire speech wave. Some excludable data are irrelevant to the recognition process while other pieces of data are redundant. The quantity of data can be reduced further by taking samples from the signal rather than trying to process the entire waveform.

2. The paucity of information in the speech sound wave

This may appear to contradict the preceding point, but it simply highlights the fact that speech is more than acoustic sound patterns. Spoken language interaction between people requires knowledge about word meanings, communication patterns, and the world in general. Words with widely different meanings and usage patterns may share the same sequence of sound patterns. These *homophones* include sets of frequently occurring words, such as "to," "two," and "too." Speech recognition systems must be able to distinguish among homophones in order to transcribe sentences. Consider the challenge this spoken sentence represents:

I want to write about this rite to Ms. Wright, right away.

The meanings of words that affect the interpretation of utterances cannot be extracted from the sound stream alone. Often, a grammar (see chapter 4) is required to assist in the process. In the sentence

Mary wrote a letter and she mailed it.

a grammar that links pronouns with nouns using distinctions like sex and animacy would, for example, link "she" with "Mary" rather than "letter." Such a grammar would not, however, be sufficient to clearly identify the link for the pronoun "they" in the following sentences:

The City Council would not give the women a permit to march because they feared violence.
The City Council would not give the women a permit to march because they advocated violence.

Knowledge of the world would be needed to determine the correct meaning of each sentence. Similar examples requiring world knowledge that is currently unavailable to computers can be drawn from newspaper headlines, such as, "LA County Spending Mushrooms" and "Man Gets Nine Years in Violin Case," as well as from our daily social communication. The question "Do you know the time?" is structured as a yes/no question, but a simple "yes" or "no" response would be viewed as offensive; a "night owl" is usually not a bird; and "My, it's drafty in here!" is often a request to close a window or retrieve a sweater.

Fortunately, the inclusion of information beyond acoustic analysis of the sound stream is not needed for many simple applications (see chapter 4). It is obvious, though, that the incorporation of such "higher level" knowledge into a speech recognition system would serve as a gateway to truly natural speech communication with machines (see chapter 4, section 4.4; chapter 10, sections 10.1 and 10.2).

3. The continuous flow of speech

Since we speak in individual words and we "hear" what other people say as sequences of words, it seems reasonable to expect the speech sound wave to consist of words with clearly marked boundaries. As described in chapter 6, that is not at all the case. Speech is uttered as a continuous flow of sounds and even when words are spoken distinctly there are no inherent separations between them. This should not be surprising since we hear foreign languages as streams of sound unbroken by our recognition of distinct words. The same phenomenon occurs for unfamiliar words and phrases in English. In fact, author Richard Lederer has written two popular books dealing with human word-segmentation errors, such as understanding "Pulitzer prize" as "pullet surprise."

Once it moved beyond single-word input, speech recognition was forced to address the problem of segmenting the speech stream into its component words.

Chapter 6 describes methods for addressing this challenge that are employed by commercial products and chapter 10 extends the view to include the systems of the future.

4. Variability

One person's voice and speech patterns can be entirely different from those of another person. Some elements of this diversity are physical. Each individual is unique, differing from others in the size and shape of their mouths, the length and width of their necks, and a range of other physical characteristics. Added to these anatomical variations are age, sex, regional dialect, health, and an individual's personal style of speech. Despite these differences, a recognition system must be able to accurately process the speech of anyone who is expected to use the speech system.

The development of speaker modeling techniques (see chapter 5) has produced dramatic advances in handling inter-speaker variability. Technology alone will not eliminate all of these issues. Resolution of a significant portion of speaker variability issues, including speaker training, vocabulary selection, and the human factors in application design, all affect the ability of a recognition system to handle inter-speaker variability. These concerns are the responsibility of application designers.

5. More variability

Even a single speaker will exhibit variability. The sound pattern of a word changes when speakers whisper or shout, when they are angry or sad, and when they are tired or ill. Even when speaking normally, individual speakers rarely say a word the same way twice. In fact, variability is a basic characteristic of speech.

When intra-speaker variability is added to inter-speaker differences it becomes difficult to identify and extract critical, word-identification information from the input. Speaker modeling techniques have been designed to extract common intra-speaker patterns of variability (see chapter 6) and produce very high speech recognition accuracy.

6. Noise

Natural speaking environments bombard the speaker with sounds of varying loudness emanating from many sources. They include people speaking in the background, street sounds, the slam of a door, music, and the hum (or roar) of machinery. Sometimes the noise in a speaking environment can be so great that people cannot understand each other. As speech recognition is embedded in more diverse products and systems, the spectrum of noises will also grow. Unfortunately, the challenging speaking environments are the ones that most characterize our daily living: busy offices, factories, loading docks, airports, automobiles, and even our own homes.

Background noise is not the only intrusion speech recognition systems must combat. They must handle

- Noise produced by the input device (telephone or microphone)
- Sounds made by the speaker, such as lip smacks
- Non-communication vocalizations made by the speaker, such as, "Uh"

Speech recognition over telephones is becoming increasingly popular, but it is one of the most challenging of speaking channels. Even people have trouble with it. Voices can be faint or full of static, but even when everything is functioning well, it may still be difficult to distinguish between similar sounding words and sounds, such as "s" and "f."

Despite these and other noise-related problems, a speech system must be able to hear and respond properly. Chapter 7 describes recent progress in this area, including work with neural networks and systems that model the human auditory system. The success of speech recognition over the telephone illustrates the progress that has been made in this area. As with other issues, the role of the application developer in addressing noise has a strong impact on the ultimate success of a speech recognition application.

The rapid technological advances of the last fifteen years augur well for achieving those goals, but the challenge should not be underestimated.

1.1.3 Driving Forces

Speech recognition has only recently achieved a level of reliability and flexibility to attract the interest of business and consumers. Its achievements are due, in part, to significant technological advances within the industry. Equally important are the external factors that have functioned as driving forces for speech recognition. Some of those external forces are technological. The 1990's have already seen

- Increasingly powerful microprocessors
- Extensive miniaturization
- Computer-telephony integration
- The growth of multimedia

1.1.3.1 Microprocessors. The dramatic and continuing growth in the speed and power of microprocessors is a primary factor in the migration of advanced speech recognition technology from laboratories to real-world applications. Figure 1.1 provides a dramatic example of that growth for Intel chips. The advent of each new generation of chips has heralded the commercialization of a new, more advanced class of speech recognition systems and technology. Intel's 80386 processor led to the commercialization of 30,000-word dictation systems and better recognition over the telephone. The 80486 allowed large vocabulary systems to grow to 60,000 words. The increased speed of the 80486 processor was exploited by Philips Dictation Systems to develop the first commercial continuous speech dictation system. The Pentium and PowerPC chips opened the door for both the development of "intelligent" recognition systems and continuous speech dictation systems with even larger vocabularies.

Increases in power have been accompanied by equally dramatic price declines. When the 60MH Pentium was introduced in May, 1993, it cost OEM's $900. One year later it cost $750. By the fall of 1994, Intel had reduced prices on Pentium chips by up to 25 percent more and they continued to cut prices following the Pentium-flaw debacle. Rapid price declines of this sort have become commonplace in all facets of computer hardware industry, including storage, memory, and peripherals. They have made it possible for speech recognition systems to follow suit. Between 1990 and 1993, the price of large vocabulary dictation systems by Dragon Systems, IBM, and Kurzweil AI dropped from several thousand dollars to below one thousand dollars. By the middle of 1994, Sensory Circuits began marketing a chip with speech recognition based on neural-network technology for under five dollars, and Verbex was selling its speaker-independent, continuous-speech, *Windows* application interface product for less than one hundred dollars. These trends facilitate the integration of speech recognition into a wider range of consumer products.

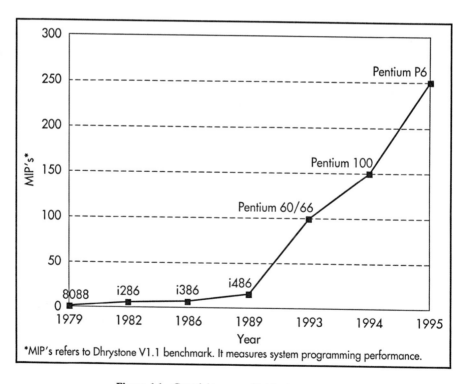

Figure 1.1   Growth in power of Intel microprocessors

1.1.3.2 Miniaturization.

One measure of progress is the increasing number of components we can cram onto a silicon chip about the size of a fingernail. For signal-processing chips, the scale of integration is about 33 percent per year. At the same time, the speed of individual components is increasing about 20 percent each year. (Pat Russo, President, AT&T Global Business Communication Systems, Keynote speech at *Advanced Speech Applications and Technologies Conference '94*)

Miniaturization of hardware is fostering the use of speech recognition in consumer products. As smaller systems become more powerful, they can support increasingly complex speech-recognition technology. Several small-vocabulary, chip-based systems were introduced in the early 1990's including AT&T's DSP-16 voice dialing chip for cellular telephones and a chip using neural network technology by Sensory Circuits. By 1995, OKI Semiconductor had begun marketing a chip with speaker-independent recognition (see chapter 5) for a vocabulary of 127 phrases; and International Meta Systems was developing chip-level technology for continuous-speech dictation using vocabularies of 5,000 words and larger.

A second effect of miniaturization has been to make speech recognition interfaces more desirable. The small size of palmtop and personal digital assistants (PDA's) makes it less convenient to use a keyboard or even a mouse. The first voice-driven PDA, the *Voice Organizer* by Voice Powered Technology, appeared in 1994 and more are on the way.

1.1.3.3 Global business.

The world is growing smaller politically and economically. International business ventures that link professionals on opposite sides of the globe are becoming commonplace. This has spawned a need to establish 24-hour and multi-lingual telecommunications capabilities. Some of these needs can be satisfied by hiring bilingual telephone operators and business professionals. That solution is not always necessary or affordable, and touch-tone technology is not widely available outside of North America.

The use of telephone-based, multi-lingual speech recognition systems is a cost-effective answer for businesses needing 24-hour telephone messaging and communication support. These and other business needs are accelerating the implementation of multi-lingual systems, more expandable vocabularies (see chapter 3), and research on speech-to-speech machine translation (see chapter 10).

1.2 HISTORICAL OVERVIEW OF SPEECH RECOGNITION

The first documented attempts to construct an automatic speech recognition system occurred long before the digital computer was invented. In the 1870's Alexander Graham Bell wanted to build a device that would make speech visible to hearing-impaired people. He ended up inventing the telephone. Sixty years later a Hungarian scientist, Tihamér Nemes, requested permission for a patent to develop an automatic transcription system using the optical sound tracks of movie films. The sound track was to serve as a source of capturing the sound patterns of speech. The system would identify the sound sequences and print them out. The request for a patent was labelled "unrealistic" and denied.

It took another thirty years before the first machine capable of recognizing speech was built at AT&T Bell Laboratories (see Davis, et al., 1952). The system compared stored reference patterns (called *templates*) of the ten English digits with utterances of individual digits. It required extensive tuning to recognize the speech of a person, but once that was accomplished, its accuracy could be as good as 99 percent. The hope of early researchers at Bell Laboratories, RCA Laboratories, and elsewhere was that speech recognition would be straightforward and easy.

By the mid-1960's, most researchers realized speech recognition was far more subtle and intricate than they had anticipated. Accepting the fact that spoken language transcription was not on the horizon, they narrowed their focus to systems capable of handling

- The speech of one person (speaker dependent)
- Input containing pauses between words (discrete-word speech flow)
- Vocabularies of fifty words or fewer (small vocabulary systems)

Speaker-dependent recognition proceeds in two stages: training (also called *enrollment*) to create stored templates (also called *word models* or *reference patterns*) followed by recognition of input. Training entails gathering spoken samples of each vocabulary item from every person who will use the recognition system. Thus, each person using an application with fifty words must provide at least one spoken sample of each of the fifty words (see chapter 5, sections 5.1 and 5.6). Other approaches to speaker modeling, *speaker independence* and *speaker adaptation*, do not require full enrollment. Speaker independent systems are designed to allow end-users to access the system without enrollment (see chapter 5, sections 5.3 and 5.8). Speaker adaptation begins with formative word models and adapts them to the speech characteristics of each end-user by extracting information from smaller samples of the user's speech (see chapter 5, sections 5.4 and 5.9).

Discrete-word, also called *discrete utterance,* recognition requires users to pause between words. Pausing assists the recognition system by reducing distortion in the input and by identifying word boundaries. It is generally contrasted with *continuous speech* recognition, which does not require pauses. Discrete-word recognition, continuous speech recognition, and other forms of *speech flow* are discussed in chapter 6.

The recognition systems of the 1960's also began to incorporate time-normalization techniques to minimize differences in the speed with which a person might say a word. They no longer sought exact or near-exact matches. Instead they tried to identify the reference pattern whose acoustic patterns most closely resembled the input. Later systems employed minimum matching thresholds to prevent incorrect recognition when the distance between the input and the best reference pattern was too great. Subsequent research programs at IBM and Carnegie Mellon University focused on continuous speech recognition, but the fruits of that work would not be seen until the 1970's and later.

The early 1970's saw the development of the first speech recognition product, the *VIP 100* system of Threshold Technology, Inc. Threshold Technology was founded by Thomas Martin, one of the first to apply time-normalization to speech recognition. The *VIP 100* demonstrated the viability of small vocabulary, speaker dependent, discrete-word recognition technology. It won a US National Award in 1972.

These initial successes piqued the interest of the Advanced Research Projects Agency (ARPA) of the United States Department of Defense. ARPA propelled speech recognition research towards large vocabulary, continuous speech recognition and helped precipitate the industry's *artificial intelligence* period. Developers focused on designing *speech understanding systems* (SUS). SUS wanted to emulate the spoken language comprehension capabilities of human listeners. Systems began to incorporate modules to handle analysis of the structure of words (lexical knowledge), sentence structure (syntax), meaning (semantics), and social behavior (pragmatics). ARPA's Speech Understanding Research project (ARPA SUR) was the largest of the projects of the 1970's. It began in 1971 and ended in 1976 and required systems to recognize

- A vocabulary of one thousand words or more
- Connected speech input
- The speech of several cooperative speakers

and have the following characteristics:

- A built-in, artificial syntax
- A well-defined, real-world task
- Recognition accomplished in "a few times real-time" or better
- An error rate of less than 10 percent

Three contractors [CMU, Bolt Beranek and Newman (BBN), and a System Development Corporation (SDC)-Stanford Research Institute (SRI) team] built a total of six systems for ARPA SUR while several other contractors, including MIT Lincoln Laboratory, focused on specific elements of the recognition process. Only one system, CMU's *Harpy*, was able to meet the ARPA SUR goals. *Harpy* recognized 1,011 words with an error rate of 5 percent (see Klatt, 1977 for a more detailed description).

The ARPA SUR systems had a profound effect on the course of speech recognition research and development. CMU's *DRAGON* system was one of the first speech systems to use a form of hidden Markov modeling (see chapter 2, section 2.3.3). Hidden Markov models (HMM's) are now found in virtually all commercial and research speech recognition systems. Three other systems, *Harpy, HWIM (hear what I mean),* and *Hearsay-II* tested vastly different approaches to structuring (called *artificial grammar* or, simply, *grammars*). CMU's *Hearsay-II* organized the information needed for speech understanding into independent knowledge sources which communicated with each other via a common database, called a *blackboard,* such as the one in figure 1.2. The structure and operation of *Hearsay-II's* blackboard model mirror the challenge of spoken language understanding. Each major level of spoken language (e.g., sounds, syllables, words, phrases) is represented as a distinct level on the blackboard and is accompanied by an independent *knowledge source.* Those knowledge sources understand the variability found at their own level and recognize that patterns found at their level are composed of data from lower levels. *Hearsay-II* successively decomposes a speech-understanding problem into smaller units until it reaches the *parameter* level where knowledge about acoustic features of individual speech sounds is analyzed. Higher-level knowledge sources evaluate and consolidate hypotheses generated by lower-level knowledge sources.

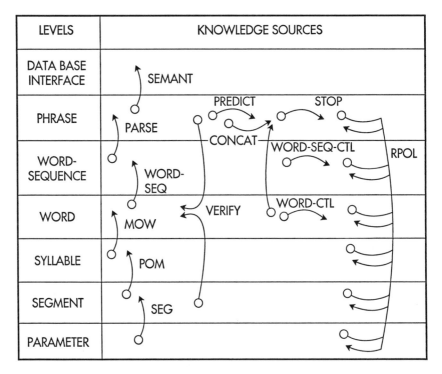

Figure 1.2   The blackboard model of *Hearsay-II* (from Erman, Hayes-Roth, Lesser & Reddy, The *Hearsay-II* Speech-Understanding System, Copyright 1980, Association for Computing Machinery)

The knowledge source for the *word* level can, for example, process variability in the pronunciation of individual words, like "speaker," and exploit information in hypotheses generated by the *syllable* level regarding the likelihood that "speak" and "er" were spoken in succession. This interactive communication continues until the system reaches a decision about the contents of the entire input.

BBN's *HWIM* system incorporated an *augmented transition network* (ATN), a grammar designed to *parse* input. Parsing systems go beyond simple recognition of word sequences. They analyze the syntactic structure of an entire sentence. ATN's are frequently used in natural language processing systems and gained renewed interest in the 1990's among researchers developing spoken language understanding systems.

Harpy took the simplest approach using a 15,000-node network, called a *finite-state grammar* (also called a *state network* or *transition network,* described in chapter 4, section 4.1) that represented all the sentences *Harpy* could recognize, and used a technique called *beam searching* (also called Viterbi search, described in chapter 3, section 3.2.2) to find the path most closely matching the spoken input. Both beam searching and finite-state grammar are among the most well-established and frequently used tools of speech recognition.

The *Harpy* and *DRAGON* systems demonstrated that simple speech recognition tasks do not require complex, human-like design. The success of *Harpy,* combined with work performed by Frederick Jelinek and his speech research group at IBM, highlighted the power of well-designed statistical modeling techniques. The ARPA SUR underlined the value of using an artificial grammar to reduce the number of choices a system must examine. This was expressed in terms of reducing the *branching factor* of a system.

The results of ARPA SUR helped redirect the focus of research towards the development of robust statistical models, including HMM's and language models. This orientation characterized work of the late 1970's and the 1980's. During the 1980's speech recognition was buoyed by continued ARPA (later called DARPA and then called ARPA again) funding and the growth of the personal computer. Personal computers made it possible to create relatively inexpensive products and tools for rapid application development. The increased PC processing power of the late 1980's fostered the integration of sophisticated algorithms into commercial products. Researchers migrated from laboratories to small speech recognition companies like Votan and Dragon Systems. A few large companies, like Exxon and Texas Instruments, also ventured into the commercial market.

The latter half of the 1980's witnessed dramatic growth in the technological sophistication of statistical techniques for speech recognition. By the end of the decade HMM's had become almost universal. IBM's work on statistical language modeling (particularly *N-gram models*) formed the basis for language models found in all commercial, large vocabulary, dictation systems of the late 1980's and early 1990's.

A major focus of the 1980's and early 1990's was on the design of large vocabulary systems. In 1985, one thousand words was still considered a large vocabulary, particularly for commercial systems. In 1986, Speech Systems, Inc. introduced the first very large vocabulary, commercial system. Their *PE100* was a twenty thousand word, phoneme-based, continuous speech, speaker-independent system running on UNIX workstations. At the same time, the research on statistical modeling of word segments produced systematic methods for representing and processing phoneme-like segments (called *subwords, phonemes-in-context* or *triphones,* see chapter 3, section 3.1.5). Subword modeling opened the door to commercialization of large-vocabulary dictation systems by transforming vocabulary development from a long, arduous process into a simple keyboard activity requiring only seconds. By the end of the decade, Dragon Systems had introduced a speaker-adaptive, discrete-word dictation system able to support a vocabulary of thirty thousand words. IBM soon followed with a long-awaited commercial version of its *Tangora* research dictation system and Kurzweil AI began offering speech recognition for medical report generation.

In the early 1980's commercial systems with continuous speech also began to appear. Among the first were systems by Verbex (small vocabulary) and the *PE100* system of Speech Systems Inc. By 1989, ITT Defense Communications, Vocollect, and other companies offered continuous speech in commercial products. During that time, Voice Processing Corporation developed small-vocabulary, continuous speech products for one of the most difficult speaking environments: the telephone.

Noise immunity improved dramatically during the 1980's, making manufacturing applications more reliable. The introduction of radio frequency transmission increased the utility of the technology for applications requiring user mobility. Speech recognition began to be used over the telephone. The first applications were limited to "yes" and "no." By the end of the decade, digits and a few basic control words had become standard for telephone applications. In 1985, Voice Control Systems tackled one of the most difficult transmission channels when it introduced the first speaker-independent cellular telephone dialing system, which it licensed to automotive companies, including Chrysler and General Motors.

The 1980's also saw the appearance of portable systems for data collection and specialized command and control. One of the earliest, The *IntroVoice* family of products by Voice Connexion, were self-contained, hand-held recognizers. By 1989, Vocollect, Mimic, and other companies had introduced wearable or hand-held portable recognizers.

The trends of the 1980's continued into the 1990's. Large vocabularies became the norm and companies that in the 1980's sold systems containing less than one hundred words for thousands of dollars began offering products with thousands of words for less than one hundred dollars. Subword modeling was extended to telephone applications and more products began offering speaker-independent recognition. In 1994, Philips Dictation Systems marketed the first PC-based, very large vocabulary dictation system with continuous speech recognition. At the other end of the spectrum, commercial speech recognition residing on single chips and chip sets made application development in consumer products a reality.

The pace of commercialization quickened. Following a great deal of research, artificial neural networks found their way into commercial speech recognition systems. Lernout & Hauspie and Sensory Circuits integrated neural networks into their commercial technology, and other companies began to seriously examine the technology. Companies began to integrate speech recognition into products ranging in size and function from VCR programmers to air-traffic control training systems. In an effort to facilitate the integration of speech recognition into software products and technology, Dialogic, Novell, and Microsoft sponsored efforts to create application programming (API) standards for speech recognition. The standards committees attracted support from outside the speech recognition industry, including Intel, Digital Equipment Corporation, NEC, Siemens, Tandem Computers, and the Centre National d'Etudes des Telecommunications.

Research to improve statistical processing continued into the 1990's as well and was accompanied by a growing emphasis on developing intelligent, *spoken language understanding* systems. The complex human factors issues related to speech recognition began to unfold, moving the industry towards better human factors design.

Prior to 1990, popular experience with speech recognition was largely limited to the technology in *Star Trek* and other works of science-fiction. By the end of 1994, many Americans had tried (or were aware of) a speech-controlled *Windows* application interface, AT&T's long-distance telephone calling system, or a voice-activated dialing system such as Sprint's Voice *FONCARD*. The perception of speech recognition as a novelty was rapidly changing to appreciation of it as a tool for everyday use.

1.3 ABOUT THIS BOOK

1.3.1 Who This Book Is For

This is an introductory book about speech recognition. It is written for application developers, technical managers, other professionals, and consumers of speech recognition who want to understand how speech recognition works, how they can use it, and how they can better evaluate the suitability of speech recognition for their application needs. Those people include

- Technology managers from CEOs to supervisors
- Human factors professionals
- Students and researchers in computer science, management, linguistics, computational linguistics, artificial intelligence, and related disciplines
- Information systems professionals in manufacturing, healthcare, law/law enforcement, entertainment, finance, service industries, consumer products, education, and government

- Personnel managers concerned about the American Disabilities Act
- Speech and language pathologists
- Management and staff of advanced technology departments
- Management and staff of technology planning departments
- Computer-based training professionals
- Not-for-profit and advocacy groups for people with disabilities
- Special education program directors

In short, this book is designed to appeal to educated consumers and application developers from any industry who are interested in understanding and using speech recognition.

1.3.2 The Goals of the Book

Using Speech Recognition focuses on two major areas:

- Applications
- Commercial Technology

It is designed as an instructional guide for application developers, but it can be used as a resource for general information about the technology as well. This book describes where speech recognition technology is today and where it is headed; it delineates application design issues; and it presents existing applications in a wide range of industries. It contains views and opinions of professionals in the speech recognition industry that are taken from their writing and from recent interviews by the author.

This book should enable the reader to accomplish the following goals:

- Evaluate (or identify) potential applications
- Evaluate speech recognition products for use in an application
- Build better applications using existing speech recognition technology
- Develop realistic expectations of the technology

These skills are critical for deciding whether to use speech recognition in an application or product, for making more informed product selections, and for designing better applications.

1.3.3 The Organization of the Book

All chapters address speech recognition applications and application development. Chapters 8 and 9 focus entirely on applications; all other chapters contain both technology and application-related information. Chapter 2 provides an overview of both the data and information needed for speech recognition as well as the three components of a speech recognition application:

- Preprocessing of the speech waveform
- Identification of the contents of the input
- Communication with the other software of the application

Chapters 3 through 7 address the major facets of speech recognition:

Chapter 3   Vocabulary
Chapter 4   Structuring the input (also called *grammar*)
Chapter 5   Modeling the speaker
Chapter 6   The style of speaking (called *speech flow*)
Chapter 7   The speaking environment

These chapters also contain reference notes that provide historical information regarding some of the concepts and approaches being analyzed. Chapter 8 examines the four basic application functions of speech recognition:

- Command-and-control
- Data entry
- Data access (also called *information retrieval*)
- Dictation

and looks closely at the use of speech recognition over the telephone. Chapter 8 also explores technological, human factors, and speaking-environment issues involved in designing applications for each of these functions. Chapter 9 provides a representative overview of applications in a range of industries. Its goal is to illustrate how speech recognition is being used today. Chapter 10 looks at the future. It describes research and application trends and explains some of the forces that are driving the industry forward.

Chapters 2 through 7 and chapter 10 are partitioned into two sections:

- Technology Focus

- Application Focus

The technology focus presents the technological issues facing speech recognition with regard to the chapter topic and describes the technological choices that exist in both research and commercial systems. Technology Focus sections contain no formulae and no code. They provide numerous examples of systems along with viewpoints of people actively involved in designing effective speech recognition systems. The Application Focus sections of chapters 2 through 7 discuss the application issues related to the chapter topic.

The Technology Focus section of chapter 3, for example, discusses what a *word* is for speech recognition systems, describes various techniques for capturing and representing words, and examines issues involved in the design of large vocabulary systems. The Application Focus of the chapter revisits the concept of *word* from the perspective of application development. It defines concepts related to vocabulary design and explains how they affect the construction of the vocabulary of an application. It then characterizes the ways in which words are incorporated into applications and delineates who can add new words once an application has been deployed. Chapter 3 concludes by providing guidelines for evaluating the vocabulary needs of an application.

Throughout the book there are quotes from researchers, product developers, and application developers. One purpose of including these quotes is to support points being made in the text. Another function they serve is as *Voices of the Industry;* they transform descriptions of technology and applications into the beliefs, goals, thoughts, and concerns of people working on speech recognition. Instances where people have changed affiliation since they made a quoted statement are annotated with the person's current affiliation and the affiliation that applied at the time of the quote.

The speed with which the speech recognition industry is changing will have a direct impact on the information contained in this book. New applications are being developed at a faster rate than ever before and technology is changing. Throughout the book attempts have been made to highlight trends, such as neural networks, that are likely to dominate in the future. Chapters 1 and 10 extend the view of this book into the future from a business perspective.

2

WHAT IS A SPEECH RECOGNITION SYSTEM?

INTRODUCTION

Speech recognition is generally used as a human-computer interface for other software. When it functions effectively in this role a speech recognition system performs three primary tasks (see figure 2.0):

- *Preprocessing*   Converts the spoken input into a form the recognizer can process
- *Recognition*   Identifies what has been said
- *Communication*   Sends the recognized input to the software/hardware systems that need it

In order to understand what these three tasks entail, the Technology Focus begins with a description of the data that speech recognition systems must handle. It describes how speech is produced (called *articulation*), examines the stream of speech itself (called *acoustics*), and then characterizes the ability of the human ear to handle spoken input (called *auditory perception*). Once this groundwork has been laid the Technology Focus examines the demands of *preprocessing* in detail. This discussion is followed by an introduction to *recognition* and *communication*. Detailed analyses of the *recognition* process begin in chapter 3.

In figure 2.0, *communication* is displayed as a bi-directional arrow. This represents the two-way communication that exists in applications where the speech interface is closely bound to the rest of the application. In those applications, software

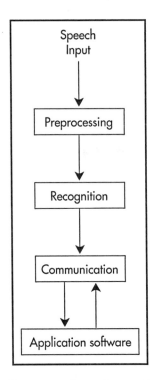

Figure 2.0   Components of a speech recognition application

components that are external to the speech recognition system may guide recognition by specifying the words and structures that the recognition system can use at any point in the application. Other uses of speech involve one-way communication from the recognition system to other components of the application.

Preprocessing, recognition, and *communication* should be invisible to the users of a speech recognition interface. The end user sees them indirectly as the *accuracy* and *speed* of the system. Accuracy and speed are tools that users call upon to evaluate a speech recognition interface. The Application Focus introduces these issues and lays the groundwork for the more detailed discussions in later chapters.

2.1 THE DATA OF SPEECH RECOGNITION

The information needed to perform speech recognition is contained in the stream of speech. For humans, that flow of sounds and silences can be partitioned into discourses, sentences, words, and sounds. Speech recognition systems focus on words and the sounds that distinguish one word from another in a language. Those sounds are called *phonemes.* The words "seat," "meat," "beat," and "cheat" are different words because, in each case, the initial sound ("s," "m," "b," and "ch") is recognized as a separate phoneme in English. The ability to differentiate words with distinct phonemes is as critical for speech recognition as it is for human beings.

There are a number of ways speech can be described and analyzed. The most commonly used approaches are

- *Articulation*   Analysis of how speech sounds are produced by speakers
- *Acoustics*   Analysis of the speech signal as a stream of sounds
- *Auditory Perception*   Analysis of how speech is processed by a human listener

These three approaches offer insights into the nature of speech and provide tools to make recognition more accurate and efficient.

This chapter contains an overview of each of the three approaches to understanding speech. Readers interested in obtaining in-depth technical analyses should consult the following references: Borden & Harris (1994, chapters 3 through 5), Ladefoged (1962), Lieberman & Blumstein (1988), and Witten (1982, chapter 2).

2.1.1 Articulation: Creating Speech Sounds

The science of articulation is concerned with how phonemes are produced. The following sections illustrate how data from articulation are used to establish a system of classification for the phonemes of a language. *ARPABET*, the notational system described below, is used by speech researchers to label those phonemes.

2.1.1.1 The vocal apparatus.

The focus of articulation is on the *vocal apparatus* of the throat, mouth, and nose where the sounds of speech are produced. The throat contains the vocal cords whose vibration produces the *voiced* phonemes, like the "ee" in the word "speech."

The mouth and nose are called *resonating cavities* because they reinforce certain sound wave frequencies. The resonating cavity of the nose is used for speech when the soft palate is lowered and air is allowed to flow into the nasal cavity. This is the way in which *nasal phonemes,* like *m* and *n,* are produced.

The vocal apparatus of the mouth consists of *points of articulation:*

- Teeth
- Alveolar ridge (the bony ridge behind the upper teeth)
- Hard palate (the firm, domed roof of the mouth)
- Soft palate (also called the *velum,* the soft, movable extension of the hard palate)

and *articulators:*

- Lips
- Tongue

2.1.1.2 Classification of phonemes. Classification systems establish consistency of analysis and facilitate communication among researchers. They are generally accompanied by a notational system. Many notational systems have been developed to represent the phonemes of languages. The system most often used in speech recognition is the ARPABET, shown in figure 2.1.

ARPABET

Accurate speech recognition requires the use of a method of classification and representation capable of providing unambiguous descriptions of phonemes. One approach, the ARPABET, is shown in figure 2.1.

    The ARPABET was created in the 1970's by and for contractors working on speech processing projects for the Advanced Research Projects Agency (ARPA) of the U.S. Department of Defense. It was designed to provide a clear, consistent representation for describing sound patterns confronting speech researchers and is used by ARPA contractors to facilitate data sharing. One ARPABET item not displayed in figure 2.1 is the symbol for silence, H#.

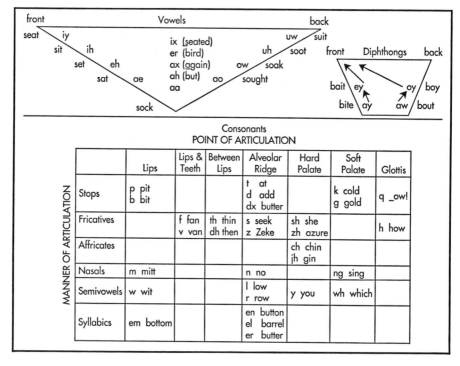

Figure 2.1 Phonemes of American English using ARPABET

Like most phoneme classifications, ARPABET separates consonants from vowels. Consonants are characterized by a total or partial blockage of the vocal tract. The effect of the obstruction is to produce noise. That noise can be the explosion of stop consonants like *p* in "pat" or the hiss of fricatives, such as the *s* in "see." The noise is present even when consonants are *voiced,* like the *b* in "bat" and the *z* in "zee." In figure 2.1, voiced consonants appear immediately below their voiceless counterparts. The voiced phoneme *b,* for example, appears immediately below the voiceless phoneme *p.*

Vowels are characterized by strong harmonic patterns and relatively free passage of air through the vocal tract. Semi-vowels, such as the *y* in "you," fall between consonants and vowels. They are often classified as a type of consonant because they contain partial blockage of the vocal tract, but they also have strong harmonic patterns like vowels.

As figure 2.1 illustrates, consonant classification uses the

- Point of articulation (also called the *place of articulation*)
- Way in which they are created (called *manner of articulation*)
- Presence or absence of voicing

Figure 2.1 displays the points of articulation found in American English consonants.

Manner of articulation classification is displayed along the left edge of figure 2.1. It groups consonants based upon how they are produced. Stops, like *b* and *k,* involve total blockage of the flow of air followed by a quick release. This often produces a noisy burst. The phoneme *dx* (under *Alveolar ridge*) is often called a flapped *t;* it consists of a tap and usually occurs between vowels, such as in the word "butter." The *q* in the column marked *Glottis* represents the catch in the throat (called a *glottal stop*) that occurs at the start of the words "out" and "up." The term *glottis* refers to the opening between the vocal cords.

Fricatives, like *s* and *zh,* narrow the vocal tract at a specific point forcing the air to flow more rapidly through the smaller opening (compare saying "ooo" vs. "sssssooooo," for example). This produces a great deal of noise. Affricates, like *jh* in "fudge," consist of complete air blockage followed by a slow release. Nasals, such as *m* and *n* (cited earlier), are produced by lowering the soft palate and allowing air to flow into the nose.

Stops, fricatives, and affricates can be voiced or unvoiced. Voicing occurs when the vocal cords vibrate as part of the utterance of a sound. Voicing is the primary difference between *t* and *d,* for example. The nasals, semivowels, and syllabics (such as *em* in "bottom") of English are almost always voiced. This is not necessarily the case in other languages.

In English, the vowel system can be partitioned into vowels and diphthongs. Diphthongs, like *aw* in "bout," consist of a vowel followed by a semi-vowel. Vowels and diphthongs are voiced phonemes with strong harmonic structure. As figure 2.1 suggests, the classification of vowels and diphthongs differs from consonant classification. Classification follows the movement of the tongue horizontally (front to back) and vertically (high to low). These effects are represented graphically by the vowel triangle on the top left of figure 2.1. The vowel *iy* in the leftmost angle of the vowel triangle positions the tongue forward in the mouth and near the upper teeth. The vowel *uw*, in the rightmost angle of the triangle, moves the tongue towards the back of the mouth. Similarly, as the vowels *iy, ae,* and *aa* are uttered the tongue moves downward and there is progressively greater opening of the mouth. In English, back vowels, (*uw, uh, ow,* and *ao*) are also produced with rounded lips.

More information about articulation from a variety of technical perspectives can be found in Borden, et al. (1994), Ladefoged (1962), Lieberman & Blumstein (1988), and Rabiner & Juang (1993).

2.1.2 Acoustics: The Signal

Articulation provides valuable information about how speech sounds are produced, but a speech recognition system cannot analyze movements of the mouth. Instead, the data source for speech recognition systems is the stream of speech itself.

Like all sound streams, speech is an *analog signal:* a continuous flow of sounds waves and silence. Knowledge from the science of acoustics is used to identify and describe the attributes of the speech stream that are important for effective speech recognition.

Four important features of acoustic analysis of speech are

- Frequency
- Amplitude
- Harmonic structure (tone vs. noise)
- Resonance

For more detailed information on acoustic phonetics consult Cater (1984), Ladefoged (1962), and Lieberman & Blumstein (1988).

2.1.2.1 Frequency and amplitude. All sounds, including speech, cause disturbances of air molecules. Some sounds, such as the plucking of a guitar string, produce prolonged, regular patterns of air movement. The simplest patterned sounds are created by *pure tone* generators, like tuning forks. Tuning forks vibrate at a single, steady rate that can be represented graphically by a simple *sine wave,* such as the ones labeled *a, b,* and *c* in figure 2.2. The wave labeled *a* in figure 2.2 displays a single *cycle.* It corresponds to a single vibration pattern of a tuning fork.

The sine wave representation shown in figure 2.2 is useful because it clearly displays the vibratory movement as an up-and-down pattern. Physiologically, this corresponds to the movement of the eardrum from its position at rest, to an inward position (in response to higher air pressure), to an outward position (in response to

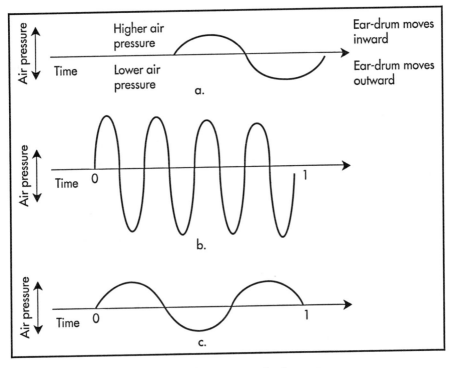

Figure 2.2 Sine wave representation for pure tones

lower air pressure), and back to its rest position. Temporal duration is represented as a horizontal (left-to-right) arrow to indicate that the wave continues over time.

The number of vibrations that a pure tone produces per second is called the *frequency* of that tone. A pure tone vibrating one hundred times per second is said to have a frequency of one hundred cycles per second or one hundred *Hertz* (in honor of the physicist Heinrich Hertz) and it is labeled as 100 Hz. Tones that sound higher have more cycles per second than tones that sound lower. This difference is represented graphically as well. The waves labeled *b* and *c* in figure 2.2 cover the same length of time. Wave *b* will sound higher than wave *c* because it has more cycles per second than wave *c*.

The loudness of a sound is a reflection of how much the air is forced to move. Loudness is described and represented in terms of the *amplitude* of the wave. Amplitude is measured in *decibels* (written as *dB*). In sine wave representation, it is indicated by the height of the wave. Wave *b* in figure 2.2, for example, has greater amplitude than wave *c* and will sound louder than wave *c*.

2.1.2.2 Resonance.   Pure tones, such as the ones described in section 2.1.2.1, are rare. Most sounds, including speech phonemes, have a dominant or primary frequency (called the *fundamental frequency*) that corresponds to our perception of the pitch of the sound, overlaid with secondary frequencies. For speech, the fundamental frequency is the rate at which the vocal cords flap against each other when producing a voiced phoneme.

Added to the fundamental frequency are other frequencies that contribute to the quality or *timbre* of the sound. It is those additional frequencies that enable us to distinguish a violin from a trumpet and to recognize the voices of specific individuals.

Some bands of secondary frequencies play a central role in distinguishing one phoneme from another. They are called *formants* and they are produced by *resonance*. Resonance is the ability of a vibrating source of sound to cause another object to vibrate. It is a common phenomenon of everyday life: the operation of heavy machinery in a factory can cause the floor to vibrate and passing trains can make windows vibrate.

Certain objects, such as the sound boxes of musical instruments, are designed to respond to sound vibrations of specific frequencies or frequency bandwidths. They are called *resonating chambers*. Since they tend to be larger than the source of the sound, they also produce larger vibrations, resulting in the amplification of the frequencies to which they respond.

The throat, mouth, and nose are all resonating chambers. They amplify bands of formant frequencies contained in the sound wave generated by the vocal cords. The formants that are amplified depend upon the size and shape of the mouth and whether the soft palate has been lowered to permit air flow into the nose. Each time we utter a different speech sound we cause the resonating chambers to change in size and shape which, in turn, causes different formant frequencies to be amplified. Formant patterns are strongest for vowels and weakest for voiceless consonants.

2.1.2.3 Harmonic structure and noise.

Multi-frequency sounds like the phonemes of speech can be represented as *complex waves*. In figure 2.3 the complex wave labeled *b* is constructed from sine waves of 100 Hz and 500 Hz with the original waves displayed in dotted lines. Figure 2.4 contains simplified representations of the complex waveforms for the vowels *ao, uw,* and *iy*. Like the complex wave in figure 2.3, each of the vowels in figure 2.4 is composed of two or more single-frequency waves. In each case one of those waves is a fundamental frequency wave of 100 Hz. The complex wave for *uw* in the middle of the figure has a secondary frequency at approximately 200 Hz (twice as fast as the fundamental frequency). It represents a formant frequency characteristic of that vowel. The vowel *ao*, shown at the top of the figure, contains a formant frequency at approximately 500 Hz, which is represented by the four smaller waves that follow the initial, higher projection produced when both frequencies disturb the air pressure in the same way. At the bottom of figure 2.4, the complex wave for *iy* not only displays a formant frequency at around 200 Hz, but the tiny projections along the pattern reveal the presence of a much higher formant frequency at approximately 3,500 Hz.

The full waveforms of these three vowels, and all phonemes, are far richer in secondary frequencies than figure 2.4 suggests. They possess a great deal of internal structure that includes both cyclic waves, such as those shown in figures 2.2 through 2.4, and acyclic waveforms of the sort displayed in figure 2.5. Acyclic

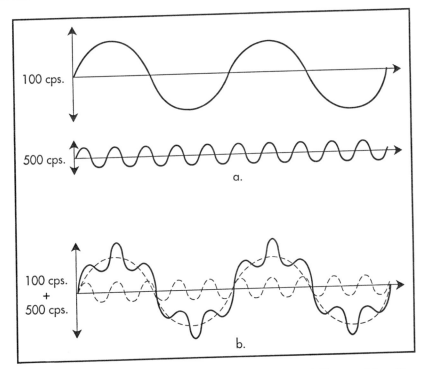

Figure 2.3   Example of a complex wave (adapted from Ladefoged, *Elements of Acoustic Phonetics*, Copyright 1962, The University of Chicago Press)

sound waves do not have repeating patterns. Sounds that produce acyclic waves are often called *noise*. They include crashes, hisses, and voiceless phonemes, such as *s* and *p*. Noise patterns are components of the waveforms generated by all consonants and by semi-vowels (see section 2.1.1.2).

The nature and frequencies of acyclic wave patterns provide critical information about the identity of the phoneme being produced. A prolonged pattern of noise signals a fricative. Silence followed by a burst is characteristic of a stop consonant. The identity of consonants is also revealed by the shift in formants that results as the articulators move from the preceding phoneme to the consonant, and from the consonant to the following phoneme. Those shifts are called *formant transitions*. The formant transitions reflect the movement of the articulators to and from a consonant and indirectly help expose the identity of that consonant.

The complexity of phoneme waveforms and the constant shifting from one pattern to the next make it extremely difficult to analyze the patterns using complex wave representations such as those in figures 2.4 and 2.5. The harmonic and noise patterns are much more clearly displayed using another type of representation: the wide-band *speech spectrogram*, such as the one displayed in figure 2.6. The spectrogram's vertical dimension (called the *frequency dimension* or *frequency domain*) displays the frequencies contained in the signal. The range of frequencies it covers

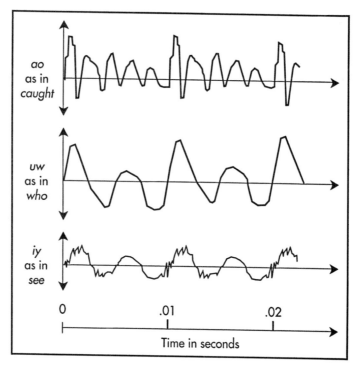

Figure 2.4 Complex waves for three vowels (from Ladefoged, *Elements of Acoustic Phonetics*, Copyright 1962, The University of Chicago Press)

(called its *bandwidth*) is 85 Hz to 8000 Hz. The horizontal dimension (called the *time dimension*) shows how the frequency patterns shift as we speak. Frequencies with greater amplitude are darker.

The spectrogram in figure 2.6 clearly represents the complex harmonic structure of the voiced phonemes *uw* and *l*. The fundamental frequency appears as a dark band at the bottom of the figure and the formants are shown as dark bands in the

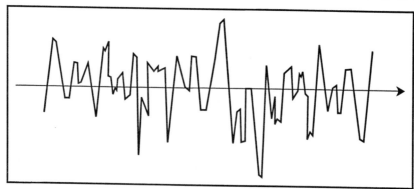

Figure 2.5 Wave produced by noise

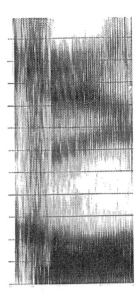

Figure 2.6   Spectrogram for the word "cool"

middle of the frequency range. The darkness of the formant bands indicates the high amplitude of the frequencies in the formants. Formant locations reflect the size, shape, and positioning of the vocal tract at the time a phoneme is spoken. Figure 2.6 shows how the formants change as the speaker's vocal apparatus moves from *uw* to form *l*. This link between acoustics and articulation is called *acoustic-phonetics*.

The location of the formants, their distance from each other, and the ways in which they change as we speak provide critical information for the identification of the phonemes and words being uttered. Formant analysis, however, is applied more easily to voiced phonemes than voiceless phonemes. Formants of voiceless conso-

---

THE SOUND SPECTROGRAPH

Prior to the use of the spectrograph there was no way to clearly display the frequency patterns embedded in speech. Oscilligrams, which trace sound pressure of the speech waveform, would hide common patterns, making utterances of the same word by the same speaker appear entirely different. In contrast, the spectrograph produces a detailed printout of the formant patterns of speech that makes changes in those patterns immediately obvious to the human eye.

The sound spectrograph was invented during World War II by Ralph Potter and his co-workers at Bell Laboratories. Initially, the sound spectrograph was seen as a tool for speech clinicians and as a means to improve communication for people with severe hearing impairments. It has been used extensively by linguists, therapists, and speech processing researchers to understand and describe speech patterns.

The first published description of the sound spectrograph appeared in issue 2654 of *Science* in November, 1945. Potter and two colleagues later published *Visible Speech* (1947), a book describing the spectrograph and its use.

nants, such as the stop k (shown at the start of the word "cool" in figure 2.6), are blurred by the acyclic noise that is part of their characteristic patterns. Those acyclic patterns are shown as dark vertical bands with poorly defined formants or no formants at all. The amplitude, duration, and onset of the noise provide clues to the nature of the phonemes but must be supplemented with formant movement information from neighboring phonemes. In figure 2.6, for example, the silence-burst pattern identifies the initial phoneme as a stop consonant, but the noise burst is too short to identify the phoneme as k. More information is obtained by analyzing the formant patterns leading to it and moving from it. They signal the positions towards which the articulators are moving and where they have been.

2.1.3 Coarticulation

The above discussions might suggest that each phoneme has clearly defined acoustic parameters and a single acoustic realization.

> Rather, the phonemes tend to be abstractions that are implicitly defined by the pronunciation of the words in the language. In particular, the acoustic realization of a phoneme may heavily depend on the acoustic context in which it occurs. This effect is usually called coarticulation. (Hermann Ney, University of Technology of Aachen, Germany & Andreas Noll, Aspect GMbH, "Acoustic-phonetic modeling in the *SPICOS* system," 1994, p. 312)

Neighboring phonemes, the position of a phoneme within words, and the position of the word in the sentence all influence the way a phoneme is uttered. The t in "to" is spoken with rounded lips because of the following uw but the t in "teeth" is said with spread lips. The t in "wait" sounds more like a d when it is embedded in the sentence "Wait a minute" because it is influenced by the voiced phonemes surrounding it. The t at the end of that sentence is unvoiced; and, because of its sentence-final position, it may even lack the characteristic burst of stop consonants.

Such inter-phoneme influences are *coarticulation effects*. Coarticulation effects and other forms of variation are so basic to the articulation process that speech professionals distinguish between the conceptual construct of a speech sound (a *phoneme*) and a specific utterance or instance of that phoneme (called a *phone*).

2.1.4 Auditory Perception: Hearing Speech

The pervasive variability in the speech signal produced by coarticulation and other sources makes analysis of speech input extremely difficult. It is astonishing how well human beings comprehend each other's speech.

The ability of the human auditory processing system to overcome these challenges suggests that an auditory-based speech recognition system would be superior to systems based on acoustics and signal processing. Unfortunately, our understanding of human speech perception is incomplete. What is known strongly suggests that human auditory processing is tuned to speech. The human ear, for example, can detect frequencies from 20 Hz to 20,000 Hz, but it is most sensitive to the frequency range critical for speech: 1,000 Hz to 6,000 Hz.

The human ear is also more sensitive to small changes in frequency for the bandwidth that is critical for speech than for the frequency bandwidths below or above that range. Furthermore, its pattern of sensitivity to changes in pitch does not correspond to the linear, cycles-per-second frequency scale of acoustics. Another scale, called the *mel scale*, was developed to represent the pitch perception patterns of the human ear.

Recent research has uncovered the fact that humans do not process individual frequencies as independent elements as the acoustic analysis of the previous section would suggest. Instead, we hear groups of frequencies, such as formant patterns, as cohesive units and we are capable of distinguishing them from surrounding sound patterns. This capability, called *auditory object formation* or *auditory image formation*, helps explain how humans can discern the speech of individual people at cocktail parties and separate a voice from noise over a poor telephone channel.

Research has already found significant improvements in recognition accuracy when coding based upon auditory models is used in conventional recognition systems. The mel scale, for example, has already been integrated into recognition systems. It is likely we will see other facets of human auditory processing slowly integrated into speech coding and recognition systems. Full utilization of models of human auditory processing must await the results of a great deal of research.

For more detailed information about the use of auditory modeling for coding consult Ghitza (1988 and 1994). Carrell (to appear), Carrell & Opie (1992), and Darwin (1981) exemplify the research being done on auditory object formation.

2.2 PREPROCESSING SPEECH

Like all sounds, speech is an analog waveform. In order for a recognition system to utilize speech data, all formants, noise patterns, silences, and coarticulation effects must be captured and converted to a digital format. This conversion process is accomplished through digital signal processing techniques. Some speech recognition products include hardware to perform this conversion. Other systems rely on the signal processing capabilities of other products, such as digital audio sound cards.

2.2.1 Capturing the Speech Signal

If each one-Hz increment in frequency displayed in the spectrogram of figure 2.6 were represented as a single byte, there would be a continuous stream of almost 64,000 bits to capture and process. The resulting quantity of data would be so great that the processing and storage requirements would be prohibitive. In order for speech recognition to function at an acceptable speed, the amount of data must be reduced.

Fortunately, some data in the speech signal are redundant, some are irrelevant to the recognition process, and some need to be removed from the signal because they interfere with accurate recognition. The challenge is to eliminate these detrimental components from the signal without losing or distorting critical information contained in the data.

One method of reducing the quantity of data is to use filters to screen out frequencies above 3,100 Hz and below 100 Hz. Most of the critical formant data and much of the characteristic noise of fricatives are included within the scope of the narrowed bandwidth. Such bandwidth narrowing is similar to using a zoom lens on a video recorder.

Another data reduction technique, *sampling*, reduces speech input to slices (called *samples*) of the speech signal. Sampling is similar to taking photographs of a busy expressway at rapid but regular intervals. The same effect can be achieved by blinking rapidly while watching a motion picture.

The number of samples that must be extracted from the signal depends upon the frequencies to be included in the analysis. Generally, the minimum sampling rate is set at twice the rate of the highest frequency of interest. This insures that the start, middle, and end of the wave cycle at that frequency will be captured. The minimum sampling rate needed to properly represent 3,100 Hz is 6,200 samples per second. Most speech recognition preprocessors take 8,000 to 10,000 samples per second.

Good analyses of sampling appear in Witten (1982, chapter 3). Cater (1984, chapter 4) and Saffari (1989) provide in-depth discussions of frequency filtering.

2.2.2 Digitizing the Waveform

The samples extracted from the analog signal must be converted into a digital form. The process of converting the analog waveform representation into a digital code is called *analog-to-digital conversion* or *coding*. To achieve high recognition accuracy at an acceptable speed the conversion process must

- Include all critical data
- Remove redundancies
- Remove noise and distortion
- Avoid introducing new distortions

Satisfaction of these requirements goes beyond simple conversion of the samples extracted from the analog signal. Most approaches to coding group the samples into 10 to 50 millisecond blocks called *frames* or *analysis windows*. The consolidation of samples into frames of a specific length is usually called *frame rate*. It is sometimes called *sampling*, but it is not related to sampling of the analog waveform (see section 2.2.1).

The preprocessor extracts acoustic patterns contained in each frame and captures the changes that occur as the signal shifts from one frame to the next. This approach is called *spectral analysis* because it focuses on individual elements of the frequency spectrum.

Two of the most commonly used spectral analysis approaches are the

- Bank-of-filters approach
- Linear predictive coding

Bank-of-filters coding uses a set of filters to segment each sample into a collection of frequency bands. Each frequency band is converted into an array (or vector) of acoustic parameters, generally using a mathematical computation called the *Fast Fourier Transform* (FFT). It defines the speech signal in terms of its component wave patterns (see section 2.1.2.1).

Linear predictive coding (LPC) has become the dominant coding methodology for speech recognition. It is predicated on the idea that it is possible to estimate the values of important acoustic parameters from an incoming sample by using the parameter values from previous samples. The popularity of LPC is due to its ability to provide accurate estimates of acoustic parameters (also called *features*) with less computation and storage than most other approaches.

LPC satisfies the dual goals of speed and accuracy and has served as the basis for other forms of coding, such as *cepstral coefficients* and *vector quantization*. Cepstral coefficients are parameters that have been shown to be more robust and reliable for accurate speech recognition than LPC coefficients. Vector quantization is one of the most effective methods developed for reducing the amount of data required to perform spectral analysis. It represents each set of spectral patterns as an entry (sometimes called a *code word*) in a dictionary of code words (called the *codebook*) so that the recognition process becomes a simple table lookup process.

Flanagan, et al. (1979), Rabiner & Juang (1993), and Schafer & Rabiner (1975) provide technical descriptions of a broad range of spectral analysis and other speech coding techniques. Cater (1984, chapter 5), Rabiner & Juang (1993, chapter 3), and Rowden (1992) provide detailed technical analyses of bank-of-filters coding and linear predictive coding. Cooley (1992) describes the history and utility of the Fast Fourier Transform. Detailed analyses of vector quantization are provided by Gray (1984) and Rabiner & Juang (1993, chapters 3 and 5).

2.3 RECOGNITION

Once the preprocessing of a user's input is complete the recognizer is ready to perform its primary function: to identify what the user has said. The three competing recognition technologies found in commercial speech recognition systems are:

- Template matching
- Acoustic-phonetic recognition
- Stochastic processing

These approaches differ in speed, accuracy, and storage requirements.

2.3.1 Template Matching

Template matching is a form of pattern recognition. It represents speech data as sets of feature/parameter vectors called *templates*. Each word or phrase in an application is stored as a separate template. Spoken input by end users is organized into templates prior to performing the *recognition* process. The input is then compared with stored templates and, as figure 2.7 indicates, the stored template most closely matching the incoming speech pattern is identified as the input word or phrase. The selected template is called the *best match* for the input. Template

---

TEMPLATE MATCHING

Template matching was the dominant recognition methodology in the 1950's and 1960's. Its failure to produce accurate recognition, and growing interest in acoustic-phonetic techniques, caused it to lose favor. Template matching experienced a resurgence following the disillusionment with acoustic-phonetic approaches in the 1970's. By that time it had been improved through the addition of techniques like dynamic time warping. The new template matching algorithms were fast, robust, and accurate enough for the requirements of the commercial systems of the early 1980's. Its dominance continued until the end of the 1980's when it was replaced by stochastic processing. Although template matching is currently on the decline as the basic approach to recognition, it has been adapted for use in word spotting applications (see chapter 4). It also remains the primary technology applied to speaker verification.

    Leedham (1992), Moore (1984), and Rabiner & Juang (1993, chapter 4) provide excellent technical analyses of template matching.

---

matching is performed at the word level and contains no reference to the phonemes within the word. The matching process entails a frame-by-frame comparison of spectral patterns (see section 2.2) and generates an overall similarity assessment (usually called the *distance metric*) for each template.

The comparison is not expected to produce an identical match. Individual utterances of the same word, even by the same person, often differ in length. This variation can be due to a number of factors, including difference in the rate at which the person is speaking, emphasis, or emotion. Whatever the cause, there must be a way to minimize temporal differences between patterns so that fast and slow utterances of the same word will not be identified as different words. The process of minimizing temporal/word length differences is called *temporal alignment*. The approach most commonly used to perform temporal alignment in template matching is a pattern-matching technique called *dynamic time warping* (DTW). DTW establishes the optimum alignment of one set of vectors (template) with another.

Most template matching systems have a predetermined threshold of acceptability. Its function is to prevent noise and words not in the application vocabulary from being incorrectly identified as acceptable speech input. If no template match exceeds the threshold of acceptability no recognition is recorded. Applications and

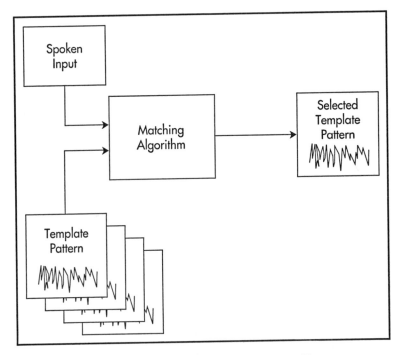

Figure 2.7 Recognition using template matching

systems differ on how such non-recognition events are handled. Many systems ask the user to repeat the word or utterance.

Template matching performs very well with small vocabularies of phonetically distinct items but has difficulty making the fine distinctions required for larger vocabulary recognition and recognition of vocabularies containing similar-sounding words (called *confusable* words). Since it operates at the word level there must be at least one stored template for each word in the application vocabulary. If, for example, there are five thousand words in an application, there would need to be at least five thousand templates.

2.3.2 Acoustic-Phonetic Recognition

Unlike template matching, acoustic-phonetic recognition functions at the phoneme level. Theoretically, it is an attractive approach to speech recognition because it limits the number of representations that must be stored to the number of phonemes needed for a language. For English, that number is around forty no matter how large the application vocabulary.

Acoustic-phonetic recognition generally involves three steps:

- Feature-extraction
- Segmentation and labelling
- Word-level recognition

ACOUSTIC-PHONETIC RECOGNITION

Acoustic-phonetic recognition supplanted template matching in the early 1970's. The successful ARPA SUR systems highlighted potential benefits of this approach. Unfortunately, acoustic-phonetics was poorly understood at the time and the equipment required to implement acoustic-phonetic systems was expensive. Since then, our understanding of acoustic-phonetic phenomena, such as coarticulation, has dramatically improved. These advances, combined with the development of powerful but inexpensive computing hardware, has led to renewed interest in acoustic-phonetic recognition by researchers. Good historical sources on acoustic-phonetic recognition include Cole (1986), Oshika, et al. (1975), and Woods (1983).

During feature extraction the system examines the input for spectral patterns, such as formant frequencies, needed to distinguish phonemes from each other. The collection of extracted features is interpreted using acoustic-phonetic rules. These rules identify phonemes (*labelling*) and determine where one phoneme ends and the next begins (*segmentation*).

The high degree of acoustic similarity among phonemes combined with phoneme variability resulting from coarticulation effects and other sources create uncertainty with regard to potential phone labels. As a result, the output of the segmentation and labelling stage is a set of phoneme hypotheses. These hypotheses can be organized into a *phoneme lattice* (see figure 2.8), decision tree, or similar structure. Figure 2.8 displays more than one phoneme hypothesis for a single point in the input.

Once the segmentation and labelling process has been completed, the system searches through the application vocabulary for words matching the phoneme hypotheses. The word best matching a sequence of hypotheses is identified as the input item.

Papers by Cole (1986) and Zue (1985) provide excellent descriptions of acoustic-phonetic recognition.

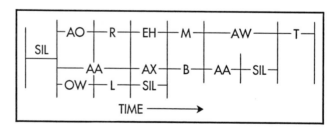

Figure 2.8   Phoneme lattice (from Rabiner & Juang, *Fundamentals of Speech Recognition,* Copyright 1993, Prentice Hall)

2.3.3 Stochastic Processing

The term *stochastic* refers to the process of making a sequence of *non-deterministic* selections from among sets of alternatives. They are non-deterministic because the choices during the recognition process are governed by the characteristics of the input and not specified in advance. The use of stochastic models and processing permeates speech recognition. Stochastic processing dominates current word-construction/recognition (see chapter 3) and grammar (see chapter 4).

Like template matching, stochastic processing requires the creation and storage of models of each of the items that will be recognized. At that point the two approaches diverge. Stochastic processing involves no direct matching between stored models and input. Instead, it is based upon complex statistical and probabilistic analyses which are best understood by examining the network-like structure in which those statistics are stored: the *hidden Markov model* (HMM).

An HMM, such as the one displayed in figure 2.9, consists of a sequence of states connected by transitions. The states represent the alternatives of the stochastic process and the transitions contain probabilistic and other data used to determine which state should be selected next. The states of the HMM in figure 2.9 are displayed as circles and its transitions are represented by arrows. Transitions from the first state of the HMM go to the first state (called a *recursive transition*), to the next state, or to the third state of the HMM. If the HMM in figure 2.9 is a stored model of the word "five," it would be called a *reference model* for "five" and would contain statistics about all the spoken samples of the word used to create the reference model. Each state of the HMM holds statistics for a segment of the word. Those statistics describe the parameter values and parameter variation that were found in samples of the word. A recognition system may have numerous HMM's like the one in figure 2.9 or may consolidate them into a network of states and transitions.

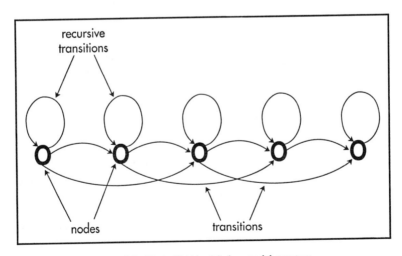

Figure 2.9   Typical hidden Markov model structure

HIDDEN MARKOV MODELS

In 1913, A. A. Markov described a network model capable of generating Russian letter sequences or predicting letter sequences using sequence probabilities acquired through exposure to Russian texts. It is used as the basis for computational models in a wide range of fields, including models of human language.

In the 1960's and early 1970's, Markov modeling was applied to multi-layer, hierarchical structures by Baum and other researchers. Since the probabalistic calculations of the underlying layers are not observed as part of the higher-level sequences these models were called *hidden Markov models* (HMM's).

Researchers began investigating using HMM's for speech recognition in the early 1970's. One of the earliest proponents of the technology was James Baker of Carnegie Mellon University (CMU), who used it to develop CMU's *DRAGON* system for the ARPA SUR project. Another early proponent of HMM's was Frederick Jelinek, whose research group at IBM was instrumental in advancing HMM technology. In 1982, James and Janet Baker founded Dragon Systems, and soon developed the *DragonScribe* system, one of the first commercial products using HMM technology.

HMM technology did not gain widespread acceptance for commercial systems until the late 1980's, but by 1990 HMM's had become the dominant approach to recognition.

For additional information consult papers by James Baker (1975a and 1975b) and Baum (1972).

The recognition system proceeds through the input comparing it with stored models. If the user were to say "fayv" the system might select the HMM shown in figure 2.9 as one of the stored models to compare with the user's input. If the user prolonged the *f* at the start of her/his input word, it is likely that when the recognizer compares the input with the HMM in figure 2.9 there would be at least one recursive transition for the first state of the HMM.

These comparisons produce a probability score indicating the likelihood that a particular stored HMM reference model is the *best match* for the input. This approach is called the *Baum-Welch maximum-likelihood algorithm*. Another common method used for stochastic recognition is the *Viterbi algorithm*. The *Viterbi algorithm* looks through a network of nodes for a sequence of HMM states that corresponds most closely to the input. This is called the *best path*.

Stochastic processing using HMM's is accurate, flexible, and capable of being fully automated. It can be applied to units smaller than phonemes or as large as sequences of words. As will be described in chapter 3, stochastic processing is most often used to represent and recognize speech at the word level (sometimes called *whole word* recognition) and for a variant of the phoneme level called *subwords*.

Papers by Moore (1984), Paul (1990), and Rabiner & Juang (1986) provide detailed technical descriptions of HMM's.

2.4 NEURAL NETWORKS

If speech recognition systems could learn important speech knowledge automatically and represent this knowledge in a parallel distributed fashion for rapid evaluation ... Such a system would mimic the functions of the human brain, which consists of several billion simple, inaccurate, and slow processors that perform reliable speech recognition. (Alex Waibel & John Hampshire II, Carnegie Mellon University, "Building blocks for speech," 1989, p. 235)

Neural networks are computer programs that emulate this type of processing. They are sometimes called *artificial neural networks* to distinguish neural network programs from biological neural structures. Since references to neural networks in this book will only be to neural network programs, we will simply use the term *neural networks* or more simply *networks*.

Neural networks are excellent classification systems. They specialize in classifying noisy, patterned, variable data streams containing multiple, overlapping, interacting, and incomplete cues. Speech recognition is a classification task that has all of these characteristics, making neural networks an attractive alternative to the approaches described earlier in this chapter.

Unlike most other technologies, neural networks do not require that a complete specification of a problem be created prior to developing a network-based solution. Instead, networks learn patterns solely through exposure to large numbers of examples, making it possible to construct neural networks for auditory models and other poorly understood areas. The fact that networks accomplish all of these feats using parallel processing is of special interest because increases in complexity do not entail significant reductions in speed.

2.4.1 What are Neural Networks?

The concept of artificial neural networks has its roots in the structure and behavior of the human brain. The brain is composed of a network of specialized cells called neurons that operate in parallel to learn and process a wide range of complex information. Like the human brain, neural networks are constructed from interconnected neurons (also called *nodes* or *processing elements*) and learn new patterns by experiencing examples of those patterns.

Groups of nodes that function in tandem are called layers. Neural networks have three types of layers: one *input layer*, one or more *hidden layers,* and one *output layer*. Figure 2.10 illustrates this basic *architecture*. The input layer receives information from the external environment and the output layer communicates the network's decisions to the external environment. Between the input and output layers are one or more hidden layers that communicate with each other and the output layer. Like hidden Markov models, the hidden layers of neural networks are *hidden* because their activities are only communicated to other neurons in the network. An outside observer cannot see their inputs or outputs. From the perspective of the net-

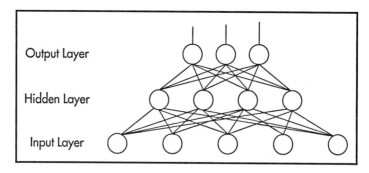

Figure 2.10   Typical neural network architecture

work as a whole, hidden layers are part of the internal abstract pattern that constitutes the network's solution to the problem to be solved.

2.4.2 Neural Network Architectures

The way in which the nodes and layers of a network are organized is called the network's *architecture*. There are several ways to classify the architecture of a neural network. The most common are on the basis of:

- Feedback loops
- Node-internal transfer function
- Learning techniques

2.4.2.1 Feedback loops.   Some networks, such as the one shown in figure 2.11, feed the results of the output layer or hidden layers back into the network. These *feedback* (also called *recurrent*) networks are good for processing data, such as speech, containing temporal information. They generally require considerably more training and operate more slowly than networks without feedback loops

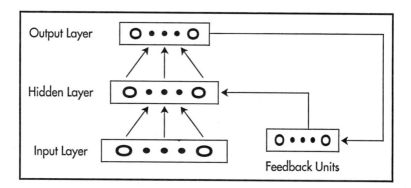

Figure 2.11   Example of a recurrent network architecture

(called *feedforward networks*). Although some recurrent networks have been developed for speech recognition, most network architectures used for speech are feedforward, such as the network shown in figure 2.10.

2.4.2.2 Transfer functions.   Each hidden or output node of a network performs internal calculations. The first calculation is to total the signals it has received from other neurons in the network, factoring into its calculations the strength of each of the input signals. This is called the weighted sum of its inputs. The node then converts the weighted sum into a form that can be processed by other nodes in the network. This conversion is called the *transfer function*.

Some transfer functions add or multiply the result of the weighted sum by a specified number. This is called a *linear* transfer function. It is the type of transfer function used by *multi-layer perceptron* (MLP) networks, a network architecture frequently used for speech recognition. A transfer function used in many types of networks is the *sigmoid function,* which establishes upper and lower limits (usually 0 and 1) on calculations to minimize the impact of extreme values. It converts the summation into a value within the specified range. The sigmoid function is an example of a *non-linear* transfer function.

2.4.2.3 Learning techniques.   In order for a neural network to learn a new pattern or set of patterns it must be exposed to samples of those patterns. This learning process is called *training* the network. It can be accomplished in a supervised or unsupervised fashion.

During *supervised training,* a network is given the correct classification or desired output along with an input pattern. A network being trained to recognize specific words might, for example, be told the identity of the word matching a set of input it is given. After processing the input supplied to it, the network training algorithm compares its independently calculated decision with the correct answer. It then corrects any errors it has made by changing the weights on the links between individual neurons of the network.

Supervised training enables a network to experience the range of variation within each category. After exposure to a large number of examples the network is said to *converge*. The network is then tested on new data before being deployed. The most common form of supervised training is *backpropagation*. During backpropagation training, error correction information is fed back into the network so that all its nodes will be updated. Backpropagation is used to train both feedforward and recurrent networks.

Unsupervised training forces a network to create its own classification system. This approach is similar to the manner in which humans learn to classify many things. Unsupervised training is often used when the patterns of classification are not fully known or are difficult to describe. The most commonly used unsupervised network is the Kohonen *self-organizing map* (SOM). The basic SOM is a feedforward network. Its architecture is a one- or two-dimensional array. An SOM network modifies itself, or learns, to detect regularities and correlations found in input patterns. Neighboring neurons adapt to become more like each other with exposure to more input. This approach is attractive for speech recognition for a number of reasons: it can capture patterns of variability in neighboring nodes; it can identify salient classification features; and it can establish a system of classification based upon those features.

Caudill & Butler (1992), Lawrence (1993), and Wasserman (1989) provide excellent overviews of neural network technology. Bourlard & Morgan (1994), Lippmann (1989), Markowitz (1993b and 1994b), Morgan & Bourlard (1995), and Waibel & Hampshire (1989) examine neural networks for speech recognition.

2.5 NEURAL NETWORKS FOR SPEECH

The allure of neural networks for speech recognition lies in their superior classification abilities. Considerable effort has been directed towards development of networks to do word, syllable, and phoneme classification. Very few vendors have incorporated neural networks into their commercial systems, but the migration from the laboratory has begun. Lernout & Hauspie used neural networks technology to generate its database of speaker-independent speaker models for its commercial technology. The RSC Series of chips by Sensory Circuits contains a neural network that performs speech recognition. Virtually all the other neural networks that will be described in this book are research systems.

2.5.1 Neural Networks for Speech Recognition

Research using neural networks for speech recognition can be characterized in terms of its ability to handle time-dimension data and inclusion of non-network structures. *Static classification* networks focus on the frequency domain of speech while making little or no attempt to process temporal information. They use presegmented (often manually-segmented) speech elements and often input speech items as whole units rather than as time sequences.

> Time alignment presents the greatest problem for neural network based systems, since connectionist learning procedures are typically defined in terms of static pattern classification tasks. (Patrick Haffner, Michael Franzini & Alex Waibel, Carnegie Mellon University, "Integrating time alignment and neural networks for high performance continuous speech recognition," 1991, p. 105)

The static classification approach was typical of early network applications to speech recognition because they were concerned with assessing the ability of neural networks to recognize units of speech.

Current networks analyze slices or streams of real speech data. Until recently, these systems were referred to as *dynamic classification* networks because they process time-dimension components of speech and because they are concerned with producing operational speech understanding systems.

Some dynamic classification networks have time alignment built into the network architecture. One of the most popular of these networks, the *Time Delay Neural Network (TDNN)* developed at Carnegie Mellon University (CMU), is shown in figure 2.12. It is a feedforward network with a sigmoid transfer function and was trained using backpropagation. The *TDNN* shown in figure 2.12 was trained to recognize the phonemes *b, d,* and *g.* It is constructed as a module to enhance extensibility. A full *TDNN* would be constructed from many modules like the one in figure 2.12.

A few researchers have used recurrent networks to capture the overlapping temporal information in speech. Recurrent networks add information about prior time slices to the analysis of the current slice. They process time shifts without having to create multiple copies of speech slices like time delay networks. Because of this, recurrent networks are seen as natural candidates for real-time speech analysis. Although recurrent networks have shown reasonably good performance on small,

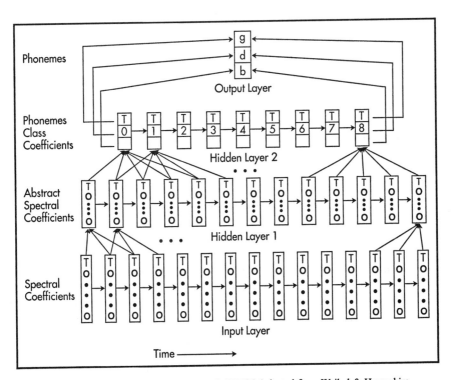

Figure 2.12 *Time Delay Neural Network (TDNN)* (adapted from Waibel & Hampshire, "Neural network applications to speech," Copyright 1991, Prentice Hall)

well-defined tasks, they are difficult to design and require more training than feed-forward architectures.

The recent focus on continuous speech recognition (see chapter 6, section 6.3) has altered the definitions of static and dynamic. Static classification has been extended to refer to systems, such as the *TDNN*, that do not process continuous speech, while dynamic classification networks are those designed to perform continuous speech recognition. Among the new class of dynamic networks are some that have recast the role of neural network processing from classification to prediction. Like linear predictive coding (see section 2.2.2), *prediction networks* are trained to use the current acoustic frame to estimate the acoustic pattern of the next frame. Accurate predictions provide indirect confirmation of phoneme classification, although prediction networks do not perform the classifications themselves.

One of the major trends in the design of neural networks for speech recognition is the construction of *hybrid models* combining neural networks with an HMM or dynamic time warping (DTW) matrix. In some instances, an HMM or DTW is attached to an existing network structure. The *TDNN*, for example, has been modified to feed its outputs into a DTW matrix. This hybrid is called the *MS-TDNN*. It performs word-level classification/recognition on continuous speech and has been used to recognize digits and the names of letters of the English alphabet. Lernout & Hauspie offer a configuration of their system that combines a neural network with an HMM, and Nippon Telegraph and Telephone (NTT) of Japan has developed a hybrid HMM-SOM network. These two hybrid systems perform phoneme classification in continuous speech.

Hybrids, predictive networks, and other dynamic systems will be discussed in greater detail in chapters 4, 5, 6, and 7. Tebelskis, et al. (1991) provide a technical analysis of their predictive system. Bourlard & Morgan (1994) and Morgan & Bourlard (1995) describe the Lernout & Hauspie network and other hybrid architectures. Waibel & Hampshire (1991) describe the *TDNN*, and Rigoll (1991) describes the NTT hybrid.

2.5.2 Neural Networks for Speech Coding

Unlike conventional approaches to coding (see section 2.2), neural networks can apply built-in parallelism to spectral analysis. This reduces computation time while at the same time enabling the preprocessor to perform more detailed analyses of the incoming data. Research has produced interesting results. Some neural network coders using supervised training have formulated abstractions in their hidden layers corresponding to important acoustic and perceptual generalizations, such as formant transition patterns.

One of the most active areas of coding using neural networks is vector quantization. Some networks have been used in conjunction with conventional systems to reduce the complexity of vector quantization codebooks. Others have been designed to perform vector quantization themselves. Multi-layer perceptron networks and Kohonen SOM's are among the most commonly used for these functions.

Neural networks have performed well as tools to reduce prediction error. The *hidden control neural network (HCNN)*, a feedforward network developed at AT&T Bell Laboratories, analyzes one sample of speech to predict the acoustic characteristics of the next sample. It receives input from two sources: digitized speech sample vectors and an independent control unit. The control unit handles temporal variation without modifying the network's other parameters and its structure parallels that of an HMM.

Levin (1990) describes the *HCNN* system and Markowitz (1993b and 1994b) present overviews of neural networks for speech coding and recognition.

2.5.3 Auditory Models

Both auditory modeling and neural networks are rooted in biological models and focus on neural activity. Consequently, the use of neural networks to implement auditory coding is a natural extension of both approaches.

Auditory modeling research using neural networks has shown a great deal of promise. Researchers doing spectral analysis based upon models of the auditory nerve have observed improvements in recognition accuracy. De Mori, et al. (1989), for example, designed an auditory-based coder using a multi-layer perceptron network. Their network produced a recognition error rate of 4.3 percent, whereas a Fast Fourier Transform generated an error rate of 13 percent.

Other research has focused on the discrimination of speech from noise. In a hybrid system developed at Wright Patterson Air Force Base, two processors based on cochlear models analyze a noisy speech signal and feed their results to a self-organizing map designed to perform phoneme recognition. This and other noise-related systems are discussed in greater detail in chapter 7.

2.6 EVALUATING RECOGNITION — AN INTRODUCTION

A recognition system must be capable of satisfying the requirements of the application for which it will be used and the needs of the people who will use it. Chapters 3 through 7 examine different components of speech recognition systems that should be part of the product selection and evaluation process.

Chapter 5, for example, discusses different types of speaker modeling. Speaker modeling should be a part of product selection and evaluation because recognition products that are *speaker-independent* (a user need not train the system to recognize her/his voice) are not appropriate for all applications. Highly personal applications, such as voice-dialing using a personalized directory ("call Mom" or "call my accountant") are handled better using a product that requires speakers to train the system to their voices.

Similarly, a full evaluation of speech recognition systems needs to include a realistic understanding of:

- Vocabulary size, type, and flexibility (chapter 3)
- Required sentence and application structures (chapter 4)
- The end users (chapters 5 and 8)
- Style of input (chapter 6)
- Type and amount of noise with which the recognizer must contend and its effect upon both the speaker and the recognizer (chapter 7)
- Stress placed upon the person using the application (chapter 7)

The evaluation must also consider why a speech recognition interface is beneficial, the type of work the recognizer must perform, the hardware and software environment in which the recognition must operate, and the types of people who will use it (chapter 8). Careful consideration of all these factors form the basis upon which a successful application is constructed.

Once the type of recognition system that is needed for the application has been identified, different products can be evaluated by testing them under conditions comparable to those of the application. This is called *performance evaluation*. Performance evaluation centers around speed and accuracy. These two criteria are strongly influenced by a number of factors:

- Vocabulary size and complexity
- Type and flexibility of the grammar
- Type and quality of speaker modeling
- Flow of speech
- Noise in the speaking environment
- Noise in the speech channel
- Type of application
- Complexity of the application
- Quality of application design

The discussions in chapters 3 through 8 are designed to provide sufficient detail to facilitate such product comparisons. This chapter presents some general evaluation concepts.

2.6.1 Speed

The speed of a recognizer's response is a critical component when recognition must be done in *real time:* recognition occurs while the user is speaking to the system. This is a characteristic of most speech recognition applications. Only a few products, such as Philips Dictation Systems' *Speech Magic,* invoke the recognition process after the user is finished using the system.

The speed of real-time recognition must be acceptable to users under both average and bad conditions. Speed can be tested by building a pilot of the target application and running it on the expected hardware platform. Another approach is to design a set of stress tests varying the demands of vocabulary, users, and grammar.

Care must be taken to ascertain whether speed problems are due to the recognition system or other factors. As with any other application, the speed of a recognition application is affected by the quality of the application design and the hardware platform. If, for example, the application is running on a PC with limited memory or if it is overloaded with other processes, speed will be reduced for all operations, including those of the recognition system.

2.6.2 Accuracy

A recognition system must be able to recognize the speech of the expected users in the target speaking environment. Even so, all speech recognition systems, including humans, make errors.

There are three basic classes of errors made by recognition systems:

- *Deletion*   Dropping of words. For example, the system hears "124" when the speaker says "1234."
- *Substitution* Replacing a spoken word with another, usually similar, word. For example, the system hears "9" when the speaker says "5."
- *Insertion*   Adding a word. For example, the system hears "12384" when the speaker says "1234."

Another type of error that is sometimes included is *rejection.* It is a form of deletion that occurs when the entire response, usually a single word or short phrase, is not perceived by the recognizer.

All errors pose problems and need to be kept to a minimum. Substitution errors are the most damaging because they replace the input with an incorrect translation. Rejection errors can be handled in some systems through the use of *time-outs.* The system may be programmed to reprompt the user when a pre-determined amount of time has elapsed without a response to a prompt. Time-outs of this sort are also useful for terminating an interaction when there is no response to several reprompts. The above list of error types is discussed further in chapter 8 (section 8.5).

If the recognizer performs acceptably on a pilot of the application, it should be stress-tested to determine whether, how quickly, and in what ways its performance degrades. Most recognition systems allow adjustments to the recognition thresholds that evaluate the match between the system's stored models and the incoming speech. Higher thresholds can result in rejection of acceptable input, whereas lower thresholds may produce substitution or insertion errors. In some applications it is preferable for the system to not hear what was said than to make an erroneous guess. The designers of those applications will set high thresholds. For applications with highly differentiated vocabulary, high thresholds may be unnecessary.

If a system makes a lot of errors at first, it may not be the result of using the wrong recognition tool. Other factors contributing to high error rates are

- The quality of speaker training
- User attitude
- Microphone quality and placement
- Poor application design
- High or variable noise levels
- Inappropriate recognition thresholds (called *rejection threshold*)

Each of these must be eliminated as the source of problems before the recognition system, or speech recognition itself, is rejected.

The most important evaluation of an application is by its users. Speech recognition is extremely sensitive to user acceptance. Good technology and design carry no weight if the people who must speak to a system refuse to use it.

2.7 RECOGNITION TECHNOLOGIES IN COMMERCIAL PRODUCTS

Template matching, acoustic-phonetic recognition, stochastic processing, and neural networks are all recognition technologies used in commercial products. They will be discussed in the following sections.

2.7.1 Template Matching

The use of template matching is waning, but it is still found in some commercial systems. It is highly effective for applications with small vocabularies but has not shown itself to be accurate enough to make the fine discriminations required for large vocabulary recognition. Applications requiring mid-size vocabularies between one thousand and ten thousand words can use template matching systems, if the number of vocabulary choices at any single point (called the *branching factor*) in the application is kept to a minimum. Another problem is that storage requirements expand in a linear fashion with growth in the size of the vocabulary. This, in turn, produces a comparable increase in computational complexity.

2.7.2 Acoustic-Phonetic Recognition

Acoustic-phonetic recognition is rarely found in the commercial systems of today. Speech Systems, Inc. is one of the few manufacturers of commercial acoustic-phonetic recognition systems although its products are migrating towards stochastic processing.

Acoustic-phonetic recognition is attractive because it promises a range of storage, computational, and vocabulary growth advantages not available with other approaches. As the size, nature, and complexity of speech recognition applications have expanded, the benefits of using acoustic-phonetic knowledge have become more important. The emergence of acoustic-phonetic systems has been hindered by the depth of linguistic knowledge and the quantity of manual labor generally required to create an efficient, accurate system.

Another fundamental issue is that recognition is performed on extremely small, yet highly variable, elements of speech (see section 2.1). This inherent variability has allowed developers a great deal of latitude in the definition of phonemes and the features used to identify them. Although interest in acoustic-phonetic representation is increasing, the absence of descriptive, methodological, and design standards continues to impede its use.

2.7.3 Stochastic Processing

Stochastic processing is currently the dominant recognition technology. It has become a component of most commercial and research recognition systems. It is fast, efficient, and *robust*. The ability of a recognition system to perform accurately under varying conditions, including different types of noise, is called *robustness* (see chapter 7, Introduction).

One of the limitations of hidden Markov models is their inability to apply linguistic knowledge to its processes for phenomena-like coarticulation. Another criticism of the current formulation of stochastic processing for word-level systems is that, like template matching recognizers, the growth of the application vocabulary produces linear increases in storage. This is not true for subword systems (see chapter 3, section 3.1.5) which exploit some of the best features of acoustic-phonetics and stochastic processing. These concerns will be discussed in greater detail in chapter 3.

2.7.4 Neural Networks

Some industry analysts view neural networks as the recognition technology of the future. Although there is extensive research applying neural networks to speech recognition, they have only begun to appear in commercial products. Sensory Circuits, one of the first to offer commercial speech recognition technology using neural networks, offers a chip-level product for less than five dollars per a chip. It is likely that neural networks will play an important role in the future. A major reason for this optimism is the ability of neural networks to learn new patterns automatically, even when those patterns are corrupted by noise and characterized by variability.

2.8 COMMUNICATING AFTER RECOGNITION IS ACCOMPLISHED

Once speech input has been identified, the application must do something with the information. From the perspective of the task to be accomplished, speech input is simply a means of achieving its goals. The ability of a recognition tool to communicate with other application hardware and software lies closer to the purpose of an application than the coding and recognition steps. Consequently, evaluating the ability of a speech recognition product to satisfy the communication requirements of an application is just as important as assessing the quality of recognition.

With the increased acceptance of speech recognition has come an appreciation of a potential design flaw in the application structure shown in figure 2.0, at the start of this chapter. That flaw is the independence of the recognition system from the other application software. One of the greatest dangers associated with the model shown in figure 2.0 is that the speech interface will lose synchrony with the rest of the application. The likelihood of this occurring increases for applications that do not maintain two-way communication between the application and the speech interface. In those applications, events may occur in either the interface or the application software that will cause one of them to move a step ahead of the other.

Figure 2.13 displays a more accurate (and more efficient) relationship in which speech recognition is an integral component of the application. Such applications are called *speech enabled* or *speech aware*. In speech aware applications, the calls to speech and the messages from speech are developed as a part of the application itself. This makes it extremely difficult for the speech to lose synchronization with the rest of the application. It adds intelligence to the speech in the form of knowledge about the current and potential states of the other application software and it clarifies the vocabulary and error conditions associated with those states. These changes make the speech interface an integral part of the application.

One example of a speech aware application was developed by the author for the Workers Compensation Department of Navistar International. As a self-insured company, Navistar had to calculate how much money to set aside to cover each worker's compensation claim. The process is called *reserving*. Since the operations of an expert system are inherently variable, the expert system was constructed so that calls to all user interface technologies, including speech, were done as a unit, making it impossible for the speech front-end to lose synchronization with the rest of the application. The rules, the graphical user interface (GUI), and the recognition system all knew the input vocabulary and navigation commands that were available at every point in the operation of the application. This melding of speech with the

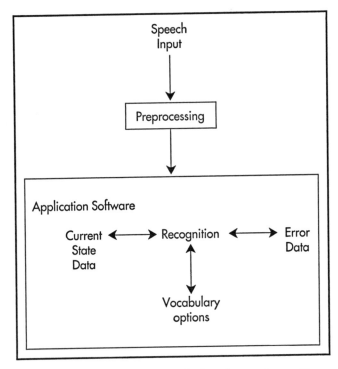

Figure 2.13   Components of an application using speech recognition

system increased the speed, flexibility, and efficiency of the application (see chapter 8, section 8.4, for more information about speech enabled applications).

Several software companies, including Novell and Microsoft, are working towards the development of speech enabled versions of their systems. The success of their efforts will have a significant effect on the speed with which speech recognition becomes an integrated part of software design (see chapter 10 for a more detailed description of these standards efforts).

3

REPRESENTING THE VOCABULARY

INTRODUCTION

One of the enduring goals of speech recognition technology is to enable system users to say what they need to say using whatever words needed to say it. This is often translated into a requirement for very large, expandable vocabularies.

In practice, the vocabulary demands of applications can vary from as few as two words to many thousands of words. Many applications require fifty or fewer words, but developers realize that by creating systems capable of processing large vocabularies they will automatically expand the range and types of applications suitable for speech recognition.

Even though phonemes are the basic sound segments of a language, most commercial recognition systems use words, rather than phonemes, as the fundamental unit of recognition. The Technology Focus section describes the dominant technologies used to represent words in both large and small vocabularies:

- Templates
- Hidden Markov models
- Sequences of phonemes
- Sequences of subwords

Each is described in terms of how it defines the concept of *word* and how it addresses variability in the way a word is spoken. The view is then expanded to examine technological issues facing large vocabulary design.

In the Application Focus, the concept of *word* is reexamined from the application perspective, comparing it to standard dictionaries and everyday word usage. Alternative methods of vocabulary development for applications are described, followed by an examination of the problem of handling acoustically similar (called *confusable*) words, such as "mine" and "nine." The chapter concludes with an overview of the vocabulary demands of applications.

3.1 WHAT IS A WORD?

Defining what a word is may seem unnecessary. To a human being, a spoken word is a sequence of sounds (see chapter 2, section 2.1.3) connected to a meaning. To a large extent, a specific word or phrase is identified because it is a concept that we already know and because its sequence of sounds is uttered in a context in which it makes sense. Such prior knowledge and contextual support enable people to interpret the question "Jeet?" as "Did you eat?" when it is uttered at noon or 6:00 P.M.

When the word or phrase is unfamiliar, or if we cannot use context to identify what has probably been said, the only source of data we have available is a stream of sounds. That sound stream is full of distortion from coarticulation and other factors, making it difficult for us to assign phoneme and word labels. These are the conditions that generate misunderstandings like "pullet surprise" for "Pulitzer Prize."

Speech recognition systems are like the person who heard "pullet surprise." Their primary source of data is a preprocessed stream of acoustic parameters that must be translated into a word or series of words. To accomplish this task, recognition systems store models (sometimes called *reference models*) of the words in an application. During recognition, they compare the stream of acoustic parameters uttered by the user with those stored models (see chapter 2, section 2.3).

Developers disagree on how reference models should be represented. The methods of representation most commonly used are

- Templates
- Hidden Markov models
- Sequences of phonemes
- Sequences of subwords

The choice a developer makes indicates both how the concept "word" is defined and the recognition methodology that will be applied.

Several members of this list have already been introduced as the tools used to perform recognition (see chapter 2, section 2.3). The overlap between the focus on representation (chapter 2) and the concern with vocabulary (chapter 3) results from the fact that recognition is generally performed at the word level.

3.1.1 Variability

All methods of representing vocabulary must address the issue of variability in the way words are spoken. Variability arises from a number of sources. One, coarticulation, was discussed in chapter 2 (see section 2.1.3). It refers to the effects of surrounding sounds. Variability is also the result of inter-speaker differences. Each speaker has a unique vocal tract configuration. We differ in the size and shape of our mouths, tongues, throats, and teeth. Speakers also vary in the way they pronounce phonemes and words. Some pronunciation patterns of large populations of speakers can be grouped on the basis of regional, class, age, or sex differences. Other patterns are idiosyncratic. Some people, for example, pronounce the phoneme *l* (as in the word "let") with the back of their tongues, while others say it with their tongue tip. Some speakers talk more slowly than others or more nasally.

Variability exists not only between speakers but within the speech of a single speaker. Words are spoken at different speeds and loudness. They reflect varying levels of emotion and fatigue. As figure 3.1 illustrates, variability is so basic to speech that one person rarely says the same word in exactly the same way twice.

Coarticulation, inter-speaker differences, and intra-speaker inconsistency interact to produce complex patterns of variation which must be addressed. The ability of a recognition system to perform well under conditions of speaker variability is one of the conditions of *robustness*. The other primary condition of robustness, accurate recognition under varying noise conditions, is discussed in chapter 7.

3.1.2 Templates

Template matching (see chapter 2, section 2.3.1) equates a word with its template representation. A template is a sequence of vectors. Each vector contains a set of values for the parameters used by the system to represent speech. The representation is simple, straightforward, and easy to generate. There is no internal structure beyond the sequence of vectors generated by the coding process. No attempt is

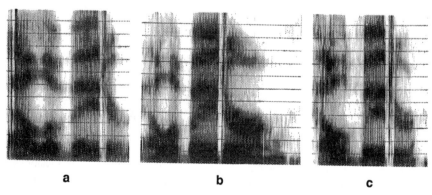

a   b   c

Figure 3.1 Spectrograms of three utterances of the word "elevator" by the author

made to analyze linguistic or acoustic relationships that might exist within the word.

In early template systems each template represented one example (called a *token*) of a word produced by a speaker. Ten spoken tokens would be stored as ten different templates and each of these templates was frozen and unmodifiable. As a result, intra- and inter-speaker variability was captured through the creation of sets of templates for each word in the application's vocabulary.

This simplistic approach to variability functions acceptably for small vocabularies containing highly differentiated words. The resource demands required for storage and searching through the templates grow linearly with the size of the vocabulary. Using this approach, template matching for vocabularies larger than one hundred words becomes unacceptably time consuming and error prone.

More recent template implementations employ *robust templates*. Robust templates are created from more than one token of a word using mathematical averages and statistical clustering techniques. These processes focus on normalizing the frequency and time patterns of the tokens for the word. Because they incorporate data from more than one token, they are better able to handle intra-speaker variability. The use of robust templates also reduces the rapid growth in storage requirements normally associated with template matching systems (see chapter 2, section 2.7.1).

Good technical analyses of template matching can also be found in Leedham (1992), Moore (1984), and Rabiner & Juang (1993, chapter 4).

3.1.3 Hidden Markov Models

In most stochastic processing systems designed for speech recognition (see chapter 2, section 2.3.3), a word is represented by an HMM, such as the ones displayed in figure 2.9 of chapter 2 and in figure 3.2. Unlike templates, HMM's are designed to capture and represent patterns of variation. The statistical information embedded in the states and transitions of the HMM contain probability information extracted from multiple tokens of a word. These tokens may be supplied by individual application users, groups of speakers, or a pre-existing database (called a *corpus*) of digitized speech.

The performance of an HMM depends heavily upon the quality of the data used to create its internal probabilities. These probabilities define the nature and scope of the variation associated with a word or other input. They guide the selection of the best path or best match (see chapter 2, section 2.3.3). If these probabilities are derived from inadequate data or from tokens that do not reflect the speech of the expected population of users, recognition using the HMM will be poor.

HMM's can be structured in a variety of ways. The most common HMM architecture found in speech recognition systems is the left-to-right, directional HMM shown in figure 3.2a. The ergotic HMM in figure 3.2b is frequently used to represent networks of phonemes or subwords (see section 3.1.5). Ergotic HMM's are non-directional and link every state to every other state.

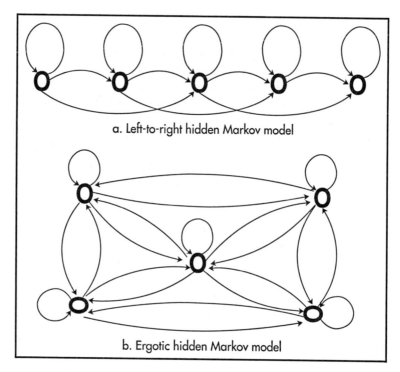

Figure 3.2   Two typical architectures of hidden Markov models

HMM's are fast, efficient, accurate, and flexible. One criticism of HMM's is that the states of an HMM are operationally independent.

> Its drawback is the inaccurate Markov assumption; namely, that acoustic realizations and durations depend only on the current state and are conditionally independent of the past . . . HMM's do not provide much insight on the recognition process. As a result, it is often difficult to analyze the errors of an HMM system in an attempt to improve its performance (Alex Waibel, Carnegie Mellon University & Kai-Fu Lee, Carnegie Mellon University [currently Apple Computer], *Readings in Speech Recognition*, 1990, p. 263).

Moore (1984), Paul (1990), and Rabiner & Juang (1986) provide detailed technical descriptions of hidden Markov models. James Baker's (1975a) classic paper introduces stochastic processing to speech recognition.

3.1.4 Phoneme Models

The acoustic-phonetic approach to recognition (see chapter 2, section 2.3.2) views words as a sequence of phonemes. The allure of phonemes is multifaceted:

- Phonemic units offer the advantage of an economic representation because most languages have only fifty or fewer phonemes.

- Vocabulary growth will not produce the corresponding linear increase in storage and computational demands associated with other methodologies.

- The fact that phonemes are basic elements of human languages suggests they might make it easier to port applications from one language to another and that they could be used for automatic vocabulary growth from one language to another.

There are many ways to create phoneme models. The traditional approach depends upon manual design of linguistic rules that express the developer's concept of the salient features of phonemes. The need to develop large, expandable, generic vocabularies has moved developers towards computational approaches, such as neural networks and statistical analysis. Manual and computational techniques may be combined to allow detailed representations capable of automated enhancement or reproduction. MIT's *VOYAGER* system, for example, blended manual and computational tools to create phonetic *seed models* for English and Japanese. Statistically-generated phonemes, called phone-like units (or *PLU's* or *context-independent PLU's*), are usually represented using ergotic HMM's (see figure 3.2b) where each PLU may be represented as a single HMM state.

There are several problems with the acoustic-phonetic approach. One is that it has been manually intensive because it requires the creation of large quantities of hand-labelled phonetic data to train the phonetic classification system. The persistence of the manual development component is a by-product of the dependence upon linguistic analysis and the lack of standards for acoustic-phonetic analysis. The details of representation are important because they are manipulated by the rules of the system. Unfortunately, researchers differ on the acoustic-phonetic features that must be represented.

Another problem facing acoustic-phonetic systems is the representation of variation. In theoretical formulations, phonemes may be represented as immutable entities, but in utterances phonemes exhibit a great deal of variability. One method of representing variability is to use the *phone*. A phone contains the acoustic information for a single utterance of a phoneme. It is excellent for representing incidental variability, but the concept of phones does not capture predictable patterns of variability produced by dialects and phonetic context (coarticulation effects).

The most common approach to handling predictable variability, such as coarticulation effects, is to design a set of rules to accompany context-independent phonemes used in acoustic-phonetic representation. The rules of an acoustic-phonetic system must capture the complex patterns of coarticulation and other variability patterns and express those patterns in terms of the acoustic-phonetic features used for representation. If the acoustic-phonetic system is constructed from a specific linguistic theory, the theory must be very well-defined. If there is no linguistic theory underlying the representation, the developers must perform extensive manual analysis or design tools to identify patterns of variation that can be transformed into rules or features of representation.

Cole (1986), Mercier, et al. (1989), and Zue (1985) provide good technical descriptions of phoneme models. Ljolje & Levinson (1991) describe an example of using an ergotic HMM to represent phonemes. Oshika, et al. (1975) provide an example of linguistic analysis for speech recognition.

3.1.5 Subwords

Subword modeling has become an increasingly more important issue because as the vocabulary capacity of recognizers increases, it becomes difficult, if not impossible, to train whole-word models (Hsiao-Wuen Hon & Kai-Fu Lee, Carnegie Mellon University [currently Apple Computer], "On vocabulary-independent speech modeling," 1990, p. 725).

This problem argues for systems that define words in terms of their acoustic-phonetic elements (phonemes) or another subword unit. The use of phonemes is attractive, but phoneme-based approaches provide little assistance handling coarticulation effects. A number of alternative subword units have been proposed that derive their information from spoken data rather than theoretical constructs. They include phones (see chapter 2, section 2.1.3), PLU's, syllables, demisyllables (one half of a syllable), and diphones. The most successful subword unit is the *triphone*, [also called a *context-sensitive* PLU (CS-PLU) and *phoneme in context (PIC)*] because it is very robust (see chapter 2, section 2.7.3 and chapter 7, introduction) and because it is feasible to develop within the bounds of existing PC technology.

PHONEMES IN CONTEXT

In the 1980's, researchers began formulating alternatives to context-independent phoneme models. One of the first to develop a phoneme in context (PIC) model with both left and right contexts was Bolt Beranek and Newman (BBN). In 1985, BBN offered a detailed proposal for using phonemes in context and integrated it into *BYBLOS*, BBN's large-vocabulary recognition system. This type of phoneme variant was called a *triphone* to express the addition of both left and right contexts.

Proprietary variants of the triphone have been developed by IBM, Dragon Systems, CMU, and other organizations working on large vocabulary systems. Triphone modeling is the default approach for large vocabulary speech recognition. Its spreading use is enabling vendors of smaller vocabulary systems to enter the large vocabulary market as well.

The paper by Schwartz, et al. (1985) is recommended, as well as Kai-Fu Lee's (1989) book describing CMU's *SPHINX* system.

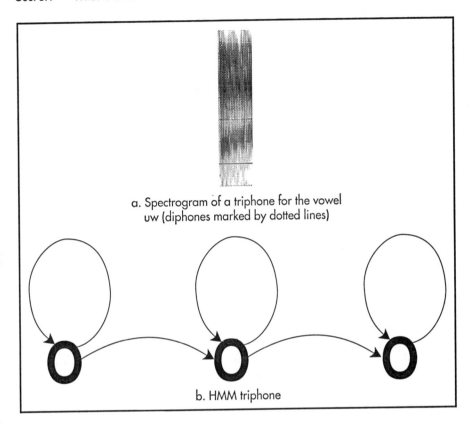

a. Spectrogram of a triphone for the vowel
uw (diphones marked by dotted lines)

b. HMM triphone

Figure 3.3   Triphones

3.1.5.1 Triphone and subword creation.   A triphone is not a phoneme, even though some vendors refer to their PICs or triphones as *phonemes*. A triphone consists of a phoneme or PLU surrounded by contextual information on both sides. A triphone for the phoneme *uw* is displayed in figure 3.3a. Like PLU's, triphone models are statistical constructs based upon analysis of very large numbers of samples. They are generally represented as HMM's, like the one shown in figure 3.3b. Usually, they contain three states representing the

- Transition from the preceding phoneme
- The phoneme
- Transition from the phoneme to the following phoneme

The statistical information represented in a triphone HMM includes variability resulting from coarticulation. In contrast with acoustic-phonetic models, analysis of coarticulation effects in the spoken input can be done using a triphone model itself rather than by invoking large numbers of coarticulation rules.

At the same time, the incorporation of coarticulation into the triphone generally entails the creation of more than one triphone model for a single phoneme. The phoneme *t,* for example, might have one triphone model for phonetic contexts involving lip rounding ("too," "toe," etc.), another for contexts without rounding ("tea," "tick," etc.), and several more for other phonetic contexts. The number of triphones needed for English is much larger than the number of phonemes.

HMM triphone models are stored in a database. During vocabulary development, triphone models are concatenated to form application vocabulary items or backup vocabulary that is stored in a system dictionary. Unlike representation using templates and word-level HMM's, new vocabulary items can be added to an application without collecting additional samples of each new word. New words are entered by keyboard; the input is segmented into graphemic subword chunks; the corresponding triphone models are accessed from the database; and the models are linked to form a model of the new word. This development process is called *subword modeling.*

> What we do is take actual tokens produced by native speakers. We break them into chunks of phonemes organized by triphones. Then we build them up again to form the models. It's like using tinker toys: You break things down and build them up again — even for words that you have never had tokens for (Mark Mandel, Product Development, Dragon Systems Inc., personal communication, 1993).

The newly created words are stored in the system dictionary with pointers to the triphones from which they have been constructed.

Technical descriptions of triphone construction and subword modeling can be found in C-F Lee, et al. (1990a and 1990b) and Deng, et al. (1990). Also recommended is Kai-Fu Lee's (1989) book describing the phoneme, triphone, and word modeling of Carnegie Mellon University's *SPHINX* system.

3.1.5.2 Issues in triphone development.

As with acoustic-phonetic modeling, the implementation of triphone models in a particular recognition system is likely to be unique to that vendor and part of the vendor's proprietary software. As a result, the triphone models of one vendor will not work with the recognition software of another vendor.

Another issue in triphone development is quality. Since it is based upon statistical analysis of data, the quality of triphone models is a by-product of the quality of the training used to create those models. It is often difficult to obtain enough samples to cover all possible phonetic contexts so that reliable triphone models can be created. This is called the *sparse data* problem. Some vendors resolve this problem by defining the vocabulary items developed through subword modeling as starting points called *baseforms.* These baseforms are designed to be molded to the speech of each user as they speak to the system. This approach is called *speaker adaptation* and will be discussed in greater detail in chapter 5. Applications developed using this method of speaker adaptation are intended to be used repeatedly by the same set of speakers.

A second method, that can be combined with baseform generation, is to develop triphone models using a *reference database* (also called a *spoken language corpus*) containing samples of large numbers of people reading words and/or sentences. One of the most widely used databases of this sort is *TIMIT*, a corpus developed by Texas Instruments and MIT to cover the entire sound system of American English.

A third type of resolution for the sparse data problem is to create a more general triphone or subword model. The *generalized triphone* approach developed at CMU is one of the most popular of these approaches. A generalized triphone is created by clustering and merging acoustic data from coarticulation contexts for a single phoneme. Although the resulting triphones are more generic, CMU found that recognition accuracy is not diminished when the models are well-trained. K-F Lee, et al. (1990a) explain generalized triphones. A number of vendors using subwords are incorporating variations of the generalized triphone approach into their systems as a means of increasing performance without introducing additional complexity.

ATTAINING LARGE VOCABULARY SPEECH RECOGNITION

In 1930 Tihamér Nemes, a Hungarian scientist, filed a patent to automatically transcribe optical sound tracks from motion picture film. The patent was rejected as untenable, so we do not know whether it would have realized the dream of large vocabulary speech recognition. Forty years later, the ARPA SUR project reactivated interest in speech recognition using large vocabularies. In that project, all participants were required to develop systems capable of processing vocabularies of one thousand words or more. It not only produced systems, notably *Harpy*, that exceeded that minimum, it established one thousand words as the definition of a large vocabulary recognition system. That definition remained in place until the end of the 1980's.

IBM's *Tangora* system was one of the earliest research efforts designed to produce a commercial system capable of recognizing vocabularies of twenty thousand words or more. It was named after Albert Tangora, once listed in the *Guinness Book of Records* as the fastest typist at 147 words per minute. The first vendor to offer a commercial system with a vocabulary significantly larger than one thousand words was Speech Systems, Inc. (SSI). In 1985, SSI's *PE100* contained a dictionary of twenty thousand words, but it required a workstation running UNIX.

The arrival of powerful PC technology opened the door to PC-based large vocabulary systems. Algorithms which would grind an 80286 to a halt ran easily in the 386 environment. The end of the 1980's saw the arrival of PC-based dictation systems with vocabularies of twenty thousand words or more. Today, a one thousand word system is considered to have a small vocabulary, and companies whose products had been limited to fewer than one hundred words in the 1980's are offering systems capable of processing several thousand words. By 1994, there were systems with available vocabularies of more than one hundred thousand words.

3.2 LARGE VOCABULARY DESIGN

One of the ultimate goals of speech recognition is to be able to communicate with a recognition system using whatever vocabulary the speaker believes is necessary to accomplish the goal at hand. If that goal is to dictate a letter, the availability of a large and expandable vocabulary is obvious. If the goal is to search a database for a specific piece of information or to enter data, the need for a large vocabulary is not immediately obvious because many systems are designed to direct or train the users to conform to the system. As the number and types of speech recognition applications grow and as the populations of users become more diverse, the need for systems capable of accommodating the vocabulary needs of a wider range of users will also increase. Ultimately, large vocabulary systems will be the norm rather than the exception.

3.2.1 Growing the Vocabulary

Large vocabulary systems use subwords to define the words in the vocabulary. This is necessary because the time, cost, and effort of developing models for ten thousand or more words would be prohibitive. Using subword design, the graphemic or phonetic representation of a word can be converted to a triphone representation in seconds.

A more challenging problem facing the developers of large-vocabulary systems is to select the vocabulary that will go into their systems. There are many frequently used words, such as digits and days of the week, that are obvious candidates, but when one is designing a dictionary of fifty thousand to one hundred thousand words for applications in a wide range of industries, vocabulary selection must include examination of print and on-line documents from a large number of disparate sources.

Most developers rely upon on-line *corpora* (also called *reference databases*) to supply the vocabularies they require. Text corpora include machine-readable dictionaries, word lists, and published materials from specific professions. Since many of those sources are not designed for use in the vocabulary development of recognition systems they must be pruned of infrequently occurring vocabulary, misspelled words, proper names, unpronounceable words (such as, abbreviations like 'lb.'), foreign words, dialect variants, and hyphenated words. The remaining vocabulary must then be converted from its text form to the representation needed by the recognition system. In addition, care must be taken to represent important word variants, such as plurals and past tenses of words.

All this involves a great deal of work, yet still offers no assurance that every word and word variant a speaker will want to use has been included. Furthermore, large vocabulary systems lack the option of acclimating system users to existing vocabulary options.

In practical large-vocabulary continuous speech recognition systems, it is nearly impossible for a speaker to remember which words are in the vocabulary. The probability of the speaker using words outside the vocabulary can be quite high (Ayman Asadi, Northeastern University, and Richard Schwartz & John Makhoul, BBN Systems and Technologies, "Automatic modeling for adding new words to a large vocabulary continuous speech recognition system," 1991, p. 305).

These concerns make the possibility of automatic vocabulary growth through machine learning extremely attractive. Such a process entails detection of the fact that a non-vocabulary item has been spoken. Existing commercial large-vocabulary systems detect new words indirectly when the system makes an erroneous word choice or when all available vocabulary fail to meet a threshold of acceptability. In the latter case the speaker is shown a set of word candidates from which to make a selection. If the desired word is not listed, the user can create a word-level model for a new word.

Neural network developers are working on automatic vocabulary expansion. One network trained on 234 Japanese words correctly recognized twenty words it had never encountered before. Another experimental system developed at AT&T Bell Laboratories has been able to learn new English vocabulary from discrete-word utterances using no typed input as a guide.

Two excellent sources of information about issues in large vocabulary development are Seitz, et al. (1990) and Jelinek (1985). Jelinek's work at IBM laid the groundwork for the vocabulary and grammar design of most large vocabulary, commercial recognition systems. Gorin, et al. (1993) describe the automatic vocabulary learning system being developed at AT&T Bell Laboratories.

3.2.2 Search Efficiency

All speech recognition systems must address the issue of accurately identifying input in a time frame that is acceptable to system users. Small vocabulary systems can allow linear search through the available vocabulary, but this is not possible for systems with vocabularies larger than one thousand words.

One solution to this type of problem is to use a *grammar* to restrict the word choices available at any point. This option will be discussed in chapter 4. Another technique is to organize the dictionary as a tree or a lattice.

Speech recognition may be treated as a tree network search problem. As one proceeds from the root towards the leaves the branches leaving each junction represent the set of words which may be appended to the current partial sentence (Douglas Paul, Lincoln Laboratory of MIT, "An efficient A* stack decoder algorithm for continuous speech recognition with a stochastic language model," 1992, p. 25).

This is the approach adopted by most large vocabulary systems. Such organization can reduce the search by a factor of seven by eliminating blocks of unlikely choices.

A third method (often combined with the tree structure) is to apply sophisticated searching algorithms. Two of the most commonly-used search algorithms are

---

SEARCHING

One of the most widely used forms of searching is *beam search* (also called *Viterbi search*). The usefulness of beam searching for speech recognition was highlighted by the success of the ARPA SUR system *Harpy*, which was able to recognize 1,011 words with an error rate of 5 percent. Beam searching moves systematically through a network matching the input to the acoustic patterns in the network. The first sounds of the input, for example, are compared with the initial states of the network taking the items that score best. All other paths are pruned from the remaining search. The paths that remain constitute the *beam* of hypotheses. This process generates a decision tree or lattice similar to the phoneme lattice described in chapter 2. Beam searching remains one of the most commonly used search strategies for both commercial and research systems.

In the 1980's, new searching algorithms were developed to handle the challenges of large vocabulary systems. One commonly-used technique popularized by IBM is *stack decoding*. As the speaker proceeds through an utterance, stack decoding generates a ranked list of candidate paths similar to the beam hypotheses of beam searching. The ranked list is called a stack. Various forms of stack decoding are being applied to research and commercial large vocabulary systems. Other approaches, called *fast match* algorithms (also called *fast search* algorithms), began to appear towards the end of the 1980's. Their aim is to decrease the time required to identify a small set of highly probable word candidates. They replace the detailed acoustic search of standard search algorithms with search-reduction strategies, such as grouping words and subwords with similar acoustic patterns.

During the same period, researchers began developing more complex searching algorithms for spoken language understanding systems. The *N-best* approach, developed at BBN, is gaining popularity. N-best employs several searching methodologies, applying simplest and fastest first, to prune unlikely candidates from consideration. The resulting list of N word candidates is called the *N-best list*. The N-best list is then sent to other, slower searching algorithms for further processing.

Additional information about beam searching is provided by C-H. Lee, et al. (1993) and Ney, et al.

---

beam search and *stack decoding*. Large vocabulary systems require complex searching methodologies capable of performing detailed acoustic analyses. As indicated in the historical note on searching, a number of *fast matching* and other sophisticated searching techniques have been developed.

3.3 WHAT IS A WORD?

In the Technology Focus a word was defined in terms of its acoustic representation. For the proper functioning of an application, two other facets of the concept of a word are as important as the acoustic pattern. They are the

- Word identifier
- Translation

3.3.1 Word Identifiers

An identifier is the unique tag or name assigned to a word. It is used to distinguish that word from all the other words in the lexicon. For ease of design and use by application developers, most commercial systems employ the graphemic or printed representation of a word as its identifier. In those systems the spoken word "one," for example, would be identified by the letters *o n e* or by the digit *1*. The use of spelling allows differentiation between homophones, such as "one" and "won." Some systems are case sensitive. In those systems the identifier *ONE* refers to a different word than the identifier *one* even if the spoken input is identical.

In many recognition systems phrases or short sentences that behave as units can be defined as words if their labels have no spaces. The utterances "end of application" and "Where am I?" would require labels like *end-of-application* or *Where-am-I*.

3.3.2 Translations

The word "translation" is not a technical term in the speech recognition industry, but it is a major component of the communication phase of speech recognition (see chapter 2, section 2.8). *Translation* refers to the conversion of recognized input into a form that other components of the application can use. Its form and content are defined by the software and/or hardware that receive the recognized input. Whether a spoken word is converted into a series of keyboard keystrokes, touch-tone telephone pulses, several paragraphs of text, or another representation, depends entirely upon the requirements of the application.

Speech recognition products vary in the type and range of translations they generate. This is a reflection of their hardware platforms, overall design, and the application types for which they were created. The ability to communicate with the other hardware and software involved in an application is a basic product-evaluation criterion.

3.3.2.1 Translation vs. meaning.

In the commercial speech recognition systems of today, words do not bear meaning as they do in human communication. The translation assigned to a word is simply a conversion from one digital representation to another, usually from HMM's to graphemes.

Some system designers recognize the potential value of word-level meaning (called *lexical semantics*) for increasing recognition accuracy. Word meanings could, for example, be used to select from among word candidates with similar acoustic patterns. They could be used to reduce the search space by restricting the number of valid word choices. They could help screen out speech errors and handle a speaker's self-corrections, and they could be used to make a system behave more like a human being. Lexical semantics techniques being tested in research systems today range from simple category class groupings, such as CITY NAMES, to complex semantic structures defined by linguistic theories. Some of the simpler forms will be incorporated into commercial recognition systems in the near future.

3.3.2.2 Multiple translations. There are no puns or ambiguities in speech recognition. A single speech pattern can have only one translation at any one point in an application. No ambiguity is permitted. This is necessary to insure speedy, accurate processing.

Many recognition products do allow more than one translation for the same word in the course of a single application. The word "one" can, for example, be used to generate the digit *1* at some points in the application and letters *o n e* at another point. In each instance the translation choice must be clear and unambiguous.

3.3.3 Word Variants

A standard dictionary with an entry for the word "recognize" might include the following information:

recognize verb PAST: recognized, FUTURE: will recognize, 3RD PERSON: recognizes. ADJECTIVE: recognizable, ADVERB: recognizably.

Speech recognition dictionaries, however, require separate entries for each of those words. This restriction is consistent with the acoustic focus of speech recognition vocabularies and is designed to minimize the complexity of the recognition process. Consequently, when the vendor of a large vocabulary recognition system reports a *total vocabulary* of forty thousand words, it means the system contains forty thousand individual word identifiers, some of which are likely to be word variants.

3.4 VOCABULARY DESIGN

Prior to 1990 most commercial recognition systems offered one of two vocabulary design options:

- Vendor-built lexicons
- Application-designer creation of word-level vocabulary

Since then the choices have expanded to include:

- Vendor-built lexicons
- Application-designer creation of word-level vocabulary
- Application-designer creation of subword-level vocabulary
- End-user vocabulary creation
- Automatic vocabulary extraction of vocabulary
- A combination of the above alternatives

3.4.1 Vendor-built Lexicons

Vendor-built lexicons are system vocabularies that have been constructed by the vendor. Large vocabulary systems, turnkey applications, systems embedded in firmware, and systems with speaker-independent user models often contain vendor-built lexicons. Vendor-built lexicons take a variety of forms, the most common of which are

- Dictionaries
- Application-specific vocabularies

3.4.1.1 Dictionaries.   Dictionaries are usually found in large vocabulary systems and serve as the backup resource for applications developed using these systems. The dictionary of a large vocabulary recognition system is sometimes called the *total vocabulary* of that system. It is where the system's coded words or baseforms reside. Its size is limited by the vocabulary development a vendor has completed and by any constraints of the storage device on which the dictionary resides. The complete dictionaries of some commercial systems hold more than one hundred thousand individual vocabulary items, each of which is represented as sequences of phonemes, triphones, or other units that form the basis of recognition for the system. They are likely to be represented in a non-linear format, such as a lattice.

Dictionaries must be designed for adequate coverage of the applications that are likely to be developed using the system. The initial vocabulary selection for a dictionary generally consists of words and phrases considered necessary for the operation of the recognizer and for the range of expected applications. They may include recognizer control words and common vocabulary, such as digits and days of the week. Additional vocabulary items may be gathered from reference databases and other on-line sources. Such items are scanned for spelling errors and evaluated on the basis of metrics-like frequency of occurrence (see section 3.2.1).

The data used to create the word models need to reflect the population of expected users (see section 3.1.3). For example, speaker-independent models designed for use with speakers of American English will not perform well if they are created using data from speakers of British English.

Jelinek (1985) is an excellent source for additional information on large vocabulary design.

3.4.1.2 Application-specific vocabularies.   Vocabularies of turnkey applications, such as a speech interface for a specific computer product, like *Excel,* provide vendor-built lexicons tuned to the functions of that application. In turnkey systems with small to moderate-sized vocabularies, such as speech front-ends for *Microsoft Windows,* the application-linked vocabulary represents the entire vocabulary of the system. As a result, the speech interface is ready for use almost immediately after it is loaded. The built-in vocabularies reduce application development

time while maintaining a high level of quality for vocabulary design. They have great appeal for computer-naive users and for people with disabilities.

In large vocabulary systems with built-in dictionaries an application-specific vocabulary represents a subset of the total vocabulary of the system. It may be called the *resident vocabulary* of the application as a means of differentiating it from the total system vocabulary found in the dictionary. The resident vocabulary is generally loaded with the application. The size and nature of the resident vocabulary varies greatly with the recognition system and the application. Some vendors offer several options as a way of satisfying different vocabulary (and pricing) requirements of their customers.

3.4.2 Vocabulary Creation by Application Developers

Application-designer vocabulary creation requires the application developer to identify the vocabulary necessary to an application and to define it for the recognition system. Little or no vendor-supplied vocabulary is provided. Instead, the recognition products contain vocabulary- and application-development tools. Most speaker-dependent recognition systems require application-designer vocabulary creation; and a growing number of small vocabulary, speaker-independent systems provide application developers with vocabulary development tools as well.

Vendors who use subword modeling have tended to create new vocabulary items themselves. Most systems allow application developers to request new vocabulary, but the subword development is done by the vendor. Speech Systems, Inc. (SSI) was one of the first to enable application developers to add words to their own dictionaries. They provided a function to convert the spelling of a new word to its phonetic representation. BBN's *HARK*, Philips Dictation Systems' *Developer's Toolkit,* and Corona's *Toolkit* (Corona is the commercial spin-off of SRI) are examples of other subword-based commercial systems that allow developers to generate a new dictionary baseform by typing a phonetic spelling for it. Since the intricacies of phonetic spelling can be confusing, vendors are beginning to implement other means of obtaining the pronunciation, such as concatenating pieces of existing subwords containing the same sound patterns (see section 3.1.5) or by basing the creation of a word on its spelling.

3.4.3 Vocabulary Creation by End Users

End-user vocabulary development is an important technique for customizing an application (called *personalizing* the application). Inclusion of such tools reflects an awareness that end users have unique individual requirements.

At first we only allowed programmers to do it but then we found that users were more likely to add things like new names (Elton Sherwin, Manager of Speech Recognition Strategy & Market Development, Power Personal Systems, IBM [currently at Lexicus], personal communication, 1994).

A second reason for incorporating end-user vocabulary development tools is that the vast majority of recognition errors made by large vocabulary recognition systems are the result of missing vocabulary. Since most systems do not possess *out-of-vocabulary rejection* capabilities, they generate a recognition by attempting to find a match from among the words in the existing vocabulary. It is not possible to predict all the words that will be needed by every user. In fact, out-of-vocabulary input is a fairly common occurrence in dictation systems, making end-user vocabulary creation tools a requirement for large vocabulary systems.

The manner in which end-users can add vocabulary to a large vocabulary system varies with the system. Even though they are fundamentally subword systems, most end-user vocabulary is entered as a speaker-dependent word-level model attached to the vocabulary of the individual who created the word. Vendors have begun to enable users to add words to the resident vocabulary, but in many cases they are still word-level representations which must be trained by each user. These approaches represent limitations in the capabilities of those systems because the trend is to generate speaker-independent models of user-added vocabulary.

Some large-vocabulary systems designed for application developers (such as Corona's *Toolkit*, BBN's *HARK* system and Philips Dictation Systems' *SpeechPro*) give developers the option of adding new items to the built-in vocabulary. The initial version of Philips' toolkit has a separate set of vocabulary development tools for the end users of applications built using the toolkit.

A few small, highly-structured turnkey applications expect users to create new words as a part of the system's operation. Cellular telephone dialing systems are the best examples of such systems. Limited end-user vocabulary construction is beginning to appear in speech interfaces for *Windows* as well.

Vendors realize that their ability to satisfy the needs of end users is central to the ultimate success of speech recognition technology. Consequently, as recognition systems grow in power and flexibility the role of end-user vocabulary development will increase.

3.4.4 Automatic Vocabulary Extraction

Automatic vocabulary extraction (sometimes called *application scanning* or *vocabulary optimization*) entails the automatic extraction of vocabulary from on-line files or systems. It represents a first step towards automatic vocabulary growth.

The value of automatic vocabulary extraction for application developers is that it transfers the process of specifying and defining the application vocabulary from the developer to the recognition system. The developer no longer needs to hunt through an application to identify needed vocabulary and then define the vocabulary and its translations for the system. For small vocabulary applications, automatic vocabulary extraction simplifies and shortens the development process. This approach can only be used for applications that utilize on-line computer systems, such as speech interfaces for computer software systems.

Vendors of large vocabulary recognizers are turning to automatic vocabulary extraction to provide a degree of personalization to the dictionary. They have begun to offer tools to scan the vocabulary of documents comparable to those that will be generated by users of the application. The frequencies of vocabulary items are calibrated to those found in the texts, but new words are not added to the dictionary. Dragon Systems was the first dictation system vendor to offer this type of automatic vocabulary extraction.

Automatic vocabulary extraction represents another way in which recognition system vendors are attempting to address the needs of their users. It is an approach that will grow in importance and availability.

3.5 SPECIAL VOCABULARY ISSUES

Active vocabulary, confusable words, the alphabet, and numbers are special vocabulary issues that will be discussed in the following sections.

3.5.1 Active Vocabulary

The *active vocabulary* of a system is the set of words the application allows or expects to be spoken at any one time. It constitutes the word candidates the system will evaluate at that point in the recognition of input. A paint inspection application might, for example, allow the following input

The paint is [peeling scratched dull uneven]

where any of the words in the brackets might be uttered after the word "is." The words in the brackets represent the active vocabulary at that point in the inspection application. The active vocabulary is rarely equivalent to the total vocabulary of a system or application, but in large vocabulary systems it can sometimes be virtually equivalent to the resident vocabulary. The concept of active vocabulary is linked to the use of grammars and will be discussed in greater detail in chapter 4.

3.5.2 Confusable Words

Confusable words are words that sound alike to a speech recognition system. When used in the same active vocabulary, such words are likely to increase recognition errors. In general, one-syllable words are more confusable than longer words because they contain less acoustic information to assist the system. Unfortunately, the two hundred most frequently used words in English are one-syllable words. Among them are function words, such as "a" and "the," whose acoustic similarity can account for more than 50 percent of a recognition system's errors.

A common technique for improving recognition accuracy of potentially confusable words is to include a similarity threshold for pattern matching between the input and the stored models. If the best match found by the recognizer fails to achieve the threshold, the system can request validation or repetition from the user. Another technique is to *cross-train* confusable words. Cross-training is a function that is provided by some commercial recognition systems. It entails removing the acoustic patterns of one of the words from the other word. This process accentuates the differences between the words and minimizes the similarities.

Whenever possible, sets of confusable words should be avoided. This is not always possible, especially for large vocabulary systems and when confusable words constitute a natural grouping of words.

SPELLING

In 1989, Voice Control Systems (VCS) developed and patented a commercial algorithm for handling spelled input. It was designed for telephone-based applications. The system minimized error through the use of a database of allowable words that limited the number of possible letter sequences (see Foster & Schalk, 1993, chapter 4). The spelling algorithm included some of the cross-training techniques available in VCS's application development systems.

By 1993, other vendors began introducing comparably structured alphabetic spelling tools for a range of applications. Several vendors offer spelling for voice-mail and other telephone-based applications. Amerigon uses Lernout & Hauspie's alphabet recognition algorithm in its voice-controlled car navigation system. That system, called *AudioNav,* relies heavily upon spelled input of street names to formulate routes between the current location of the user and the destination. A few vendors of desktop systems, such as SRI (and Corona, its commercial spin-off) and BBN include alphabet letter names in their dictionaries as basic vocabulary items, but most other vendors of desktop systems have not yet integrated alphabetic spelling into their commercial products.

3.5.3 The Alphabet

Names of letters of the alphabet constitute the most troublesome set of confusable words in English. One group of letter names is so troublesome for recognizers and human beings it has a special name: the *E-set.* The E-set refers to names for letters that end with the phoneme *iy* (including "b, c, d," and "g"). Two other groups of confusable letter names in American English can be labelled the *a-set* (including "a" and "h") and the *eh-set,* which includes "m, n, s," and "f."

Because the ability to spell words is an important facet of many applications, a great deal of attention has been given to creating tools to handle spelling. The fact that only a few commercial recognizers have implemented alphabetic spelling is an indication of the level of difficulty involved. Some vendors still urge users to substitute the military alphabet ("alpha, bravo, charlie. . . ") or a comparable set of more highly distinguishable words.

Application developers working with a recognition product that does not offer alphabetic spelling can use a technique that has been employed by Amerigon in its *AudioNav* product, by the MIT Media Laboratories, and by others. The system reduces the E-set effect by using both acoustic data and acceptable spelling patterns.

Like most other existing approaches to spelling it requires a reference list. The method used by the MIT Media Laboratories for discrete letter spelling of proper names is to build a *confusability matrix,* such as the one displayed in figure 3.4. The confusability matrix reflects the patterns of confusability found during testing of the recognition system on spelled input. Input of the letter "b," for example, was recognized as "a, b, d, e, p, v," and "z." If no names on the reference list begin with "v" or "z," the only choices the system retains are "a, b, d, e," and "p." Each succeeding letter provides a new set of alternatives that are combined with previous options and compared with the list of names until one option remains. Since each recognition product and input device exhibit unique patterns of confusability, the matrix used by MIT cannot simply be appropriated. Once the matrix and algorithms are created, it is important to submit them to extensive testing prior to fielding.

More information about the MIT Media Laboratories' approach to spelling can be found in Marx & Schmandt (1994). Another approach using neural networks is described by Fanty, et al. (1992).

3.5.4 Numbers

Many recognition systems require that numbers be spoken as a list of single digits. When using such systems a user would need to input the number 1445 as "one four four five." This is a by-product of the need for speech recognition systems to restrict processing to one translation per word. If the translation for "thousand" is '000' when a speaker says "one thousand" the system will respond with '1000.' If the speaker says "one thousand four" the system will respond with '10004.'

This limitation began to disappear in the early 1990's when the increased speed and power of computing hardware made it easier to include macros to handle more complex structural analysis. By the middle of 1994, natural numbers had become a feature of several commercial systems, including IBM's *True Type* technology (formerly, their *Personal Dictation System* and *Continuous Speech System*), BBN's *HARK,* Lernout & Hauspie's technology, and Corona's *Toolkit.*

An application developer can create a natural number algorithm that accepts the sequences recognized by the recognition product and reanalyzes them. The development and testing processes would be similar to those required to create alphabetic input (see section 3.5.3).

a -- > ah	h -- > ah	n -- > anrs	t -- > dept
b -- > abdepvz	i -- > iy	o -- > lo	u -- > qu
c -- > ctz	j -- > adgjktz	p -- > cdepvz	v -- > bdepvz
d -- > cdvz	k -- > adjkq	q -- > qi	w -- > fmnw
e -- > e	l -- > l	r -- > iry	x -- > sx
f -- > fx	m -- > mn	s -- > fs	y -- > y
g -- > gt			z -- > defnstvxz

Figure 3.4   Confusability Matrix (from Marx & Schmandt, "Reliable spelling despite poor spoken letter recognition," Copyright 1994, Matt Marx and Chris Schmandt)

3.6 EVALUATING THE VOCABULARY REQUIREMENTS OF AN APPLICATION

An evaluation of the vocabulary needed by an application should include the following considerations:

- An informed estimate of the vocabulary size
- Careful matching of the application vocabulary needs with a product
- A determination regarding how the application vocabulary will grow

3.6.1 Vocabulary Size

Despite the fascination with unlimited vocabularies, most applications involve much smaller vocabularies than one might expect. Dialing a car telephone, for example, requires fewer than twenty words and most manufacturing applications use fewer than one hundred words. Even the vocabularies required for dictation applications are not infinite. The original radiology report generator system developed by Kurzweil AI, for example, required only five thousand words.

3.6.2 Matching a Recognition Product to Vocabulary Needs

Large vocabulary systems are very attractive, but they are designed for dictation applications and may be poorly suited to smaller-vocabulary data entry and equipment control applications.

If the vocabulary of the application is large and highly variable there may be a high branching factor. If this is the case, a recognition system should be evaluated in terms of how sensitive it is to large numbers of choices. Claims about vocabulary size are irrelevant if a system requires the size of the resident or active vocabulary to be very small.

If the application requires switching among sub-vocabularies or between the recognizer's base vocabulary and a specialized vocabulary, the time required to switch from one sub-vocabulary to another should be evaluated.

If a system with a built-in dictionary is appropriate, it is important to verify that its vocabulary matches that needed by the application. If the differences are extensive, the recognizer may not be appropriate for the application. If no recognizer fits the application vocabulary requirements, the application developer or the vendor may need to create new vocabulary for the application.

The data used to create the models in the dictionaries need to reflect the speech characteristics of the expected user population (see section 3.1.3). This is particularly important for speaker-independent models (see chapter 5). Reference models created using samples from males are not suitable for populations of female users; models based upon data from speakers of American English should not be used for speakers of Australian English; even models built from samples provided by residents of Boston may not perform well in Mississippi. Whenever questions arise about the suitability of reference models for a new population of users, the models should be tested and, if there is a problem, the vendor should delineate the methods that would be used to modify those models.

3.6.3 Growing the Vocabulary

Section 3.4 examined a variety of vocabulary design methods. These methods apply to expanding an existing vocabulary as well. One important question to resolve is whether end users will need to add vocabulary to the application. If it is likely they will need to add vocabulary, the developer must determine how that will be accomplished. If the vocabulary will evolve through the addition of vocabulary supplied by the vendor or created by the application developer, users must be made aware of the newly added items and may need to provide spoken samples of the newly added items before they can be used.

4

ADDING STRUCTURE

INTRODUCTION

Speech recognition applications do not consist of an unorganized conglomeration of words. They possess the same structure and sequence as the tasks to which they are linked. That structure can be as rigid as a command sequence for controlling a piece of equipment or as flexible as dictation.

The methods used to organize application vocabularies have a variety of names. Most often, they are called *grammars, models,* or *scripts*. The term *grammar* is the most suitable since it refers to the relationship of the words in a sentence. Unfortunately, it conjures specters of elementary school exercises and is avoided by some vendors. The word *model* is applied to probabilistics/statistical approaches, expressing the basic process of those grammars: to create models of language patterns. The label *script* is most often applied to telephone-based applications. It emphasizes the focus on structuring the interaction between the caller and the recognition system.

The most commonly used forms of structuring are

- Finite-state grammars
- Probabilistic models
- Linguistics-based grammars

These approaches differ in their

- Goals
- Implementation

- Flexibility
- Handling of large vocabularies
- Handling of complex language patterns

These differences affect their suitability for use in specific types of applications. The Technology Focus begins with a more extensive explanation of the role of structuring techniques. This is followed by an examination of the principal forms of grammar found in commercial and research systems. Each form of grammar is characterized in terms of its flexibility, limitations, and standard implementation in speech recognition systems. The Application Focus examines application design issues associated with the types of grammar used in commercial recognition systems. These themes include naturalness and accuracy.

In addition to this chapter, the book by Terry Winograd (1983) listed in the chapter references is an excellent source of information about grammars used in a wide range of computer systems.

EARLY GRAMMARS

Like many components of existing speech recognition technology, the use of structuring techniques in speech recognition applications is a by-product of the ARPA SUR project of the 1970's (see chapter 1, section 1.2). The ARPA SUR systems were required to handle vocabularies of one thousand words or more, forcing application designers to focus on ways to reduce the amount of searching the system had to do to locate the best match. The value of using *finite-state grammar* for structuring speech recognition applications was clearly demonstrated by Carnegie Mellon University's *Harpy* system, which outperformed the other systems in the project.

CMU's *Hearsay-II* system introduced the *blackboard model* to speech recognition. A blackboard uses multiple knowledge sources to recognize and understand spoken language. Knowledge sources in *Hearsay II* ranged from phonetic parameters (such as voicing) to phrase-level structures. These knowledge sources reflect the range of information that is applied to understanding speech. During the analysis process, knowledge sources generate hypotheses about segments of the input. Since the knowledge sources constitute vastly different types of information, adjacent knowledge sources communicate with each other about their hypotheses using a message center, called a *blackboard*.

Bolt Beranek and Newman's *Hear What I Mean (HWIM)* system was the first speech recognition system to employ an *augmented transition grammar* (ATN) containing syntactic and semantic components.

All three of these approaches continue to be used in speech recognition, although only finite-state grammars have achieved commercial success. Other early approaches to structuring, notably linguistics-based grammars, are experiencing a resurgence resulting from the push to develop *spoken language understanding systems* (SLU's). SLU's do not recognize the input as sequences of acoustic patterns. They attempt to understand more about the input, including its meaning and syntax.

Consult Baker (1975b), Erman, et al. (1980), and Klatt (1977) for more detailed information on the ARPA SUR project.

4.1 WHY USE STRUCTURING TECHNIQUES?

The use of structure in commercial speech recognition systems is directed toward specifying allowable and/or likely sequences of words. This is sometimes called *syntax*. Linguistics-based grammars (discussed in section 4.4) extend the coverage of grammar to include meaning, social rules of interaction, word structure, and other facets of verbal communication.

The primary objectives of structuring of any sort are to

- Reduce perplexity
- Increase speed and accuracy
- Enhance vocabulary flexibility

4.1.1 Reducing Perplexity

The recognition step of the speech recognition process (see chapter 2, section 2.3) involves searching through the application vocabulary to locate the best match for spoken input. The set of vocabulary items the recognizer must evaluate to accomplish this goal is called the *active vocabulary*. The number of items in the active vocabulary at a single point in the recognition process is called the *branching factor* of that point in the application. The *average branching factor* refers to the amount of branching found in an entire application. The term *perplexity* is often used as a synonym for average branching factor, but it has a slightly more complex and precise definition (see Jelinek 1968 and 1985 for more detailed discussions of the precise technical meaning of the term *perplexity*).

Recognition applications can be characterized using perplexity. An application consisting entirely of "yes" and "no" responses, for example, has a perplexity of two, whereas the estimated perplexity of general business correspondence has been estimated at ranges from one hundred to several hundred.

Reducing perplexity automatically lessens the amount of searching the recognizer must do. The reduction of perplexity also increases the speed of an application during use and can be used to enhance its accuracy as well. Grammars reduce perplexity by limiting the words in the active vocabulary or by assigning a probability ranking to those items. An application with a total vocabulary of one thousand words may, for example, receive input such as

Take the toll road to Milwaukee

If that application has no grammar, the branching factor at each point in the sequence is one thousand. This means the recognizer must examine each of the one thousand words in the vocabulary six times to find the correct sequences of input items. Without a grammar, the perplexity of that application is one thousand.

If the application contained a grammar with the allowable input sentence:

Take the TYPE road to PLACE

in which TYPE and PLACE are variable slots that can be filled with one of the following:

TYPE = high OR toll OR long-and-winding OR back OR rocky
PLACE = Milwaukee OR Kokomo OR nowhere OR Araby OR Rio

the perplexity of the application is far less than one thousand. The branching factor for the first word is one (its active vocabulary is "take"). The branching factors for the second, fourth, and fifth words are also one. The branching factor for the third input item is five and its active vocabulary consists of the items that can fill the TYPE variable slot (high, toll, long-and-winding, back, and rocky). The sixth word also has a branching factor of five. At no point in the utterance would the system be required to search the entire vocabulary.

Recognition products can be described in terms of the perplexity they can handle, making perplexity an important component of system evaluation.

> We assume that reducing the perplexity of a language model on a test corpus will result in a lower recognition error rate on that corpus and we, therefore, use perplexity as the measure of the quality of a language model (Frederick Jelinek, Robert Mercer, and Salim Roukos, senior researchers, IBM Watson Research Center [Jelinek is currently at the University of Pittsburgh]. "Classifying words for improved statistical language models," 1990, p. 621).

More information on perplexity can be found in Jelinek (1985).

4.1.2 Increasing Speed and Accuracy

When there are fewer items for a recognizer to evaluate, the time required for recognition is automatically reduced. If an application with a total vocabulary of one thousand words need only examine five of those words at a single point, the time required for recognition at that point becomes approximately .005 of the time that would have been required to examine the full vocabulary. The importance of eliminating unnecessary searching increases with the size of the application vocabulary. Accuracy increases because there are fewer word candidates in the active vocabulary to cause an error.

4.1.3 Enhancing Vocabulary Flexibility

The careful design of active vocabularies enhances accuracy when the words within each active vocabulary are acoustically distinct. Confusable words, such as "mine" and "nine," and homophones, such as "to," "too," and "two" can still be included in a single application, but the recognition errors they often produce are minimized by placing them in different active vocabulary sets. A grammar might, for example, specify that only numbers, like "two," will be recognized at a certain point, thereby eliminating potential errors from the homophones "to" and "too." Since natural sets of words may contain confusable words, such as names of the letters of the English alphabet, it is not possible to eliminate confusable words from a single active vocabulary.

FINITE-STATE GRAMMAR

Finite-state grammar gained prominence as an effective tool for structuring speech recognition applications during the ARPA SUR project of the 1970's. A finite-state grammar was used by the only system that satisfied the ARPA SUR accuracy requirement, Carnegie Mellon University's *Harpy*. In the 1980's, finite-state grammar became the dominant technology used in commercial speech recognition systems. It remains the principal form of grammar found in commercial systems containing small and mid-size vocabularies. It is also employed in some large vocabulary systems, including Speech Systems Inc.'s (SSI) products and BBN's *HARK* system.

Winograd (1983, chapter 2) contains an excellent technical analysis of finite-state grammar.

4.2 FINITE-STATE GRAMMAR

The most frequently used grammar in automatic speech recognition is the finite-state grammar. Finite-state grammars have been successful in improving recognition accuracy in limited-domain recognizers (L. Miller & S. Levinson, senior researchers, AT&T Bell Laboratories, "Syntactic analysis for large vocabulary speech recognition using a context-free covering grammar," 1988, p. 270).

A *finite-state grammar* reduces perplexity by delineating the words that are allowable at any point in the input. This is the type of grammar illustrated in section 4.1.1.

4.2.1 The Power of Finite-State Grammar

Finite-state grammars constitute one of the most straightforward methods of reducing perplexity in speech recognition applications. They are easy to understand and, depending upon the requirements of the application, they can be relatively simple to create.

The use of a finite-state grammar simplifies application development by replacing listings of allowable utterances with generic descriptions. For example, a recognition system used in a manufacturing plant could include the pattern

SENTENCE1 = Part-number NUMBER^{multiple}

which is all that is needed to recognize the input utterances

Part-number 1 2 4
Part-number 2 2 1 5

Part-number 9 2 5 4 7
Part-number 3 8 2 9 4 1
Part-number 8 2 4 2 6 1 7 5 9

and any others that consist of the word "part-number" followed by one or more digits in any order. The indicator "multiple" after the variable NUMBER indicates that
the grammar can handle more than one digit. Similarly, if the variable TYPE is defined as

TYPE = ID-number OR Station OR Department-number

the grammar pattern

SENTENCE2 = TYPE NUMBER^{multiple}

can be used to recognize utterances like

ID-number 1 2 4
Station 3 6
Department-number 3

Structures such as SENTENCE1 and SENTENCE2 can be embedded in other
structures to form longer sequences, such as

LONG-SENTENCE = SENTENCE2 SENTENCE1 inspection report

Using structures like SENTENCE1, SENTENCE2 and LONG-SENTENCE in a
finite-state grammar can represent a wide range of utterances. By eliminating all
information other than the acoustics of the current active vocabulary from consideration, finite-state grammars promote speed and accuracy.
    When used in structured applications, finite-state grammars are fast, effective,
and easy to construct. Their simplicity and robustness account for the success they
have brought to commercial speech recognition.

4.2.2 Weaknesses of Finite-State Grammar

The *deterministic* nature of finite-state grammars makes them rigid. Only
the word and sentence sequences that have been programmed into the grammar
can be recognized. Users cannot deviate from those patterns. Once the user begins to say a sequence, it must be completed in one of the ways specified by the
grammar.
    Finite-state grammars do not understand syntactic patterns that underlie the
word sequences they are programmed to accept. Because of this, they cannot monitor their recognition to insure that commonly-occurring, context-dependent patterns
of human languages are correctly recognized. One of those patterns is subject-verb

agreement ("She *goes*" vs. "They *go*"). In this pattern, the active vocabulary of the second word often contains acoustically similar, confusable words, such as "go" and "goes," making the application vulnerable to errors like "She go" and "They goes." Furthermore,

> the finite-state grammar is not powerful enough to effectively increase recognition in versatile, large vocabulary speech recognition systems. Many major language constructs can not be properly characterized in the finite-state domain. A more powerful grammar is necessary (L. Miller & S. Levinson, senior researchers, AT&T Bell Laboratories, "Syntactic analysis for large vocabulary speech recognition using a context-free covering grammar," 1988, p. 270).

Consequently, finite-state grammars are inappropriate for applications, like dictation, that require a great deal of flexibility.

Another failing of most finite-state grammars is an inability to rank active vocabulary in terms of their likelihood of occurrence. An input sequence, such as

FURNITURE-ITEM and FURNITURE-ITEM

where

FURNITURE-ITEM = table OR chair OR sofa

the word "table" is most likely to be followed by "chair" and least likely to be followed by a second utterance of "table." Organizing the search using probability of occurrence would improve search speed and efficiency.

Finite-state grammars have no inherent way of coding such prioritization within the active vocabulary. All members of the active vocabulary have the same likelihood of occurrence. A few commercial recognition products, such as BBN's *HARK*, contain finite-state grammar tools that have been adapted to permit manual assignment of priorities to individual words within an active vocabulary. Those priority assignments help guide the searching process during recognition. Some research systems employ a more extensive, automated variant of probabilistic finite-state grammar.

4.2.3 Implementing Finite-State Grammar

Finite-state grammars are generally represented using *finite-state networks* (also called *finite-state machines* or *transition networks*). Like hidden Markov models, a finite-state grammar consists of states linked by left-to-right, directional transitions, and recursive transitions (see chapter 3, section 3.1.3). The finite-state network shown in figure 4.1 defines sixteen sentences of a finite-state grammar for a hotel reservation application with a total vocabulary of twenty-four words. True to the objective of perplexity reduction, the grammar in figure 4.1 has a maximum branching factor of four (at state 2).

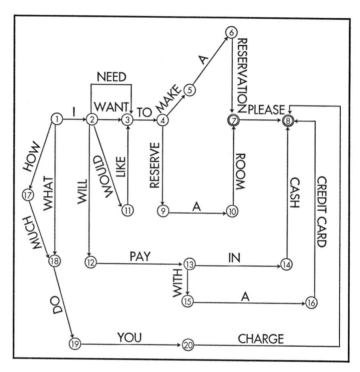

Figure 4.1   Finite-state network for hotel reservation

Unlike hidden Markov models, neither the states nor the transitions of finite-state networks are characterized by probabilities. Since a single finite-state network may represent all the allowable utterances of a task, the networks tend to be much larger than individual hidden Markov models.

Generally, the allowable sequences represented by a finite-state grammar are identified, defined, and coded by the application developer. Commercial systems are beginning to offer tools to extract structural patterns from collections of sample sentences. Some graphical user interface (GUI) application interfaces offer automatic pattern extraction as a component of their vocabulary extraction tools.

4.2.4 Word Pair Grammar

Word pair grammar can be viewed as a variant of finite-state grammar. Each word in the vocabulary specifies the words that can follow it. It is generally implemented as a finite-state network and can be used with word-level or subword models. In a word pair grammar for the hotel reservation application represented in figure 4.1, the word "I" (node 1) would specify "need," "want," "would," and "will" as the list of words that can follow it in an input utterance.

When word pair grammar is implemented using subword models, each word-final subword is linked to a list of possible word-initial subwords. Pieraccini, et al. (1991) provide a detailed description of a word pair grammar implementation using triphone models.

4.3 STATISTICAL MODELS

Statistical models are most often used in dictation systems. Rather than specifying what is allowable, statistical/probabilistic language models examine what is likely (or probable). These approaches acknowledge the flexibility and structural variation that constitute natural spoken language. They seek to balance that naturalness with control of perplexity and simplicity of implementation. Since the focus of these grammars tends to be on predicting word-sequences, they are often called *stochastic language models*.

There are two principal forms of statistical modeling found in commercial and research systems:

- N-gram models
- N-class models

N-GRAM MODELING

The N-gram approach was first advocated for speech recognition in the 1970's by Frederick Jelinek of IBM, and later used to develop IBM's *Tangora* recognition system. By the end of the 1980's, Dragon Systems had incorporated bigrams, a form of N-gram modeling, into its *DragonDictate*. It has since become the dominant grammar methodology in large vocabulary systems where it is most often implemented as a bigram or trigram model.

4.3.1 N-Gram Models

N-gram modeling is the most common form of statistical modeling used in speech recognition systems.

4.3.1.1 The power of N-gram models. An *N-gram model* identifies the current word (the unknown word) by assuming that the identity of that word is dependent upon the previous N-1 words plus the acoustic information in the unknown word. A trigram model, where N = 3, would use the two words spoken prior to the unknown word. In the utterance

This is *my printer* [unknown word]

the unknown word would be identified using the two words, "my printer," spoken prior to it. What is identified using the words "my printer" is a list of word candidates ranked according to the probability that the word candidate will be the unknown word. N-gram modeling recognizes the unknown word by combining those probabilities with the acoustic information provided by the unknown input word. No other information is used. During recognition, the N-gram model consists of a moving window which is N-1 words wide that generates lists of ranked word candidates. This method of restricting the scope of analysis contributes to the simplicity and speed of the N-gram approach.

The active vocabulary of an N-gram model can, conceivably, include the entire vocabulary of an application; but in most cases it is narrowed through the use of probability thresholds. Search is guided by a combination of the acoustic patterns of the input and the ranking of word candidates based upon probability of occurrence. This approach provides the flexibility missing from finite-state grammars.

> Statistical language models based on . . . N-gram models have been shown to be useful for improving the accuracy of speech recognizers. One very useful aspect is their simplicity; large amounts of text training data can be used to estimate the model parameters (Marie Mateer, Renssalaer Polytechnic Institute, & J. Robin Rohlicek, BBN Systems and Technologies, "Statistical language modeling combining N-gram and context-free grammars," 1993, p. 37).

The N-gram approach is well-suited to large-vocabulary dictation applications. It seeks to offer the maximum flexibility, speed, and search-space parsimony with the minimum computational overhead. These are the attributes underlying its success.

Jelinek (1985) and Jelinek, et al. (1975) are good sources of additional technical information about N-gram language modeling.

4.3.1.2 Weaknesses of N-gram models.

A double-edged criticism has been levelled at N-gram models based upon the limited window used for recognition. The following two strings of words:

> This is a printer [unknown word]
> It is necessary for you to insert a printer [unknown word]

would be considered identical to a trigram model because the last two known words are identical. In both cases, only those two words would be used to generate a list of word candidates for the unknown word. Critics claim such a narrow focus is not sufficient to capture real differences found in many conceptual and linguistic patterns. When they are examined in the context of the longer structures of which they are a part, they may not be equivalent at all, as the following sentence segments indicate:

> The gardener likes to *plant with* [unknown word]
> The coleus is the *plant with* [unknown word]

Understanding the structure of the entire sentence segment would eliminate unacceptable choices from the list of options. The words "trowels" and "gusto" might be reasonable candidates for the unknown word in the first sentence, but not the second.

On the other hand, two- or three-word patterns classified as distinct because they end with different words, may be equivalent patterns. Although they contain different words, the following sentences are structurally and semantically parallel:

> Mary is a good attorney.
> Rose is a fine lawyer.

Both criticisms are responses to a form of myopia that can lead to nonsensical recognition errors, such as acceptance of the non-sentence

> Which of the flight on Delta airlines?

as a valid query, or accept as meaningful text the following other-worldly sequence:

> If you don't have to be a good deal of the world."
> "I said.
> She was a good deal of the world. But the fact that the only one of the world. When the first time in the world (Lalit Bahl, Peter Brown, Peter deSouza & Robert Mercer, Senior researchers, IBM Watson Research Center, "A tree-based statistical language model for natural language speech recognition," 1989, p. 1008).

In these examples, successive three-word patterns are acceptable, but the longer strings are nonsense.

> While statistically based . . . N-gram models have been shown to be effective for speech recognition, there is, in general, more structure present in natural language than N-gram models can capture (Marie Mateer, Rensselaer Polytechnic Institute, & J. Robin Rohlicek, BBN Systems and Technologies, "Statistical language modeling combining N-gram and context-free grammars," 1993, p. 37).

Therefore, if the purpose of using speech recognition is to capture and comprehend what the speaker is communicating, N-gram models, by themselves are insufficient. If, however, the goal of recognition is to identify verbatim what is being said, an N-gram approach works very well.

> If the goal is to recognize what the person says, you need to recognize those ungrammatical sentences. It is more important to accept the right thing than reject the wrong thing. The N-gram approach will accept any sentence with some sort of probability assigned to it. This gives the approach a level of robustness you don't get from a more highly structured, linguistic model (Richard Schwartz, Senior Researcher, BBN Systems and Technologies, personal communication, 1994).

The weaknesses of the N-gram model for language comprehension become advantages when used for dictation and other verbatim records of spoken language, such as court reporting.

4.3.1.3 Implementing N-gram models. N-gram models extract word-sequencing patterns directly from large quantities of language data. Once found, those sequences are coded in terms of the probability that the Nth word of the sequence will follow the previous N-1 words. This process is called *training* the system.

The training procedures produce an N-gram language model. That model is generally represented as a lattice or linked list whose links contain the probabilities found during training. During the operation of an application, those probabilities are used to select, eliminate, and rank word candidates.

The amount of language data needed to create a good language model increases with the size of the vocabulary in the application and the size of N. Even a small N, such as 3, requires a great deal of language data. Jelinek (1985) estimated that to find all possible trigrams ($N = 3$) for a vocabulary of five thousand words would require a corpus of 125 trillion words.

Unfortunately, these probabilities cannot be approximated directly by relative frequencies obtained by counting trigrams occurring in some large text, since the vast majority of possible English word trigrams will not take place even in very large databases (Frederick Jelinek, IBM [currently at the University of Pittsburgh], "The development of an experimental discrete dictation recognizer," 1985, p. 589).

Bigram ($N = 2$) and unigram ($N = 1$) probabilities are used to supplement missing trigrams. For each trigram sequence

word1 word2 word3

the bigram prediction for word2, given word1, and the bigram prediction for word3, given word2, are calculated and used to extrapolate the trigram prediction for word3 in the sequence. If the sequence word1 word2 does not appear in the corpus, a unigram (single-word occurrence) prediction is used to make a bigram estimate. This process of moving from trigram to unigram is called *backing off*.

Alternatives to backing off are being explored in research systems. Some involve gathering additional data from a word's structure (called *morphology*), part of speech, or semantic class (such as *date* or *number*). Jelinek (1990) has suggested including *collocations* for low-frequency words. Collocations are words frequently used in conjunction with a target word but are not necessarily adjacent to it. The word "saucer," for example, is a collocation of the word "cup." Researchers specializing in information retrieval and natural language processing have extracted a considerable amount of data on collocations from printed materials. Both the methodologies and the findings could be imported into speech recognition.

Detailed technical information on the implementation of N-gram models can be found in any of Jelinek's publications. Technical descriptions of backing off and some alternatives to it are described in Jelinek (1985 and 1990) and in Maltese & Mancini (1992). More information about collocations and other lexical relationships can be found in Evens, et al. (1980), Grishman & Sterling (1993), and Markowitz, et al. (1986 and 1992).

4.3.1.4 Personalizing N-gram models. When a dictation system reflects the style and vocabulary preferences of a user, it is both easier to use and more efficient. The molding of a system to the behavior of the user is called *personalizing*. There are two primary ways to personalize a system. One entails the ability to add new vocabulary items (see chapter 3, section 3.4.3). The other involves using an internal grammar that reflects the style and language patterns of the user.

When a speaker creates a new word, the system must assign it a word-sequencing probability. Since it has no training data upon which to base its assignment, it must find another method. The approach generally used is to base the probability upon general word-frequency estimates. This practice often results in grossly inflated or deflated probabilities. Another approach, used by IBM, is called *adaptive cache*. It adjusts the probabilities of bigrams in the existing language model to reflect situations involving newly added words.

The process of personalizing the grammar itself can be exemplified by two techniques used in Dragon Systems' *DragonDictate*. Prior to using the system in an organization, the system can adapt its internal grammar by scanning word-sequence patterns found in relevant organization documents. During the operation of the system it will modify its probability assignments to better reflect those of its users.

4.3.2 N-Class Models

N-class models extend the concept of N-gram modeling to syntactic (or semantic) categories. Bi-class modeling calculates the possibility that two categories will appear in succession; tri-class modeling extends the frequency patterns to three successive classes. In a bi-class system for English, for example, the words "a," "an," and "the" might be grouped into the *article* class and words like "table," "book," and "shoe" might be members of the *countable-noun* class. The probability of the bi-class *article countable-noun* occurring is calculated by finding:

1. Total occurrences of the *article* category in the training text (total-articles)
2. Total occurrences of the *article* category followed by the *countable-noun* category (sequence)
3. $\dfrac{\text{total-articles}}{\text{sequence}}$

This process requires all words in the data to be classified. Although some classification can be done automatically, language training process is lengthened.

Bi-class and tri-class modeling has been implemented at IBM and in several European recognition systems. One French implementation generated bi-class and tri-class models for 150 categories from a 170,000 word lexicon. In the United States, use of N-class modeling is growing as a means of reducing some of the training issues of N-gram modeling and as an alternative to backing off.

N-class modeling has been found to produce accurate, robust language models from corpora much smaller than those required for N-gram modeling.

> The amount of data necessary to train . . . a trigram model, will be large. In the case of using grammatical categories [N-class models], the text will have to be labelled, but can be shorter. Moreover, if a new word is introduced in the dictionary it can inherit the probabilities computed for the words having the same grammatical category (J. Mariani, Centre National des Recherches Scientifiques, "Automated voice dictation in French," 1993, p. 173).

These are important features for a grammar because they facilitate grammar construction and the porting of large vocabulary systems to new domains. The language patterns and vocabulary used for a business involved in exporting is, for example, unlikely to resemble those found in a brokerage.

Mariani (1993) provides an excellent description of bi-class and tri-class modeling. Pieraccini & Levin (1992) describe a similar approach being developed at AT&T Bell Laboratories, and Placeway, et al. (1993) describe the use of N-class modeling with both small and large corpora. Jelinek, et al. (1975) contains a technical description of an early N-class proposal, and Jelinek, et al. (1990) describe how an N-class approach might effect better integration of new words into a trigram model.

4.4 LINGUISTICS-BASED GRAMMARS

Grammars designed by linguists are intended to describe all the features of verbal communication displayed in figure 4.2. Such grammars may include a finite-state grammar and/or a probabilistic language model as a component, but the focus is on designing a system that understands the sense of what a user has said as well as (or, sometimes, instead of) identifying the spoken words. This objective transforms the

```
Sound system                   -- > Phonetics and Phonology
Words and word structures      -- > Morphology and Lexicology
Phrase and sentence structures -- > Syntax
Meaning                        -- > Semantics
Social rules of communication  -- > Pragmatics
```

Figure 4.2   Contents of a linguistic grammar

LINGUISTIC GRAMMARS

Linguistic grammars dominated the speech research effort in the mid-1970's but were supplanted by other approaches more capable of moving from the laboratory to the marketplace. In the 1990's, renewed interest in linguistic grammars is a natural by-product of the recent growth in computing power, greater understanding of linguistic principles, and the maturation of speech recognition. As in the 1970's, the recent upsurge of research using linguistic grammars has been spurred by interest and funding from ARPA, other federal agencies, and government-sponsored projects in Europe and Asia. The aim of the funding is to link speech research with natural language processing as a way of creating systems capable of performing speech-to-speech or speech-to-text translation and systems that are able to participate in natural verbal interaction with humans (called *discourse*).

---

acoustics-oriented process of speech recognition into the cognitive-linguistic process of *spoken language understanding*. Virtually all linguistics-based grammars for spoken language understanding are research systems.

There are a variety of reasons why the speech recognition industry would like to understand language rather than to simply recognize speech. One is that the use of additional knowledge, such as the goals of the user and topics already covered in the conversation, will refine the active vocabulary by eliminating illogical or impossible choices.

> Appropriate use of constraints from natural language processing reduces the perplexity of the speech recognition task, increasing word recognition accuracy (Hy Murveit & Robert Moore, SRI International, "Integrating natural language constraints into HMM-based speech recognition," 1990, p. 573).

Another reason is that cognitive, behavioral, and linguistic knowledge are natural components of human interaction.

> Many of the applications suitable for human/machine interaction using speech typically involve interactive problem solving. That is, in addition to converting the speech signal to text, the computer must also understand the user's request, in order to generate a response (Victor Zue, James Glass, David Goodine, Lynette Hirschman, Hong Leung, Michael Phillips, Joseph Polifroni & Stephanie Seneff, MIT, "From speech recognition to spoken language understanding: The development of the MIT *SUMMIT* and *VOYAGER* systems," 1991, p. 256).

Natural, flexible, user-friendly, human-like speech recognition is a by-product of including non-acoustic knowledge about human communication.

Linguistic-based grammars have taken many forms. Most contain separate modules for each of the functions displayed in figure 4.2. Some are based upon formal linguistic theories.

4.4.1 Context-Free Grammar

Context-free grammar represents the most widely used approach to syntactic analysis found in linguistic-based speech recognition systems. It may be implemented alone or as a component of a larger model.

4.4.1.1 The power of context-free grammar. Like finite-state grammars, context-free grammars are *deterministic:* they define allowable structures. Their ability to represent and control relationships within the utterance makes them more powerful than finite-state grammars. A finite-state grammar can be used for an application requiring the construction of an identification code consisting of digits followed by letters. A finite-state grammar could not be used for a code consisting of a variable number of digits followed by an equal number of letters. A context-free grammar would be needed for that application and for applications requiring number agreement of subject and verb within a sentence. This is accomplished through the use of rewrite rules and tree representations, such as those shown in figures 4.3 and 4.4.

Each rule displays one category, or symbol, on its left-hand side which is converted (called *rewritten*) to one or more other symbols. The left-hand category encompasses the categories on the right. The first rule in figure 4.3, for example, rewrites the category *sentence* as a sequence of two categories: a *noun phrase* followed by a *verb phrase*. A full grammar would contain many such *rewrite rules* for the *sentence* category and the other linguistic categories included in the grammar. The rewrite rules of figure 4.3 are represented graphically as a tree in figure 4.4a.

Part of the flexibility of context-free grammars is that they can represent a variety of linguistic approaches. The context-free rules in figure 4.3 and the corresponding tree in figure 4.4a, for example, depict an immediate constituent grammar. The tree in figure 4.4b and the context-free rules that underlie it represent a head-and-modifier theory of grammar.

Its power, flexibility, and simple representation have made context-free grammars a popular choice for linguists, computer scientists, and speech system researchers. Winograd (1983, chapter 3) describes context-free grammars in detail.

S - > NP VP	VP - > AUX VP
NP - > DET NP	VP - > V PP
NP - > ADJ N	PP - > PREP NP

KEY:		
S = sentence	ADJ = adjective
NP = noun phrase	N = noun
VP = verb phrase	AUX = auxiliary verb (is, can, etc.)
PP = prepositional phrase	DET = determiner (a, an, the)
V = verb	PREP = preposition (on, behind, etc.)

Figure 4.3   Context-free rules

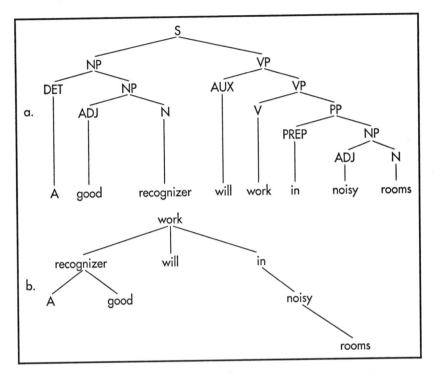

Figure 4.4   Tree representation for context-free grammar shown in figure 4.3

Ney (1991) provides an example of the combination of context-free rules with probabilities.

4.4.1.2 Implementing context-free grammar.   One of the most frequent computational implementations of context-free grammars is the *chart parser*. Chart parsing constitutes a dynamic approach to parsing. It applies the context-free rules of the grammar to the spoken input and keeps track of the rules that were successful by placing them on a *chart*. Figure 4.5 displays a chart containing a partial parse for the sentence "The rabbit with a saw nibbled on an orange." It shows that the structure of the chart is similar to that of a finite-state network. As the chart parser works through the speech it extends and removes alternatives until it has an interpretation of the complete utterance. Winograd (1983, chapter 3) provides a detailed description of chart parsers.

4.4.2 Grammars with Multiple Knowledge Sources

Speech recognition research is producing a highly differentiated array of grammars that combine syntactic analysis (often context-free grammar) with semantics, statistics, and other sources of knowledge.

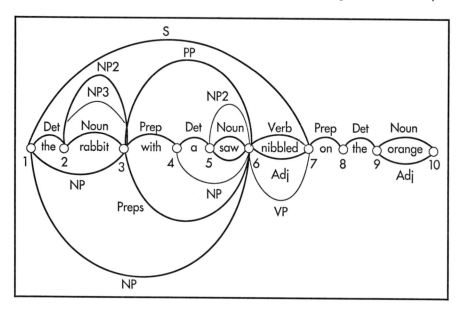

Figure 4.5   Chart parser showing chart for the sentence "The rabbit with a saw nibbled on an orange" (Winograd, *Language as a Cognitive Process, Volume I Syntax,* Copyright 1983, Addison-Wesley).

The *Spoken Language System,* developed by BBN, is a good example of how diverse approaches have been blended into a single spoken language understanding system. *BYBLOS,* its speech recognition component, contains bigram and trigram language models supplemented with a modified form of backing-off. It has been merged with *DELPHI,* BBN's language understanding system. *DELPHI* contains a context-free grammar implemented as a chart parser. The context-free grammar has been enhanced to integrate semantic knowledge. *DELPHI* uses statistics to rank the context-free rules to help process poorly-formed spoken input. The interface between *BYBLOS* and *DELPHI* is an N-*best* list of word candidates (see chapter 3, section 3.2.2).

MIT's *TINA* system combines context-free rules with probabilities. As with the *Spoken Language System,* the statistical probabilities assist in reducing the processing requirements of the linguistic model. *TINA* uses an *augmented transition network (ATN).* The structure of an ATN is similar to that of a finite-state network. Unlike finite-state networks, the nodes of ATN's contain additional grammatical information used to select the outgoing path from a node. That information can represent context-free rules or contain more detailed linguistic data. The states of *TINA's* ATN contain syntactic and semantic information. Unlike typical ATN's and finite-state networks, the links of *TINA's* ATN contain probabilities derived from statistical training.

Developers of spoken language understanding systems realize that true speech understanding must go beyond the sentence to include analysis of the conversational interaction with the user (called *discourse processing*). The CMU system, *MINDS,* is an example of a system designed to do discourse processing. It contains triphones, bigram and tri-class modeling, finite-state networks, rules for word class and semantic functions, frames (an object-oriented programming structure) containing the history of the discourse, speaker and topic knowledge, and layers of *pragmatic constraints.* The pragmatic constraints are knowledge sources used to predict the content of the user's next utterance. Predictions generated by the constraints are ranked based on the amount of control they impose upon the user's response and upon their likelihood of occurrence. Such layering allows *MINDS* to parse and reparse input until a good match for it is found. Comparative testing of recognition for a one thousand word, problem solving domain showed a drop in perplexity from 279 (without constraints) to eighteen (with constraints).

   JANUS is a spoken language translation system developed as a joint effort called *C-STAR* involving CMU, the University of Karlsruhe, Siemens AG, and the Advanced Telecommunications Research Institute. The recognition process begins with a neural network (several variants have been used) to analyze continuous speech input. The network sends its findings to an N-best search to identify and rank from six to one hundred viable sentence-level hypotheses. These hypotheses are screened and reranked by a trigram model and sent to a specialized context-free parser. If there is garbled input or if the parser has difficulty identifying the input, a neural network parser, called *PARSEC,* serves as a backup system. The translation process includes the semantic and pragmatic components of the *MINDS* system.

   A blackboard system called *SUS* was designed by De Mori of Concordia University and implemented as an object-oriented system. Its knowledge sources fill the slots of object instances with hypotheses and information. Most of *SUS's* linguistic experts represent their knowledge as sets of rules that take into account contextual constraints of concern to that knowledge source.

   Bates, et al. (1993) describe BBN's *Spoken Language System,* Seneff (1992) describes *TINA,* Young, et al. (1989) describe *MINDS,* and Osterholtz, et al. (1992) describe *JANUS.* Markowitz (1993e) provides a detailed overview of other linguistic and multiple-knowledge source grammars in speech recognition. Additional information on the *SUS* blackboard system can be found in De Mori (1983).

4.5 WORD SPOTTING

The goal of word spotting is to locate and extract one or more target words embedded in continuous speech. Word spotting applications contain models of each of the target words of the application as well as models for silence, noise, and non-keyword speech (called *garbage* or *junk models*). These models have been implemented using a wide range of approaches, but the principal techniques are hidden Markov models and templates.

WORD SPOTTING

Interest in the design of systems capable of detecting specific words in continuous speech has existed for more than twenty years. It has been approached using templates and HMM's. In 1973, Bridle published the earliest proposals using templates and dynamic time warping. His system calculated a separate score for every keyword template matched against every portion of the input. The positions in the input containing possible keywords (called *putative hits*) frequently overlapped and had to be normalized. Later proposals replaced the overlapping putative hits with two types of templates: keywords and fillers. Fillers represented non-keyword speech patterns. The input was viewed as a sequence of filler and keyword patterns. In the 1980's, HMM's began to replace templates, and fillers were supplanted by more detailed acoustic representation of non-keywords, called *garbage models* (also called *junk models*).

One of the first commercial applications of keyword spotting was AT&T's *Voice Recognition Call Processing (VRCP)* system which was deployed in the late 1980's to handle long-distance telephone calls (see chapter 8, section 8.3.1.4). Word spotting did not appear as a feature of commercial products for application developers until AT&T's *Conversant* offered it in the early 1990's. By the middle of 1994 it had become a feature of several other commercial products targeting telephone-based applications.

For more historical information on word spotting consult Biddle (1973) and Rose & Paul (1990). Wilpon, et al. (1985) provide a detailed discussion of the AT&T findings for the *VRCP* system.

Since word spotting generally operates in noisy environments with unpredictable users, word spotters can erroneously signal the detection of a keyword (called a *false alarm*), or fail to detect a keyword when it is uttered (called a *false reject*). Considerable effort is being directed towards minimizing such errors. One technique is to ascertain that keyword sets do not contain confusable words. Taking another approach, SRI has found that the more word models of non-keywords a system contains, the better word-spotting systems perform. Similar findings have been obtained by researchers at AT&T Bell Laboratories. Other approaches focus on separating the speech signal from the background and speech channel noise (see chapter 7) or on better ways of locating the beginning and ending of words (see chapter 6, section 6.3).

Word spotting has internal structure. That structure is based upon the patterns of silence, keyword utterance, and extraneous speech that were found in the original AT&T research.

A typical word spotting grammar has the following form:

UTTERANCE = silence extraneous-speech keyword extraneous-speech silence

This grammar is part of a continuous speech recognition system. The original models for extraneous speech were taken from actual samples of speech taken from the test data, but more recent modeling has been derived from large vocabulary speech databases and enhanced through the use of detailed acoustic parameters.

4.5.1 Neural Networks for Word Spotting

Most neural word spotters are hybrid systems that combine a network with dynamic time warping (see chapter 2, section 2.3.1). Networks used in this way include CMU's *MS-TDNN*, recurrent networks, and a range of feedforward networks.

One promising network is the *generalized probability descent minimum classification error (GPD/MCE)* network. It is a variant of the feedforward, *learning vector quantization (LVQ)* network. It attempts to minimize errors by defining a gradient along which the quality of membership in a classification is evaluated (generalized probabilistic descent). The network is trained to penalize recognition errors that differ greatly from the correct string (minimum classification error).

More information on GPD/MCE networks for word spotting can be found in McDermott & Katagiri (1993). Zeppenfeld, et al. (1993) discuss the use of the *MS-TDNN* for word spotting. English & Boggess (1992) explain the benefit of using backpropagation training for networks doing word spotting.

4.5.2 Gisting

Gisting extends the concept of word spotting to structured dialogues between two people, with the recognition system acting as an unobtrusive observer. It is an outgrowth of ARPA-sponsored research to extract information from messages and large quantities of text. The objective of gisting is to locate information known to exist in the conversation. Unlike standard word spotting, the information of interest is defined by type and is not limited to specific vocabulary items. A gisting system might, for example, scan the speech of one speaker for language indicating that person has uttered a personal identification code.

A prototype system for air-traffic control (ATC) communication developed by BBN illustrates the capabilities and limits of current gisting technology. The system identifies flight identification data and determines whether the airplane is landing or taking off. It extracts that information from radio transmissions between air traffic controllers and pilots in real time. Each controller maintains multiple, interleaved dialogues with pilots over a noisy communication channel. The speech is rapid, free flowing, and idiomatic. It is also spoken by individuals who are not actively co-operating with the gisting system. Since the function of ATC communication is to guide pilots, the interactions are short and the information sought by the gisting system is clearly present in some form.

In order to identify relevant pieces of information embedded in the communication, gisting requires the use of both artificial intelligence and statistical techniques. It relies on object-oriented representation, techniques of knowledge-based systems, and tools to perform limited natural-language understanding. Robust word spotting and good speaker modeling techniques enable the system to distinguish the voice of the controller from the pilots and to differentiate among the voices of the pilots. The task dialogue must be well-defined and thoroughly understood to support real-time processing.

Funding by government agencies is fostering research on gisting that will make it more powerful and extend its application to less structured conversations. A sizable portion of that funding comes from the intelligence and military communities. In the United States, for example, one of the most active sources of funding for this work is Rome Laboratory of the United States Air Force. The potential applications of gisting extend to extraction of information from large quantities of speech or discourse that can be tagged with a topic and summarized.

More information on BBN's gisting prototype is provided by Denneberg, et al. (1993). Sundheim (1989 and 1993) describe techniques that have been developed to extract information from text.

Virtually all commercial recognition systems contain one or more of the following grammars:

- Finite-state grammar
- N-gram model
- Word spotting

4.6 FINITE-STATE GRAMMAR IN COMMERCIAL RECOGNITION SYSTEMS

Finite-state grammars are most effective in structured applications, such as data entry and voice command-and-control of equipment. They enhance speed and accuracy by limiting the size of the active vocabulary. When they are well-designed, they are fast, efficient, and accurate.

Most finite-state grammars are constructed by an application developer and tailored to the requirements of a specific task. In general, finite-state grammars are easy to understand and construct. The most difficult facets of grammar design are identifying and defining the linguistic and structural requirements of the task (also see section 4.9.1). The recent appearance of automatic vocabulary extraction, now available in some GUI application interface products (also see chapter 3, section 3.4.4), is making the design process even easier.

A challenge for applications containing finite-state grammars is to insure that the people using the system speak only the allowable words and word sequences. If the users consist of a small, well-defined group of people who will employ the system regularly, they can be given a training program to assist them. The application might also include a help system. These techniques are less useful for applications that expect large populations of one-time users. In such cases, it is possible to use finite-state grammars to create speech structures that appear natural to the system users. This requires a full understanding of the ways in which users proceed through the task, the language they are likely to use, the impact of different types of prompts on user behavior, and good error correction.

4.7 N-GRAM MODELS IN COMMERCIAL RECOGNITION SYSTEMS

Most large vocabulary systems use bigram and/or trigram language models. These models increase speed and accuracy by ranking the items in the active vocabulary. They foster naturalness by allowing users a great deal of flexibility.

Good N-gram models are difficult to construct because they require huge quantities of language data and sophisticated statistical analysis. Because of the difficulty obtaining good sources of data, most N-gram models are developed by technology vendors. Some vendors provide tools to application developers to modify the language model; some have automated the model adaptation process. Such tools are important because an N-gram language model reflects the word sequencing patterns found in the data used to train it. The language patterns of one industry are likely to be quite different from those of other industries. Models constructed from issues of the *Wall Street Journal,* for example, may not work well for the transportation industry; they may even be inappropriate for diverse organizations within the financial industry. Consequently, the language models of a dictation product need to be tested on a representative sample of the expected forms of dictation.

The documents of an organization or an individual constitute the best corpora for the development of a probabilistic language model. Additional subword modeling can be used to mold the resident vocabulary of an application to satisfy the needs of an individual organization. Some products adapt the language model to reflect word-sequence patterns found in the documents. These language modeling tools vary in their ability to incorporate statistics for any new words found in the documents.

Some products contain language models that adapt during use to match the word-sequencing patterns of the person using the system. This may or may not include the integration of new vocabulary into the language models. Other vendors rely on generic estimates of frequencies for unknown words but do not modify their existing language models when new words are added.

4.8 WORD SPOTTING IN COMMERCIAL RECOGNITION SYSTEMS

Word spotting is typically used for small, highly structured applications involving large and varied populations of one-time users. The number of potential users, the lack of commitment on the part of users to a word spotting system, and the transient nature of their contact with it has inspired David Pallett of the National Institute of Standards and Testing (NIST) to refer to such interactions as *promiscuous speech.*

The unobtrusiveness of word spotting allows speakers unfamiliar with speech recognition systems to communicate naturally. For that reason word spotting is becoming increasingly popular for telephone applications. The invisibility of word spotting is a by-product of careful application design and extensive testing. The selection and coding of keywords, the design of speech instructions and prompts, and the structure of the interaction all need to match the likely behavior of the user population. All of these factors contribute to the naturalness, effectiveness, and accuracy of the application.

4.9 USING A GRAMMAR

Designing a successful grammar depends upon task analysis, response time, speech-aware applications, and expecting the unexpected; all of which are discussed in the following sections.

4.9.1 Task Analysis

The most challenging part of grammar design is task analysis. It requires a thorough understanding of

- The organization of the task and its subtasks
- Vocabulary needed for the task
- Language patterns of the task
- Application control patterns
- Expected range of behavior of people who perform the task

Application control patterns include natural-seeming methods of turning speech recognition on and off, correcting errors, backing up to a previous state of the application, getting help, and giving verbal instructions and feedback to users.

For free-form dictation systems, the greatest challenge is insuring that important words are in the resident vocabulary. For all other types of applications, including structured report generation, task (and user) analysis is a central feature of the acceptability of the application and naturalness of the speech interface. Automatic vocabulary extraction is helpful if speech is being added to a computerized system. These tools extract vocabulary and structure from computer applications. As a result, they are useful for understanding the implementation of the task. The findings of automatic vocabulary extraction will not necessarily parallel natural human behavior and, consequently, will need to be evaluated in terms of the expected behavior of users when performing the task. The menus of a *Windows* application, for example, are likely to support the pattern "File open" and "File close" because these word sequences reflect the requirements of menu-based *Windows* applications. In contrast, a human is more likely to say "Open the file" and "Close the file." When used in this way, speech is truly a keyboard or mouse substitute, but it fails its goal of being a more natural, human-based input device.

One way to maximize naturalness is to involve system users in the system design and testing. Another technique is to test specific features of the application as pilots or prototypes. A third approach is to use iterative design and testing. Chapter 8 (section 8.2) describes some of these methods in greater detail.

4.9.2 Response Time

One facet of user acceptance is a reasonable response time. Users impose limits on the time they are willing to wait for a recognition system to accomplish its work. This limit may be extremely short and is unlikely to expand with the size of an application's vocabulary.

The design of a finite-state grammar will affect response time. One component is the size of the active vocabulary. The organization of the grammar and interaction between the structures within the finite-state grammar can also have an impact on the speed of the system. Simpler structures containing little recursion run faster than larger, complex structures.

4.9.3 Speech-Aware Applications

Most recognition systems are designed to function in parallel with an application. Their structures mimic the organization of the task, but they are bound to the task. As a result, they can become out-of-sync with the application.

The best solution to this problem is to design a *speech-aware* (also called *speech-enabled*) application. In speech-aware applications, the application software identifies the vocabulary and structure required to accomplish a specific subtask and communicates that information to the speech system. Application software developed within an organization or built in conjunction with the design of the speech recognition front-end are the easiest to construct as speech-aware systems. Most commercial software do not yet allow this type of link for speech. The discussion of speech-aware application design continues in chapter 8 (section 8.4).

4.9.4 Expecting the Unexpected

No matter how well an application is designed, and how much it is tested, good developers expect the unexpected. Some unexpected events may arise from platform, channel (see chapter 7), or equipment communications problems, but the majority will be generated by users. This is particularly true for applications designed for one-time users. System parameters, such as time-out or input loudness thresholds may need to be adjusted. Prompts may need to be changed and some features may need to be resequenced.

Even sophisticated users can become distracted, confused, or forgetful. If the cost of making a recognition error is high, the system should be designed with frequent confirmation of recognized input. If users can be distracted, the developer can add reprompting and/or features to remind users where they are in the application.

The best protection for the unexpected is the development of a small prototype or pilot for testing. It is far easier to correct problems in a prototype system than it is to reengineer a large application.

> If you do something as simple as that you will have better applications and you can even decide whether or not speech recognition will work for you in the application. AT&T, with all our experience, usually does trials of this type (Judith Tschirgi, Director, Services and Speech Technology, AT&T Network Systems, personal communication, 1994).

Another useful technique is called the *Wizard of Oz* approach (see chapter 8, section 8.2.3). It entails simulating the recognition application. System users believe they are communicating with a recognition system but they are actually interacting with a human. Wizard of Oz testing is excellent for identifying behavior variables and points of confusion.

4.10 SPOKEN LANGUAGE UNDERSTANDING

Spoken language understanding is an area of active research that is strongly supported by funding from ARPA and government agencies of other countries. Language understanding is a complex, multi-faceted task (see section 4.4), and it is unlikely that commercial spoken language understanding systems will emerge in the near future. Elements of language understanding have, however, already begun to appear in commercially-oriented prototypes.

Speak2Directions, for example, is a prototype developed by Pure Speech for the highly-structured and well-defined communication for getting directions over the telephone. It utilizes a *semantic frame* with two objects: a *discourse object* and a *history object.* The discourse object stores the goal of the interaction along with important information about that goal in the object's *slots* (also called *attributes*). In the *Speak2Directions* prototype the goal is to get directions, necessitating slots to represent the person's current location and destination. The history object monitors the information gathered in the course of the dialogue. It is used to identify the reference of pronouns and words like "here." If a caller wishes to go to the Cambridge Marriott, *Speak2Directions* will consult its discourse object to determine whether it has been told the caller's current location. If not, it will ask for that information. Later in the conversation, the history object might be called upon to interpret the word "here" as the caller's current location.

4.11 SYSTEMS WITH NO GRAMMAR

Some vendors claim their products have no grammar. Generally, this means there is no finite-state grammar. Most products described in this manner utilize a statistical language model, usually a bigram or trigram model. If the vendor insists there is no grammar of any sort in the product, they should be prepared to explain (and demonstrate) how the product handles high perplexity.

5

SPEAKER MODELING

INTRODUCTION

A speech recognition system must understand the speech of anyone who needs to use it. That might include a small, well-defined group of regular system users or a large, diverse population of one-time users. Given this requirement, the focus of speaker modeling is on devising ways of representing speaker variability that enable recognition systems to perform well with the speech of all potential system users. The approaches created to accomplish this goal can be grouped as

- Speaker-dependent modeling
- Multi-speaker modeling
- Speaker-independent modeling
- Speaker adaptation

This chapter examines the technologies required to generate various forms of speaker modeling and the application issues related to each speaker modeling approach. The Technology Focus begins with definitions of each of the approaches to speaker modeling and discussions of technological challenges associated with them. Special attention is given to the two forms of modeling that are gaining dominance: speaker independence and speaker adaptation.

The Application Focus characterizes the four approaches to speaker modeling as points along a speaker-modeling continuum. Further discussion of individual speaker-modeling approaches focuses on the strengths and weaknesses of each approach, its accuracy, and the ease with which new words are added to applications.

Finally, some general speaker-modeling issues, such as the effect of stress on speech, are discussed.

In chapters 2 and 3 we described the major technologies used to represent words:

* Templates
* Hidden Markov models
* Neural networks

Each technology can be used to create a digitized representation for every vocabulary item in an application or system. The patterns that are stored as part of an application are called *reference patterns*. Recognition is accomplished when incoming speech is compared with these stored reference patterns and a good match is found. The acoustic information coded into the internal reference patterns created by these technologies differs depending upon which of the four speaker-modeling approaches is being used.

For additional information regarding speaker modeling, consult Markowitz (1990 and 1993a), Rabiner & Juang (1993), and Huang & Lee (1993).

5.1 SPEAKER-DEPENDENT MODELING

A recognition system using speaker-dependent modeling creates a special speaker model for each of the people who will be using the system. A speaker model contains the speech attributes of a single authorized speaker. Most commercial systems store each speaker model in a separate file. When an authorized user wishes to access the recognition system, she/he enters a personal identifier that causes the system to load that person's speaker file.

The creation of any speaker-dependent model entails three steps:

* Data collection
* Calculation
* Model construction

The data collection process is called *training* or *enrollment*. It consists of eliciting one or more spoken samples (called *tokens*) of each word in the application from the speaker. The subsequent calculation and model construction steps depend upon whether the model is created using templates or HMM's.

Because speaker-dependent representation attempts to capture the acoustic patterns of a single individual, it can produce excellent models.

Because of between-speaker variabilities, well-trained speaker-dependent speech recognition systems outperform speaker-independent systems by a factor of two to three (Xuedong Huang & Kai-Fu Lee, Carnegie Mellon University [Huang is currently at Microsoft Corporation. Lee is currently at Apple Computer Corporation], "On speaker-independent, speaker-dependent, and speaker-adaptive speech recognition," 1993, p. 150).

5.1.1 Template Models

Calculation for template creation consists of computing norms for acoustic parameters within those tokens. One or more templates are constructed using the results of the calculation process.

Early template systems created a template for each training token. Each template became a separate reference pattern for its vocabulary item. Because of its poor utilization of storage and the high level of computation required to compare incoming speech with each template, applications developed using this template construction methodology were characterized by small vocabularies. Furthermore, this methodology could neither handle intra-speaker variability effectively nor minimize the effects of errors made during enrollment.

Improvements in template technology have made it possible to construct reference model templates from two or more tokens. Each frame of the reference template represents the statistical average of the acoustic data contained in the tokens used to generate the frame. This approach, called *robust training,* avoids many of the problems that characterized earlier template systems.

5.1.2 Hidden Markov Models

The calculation step for hidden Markov models (HMM's) employs more sophisticated statistics than the averaging calculations used for template generation. The statistics are designed to capture the speaker's patterns of variability as well as norms. The results of the calculations are embedded in the states and transitions of the HMM word model (see chapter 2, section 2.3.3 and chapter 3, section 3.1.3). The most commonly used HMM model-creation technique, the Baum-Welch algorithm, updates and recalculates the acoustic parameters of an HMM based upon the tokens it is provided. This process is called *reestimation.*

Good technical analyses of speaker-dependent modeling are provided by Rabiner & Juang (1993, chapters 5 and 6) and by Moore (1992).

5.2 MULTI-SPEAKER MODELING

Multi-speaker modeling is an extension of speaker-dependent modeling, and speaker-dependent recognition systems are generally used to create them. The models are designed to represent the speech attributes of a group of individuals. The creation of accurate, high quality multi-user models requires a known, well-defined population of authorized speakers. All users supply one or more tokens of each vocabulary item they will be using.

Because multi-speaker modeling attempts to represent the speech patterns of more than one speaker using speaker-dependent technology, it is inherently less precise than speaker dependence. Its accuracy declines as the members of the speaker group grow more diverse.

5.3 SPEAKER-INDEPENDENT MODELING

Applications with speaker-independent models are designed to be used by people with no enrollment. The reference models for many of these applications must recognize large, heterogeneous populations of speakers. Given the range of individual differences, dialects, foreign accents, and speech impediments exhibited by speakers, that is a difficult goal to achieve.

Reference models designed for speaker-independent recognition represent the expected acoustic parameters of the entire population of speakers. All speakers use the same set of reference models. Consequently, reference models developed for speaker-independent applications are more complex and difficult to construct than those created for speaker-dependent recognition.

> With speaker dependence you do not need to be as concerned with variability as you do with speaker-independent recognition. A single person varies speech from day to day and morning to night, but the range of variability is far less than that required by a speaker-independent model for the entire country (Jeff Hill, Vice President of New Product Development, Voice Processing Corp, personal communication, 1993).

To minimize errors, speaker-independent systems have traditionally had small vocabularies and have avoided confusable vocabulary items (see chapter 3, section 3.5.2). The advent of faster, more powerful PC hardware combined with inexpensive memory chips has fostered the commercialization of more complex modeling and recognition techniques. The resulting models are more accurate and capable of discriminating among large numbers of word candidates.

The three principal methodologies used to create speaker-independent reference models are

- Sampling
- Subword modeling
- Neural networks

5.3.1 Sampling

Sampling produces high quality models that are tuned to the target population and the speaking environment of an application. It follows the same three-step process applied to speaker-dependent modeling (see section 5.1).

Data collection is more extensive and complex than that required for speaker-dependent model generation. The number of tokens that need to be gathered for each vocabulary item depends upon a variety of factors, including

- Population size and diversity
- Vocabulary type
- Speech flow
- Word similarity
- Speech environment

Sampling for large, diverse populations requires more tokens than sampling for homogeneous speaker populations. The population is partitioned into subgroups based upon demographic information about age ranges, sex, dialect patterns, and other characteristics likely to affect speech. Data collection from subgroups reflects the population proportion of that group.

> For speaker independence you must get a good mix of male and female. You want to mirror the sort of people who will be using the system. The same is true of dialects (Ed Tagg, Vice President of Engineering, Voice Control Systems [currently with ConnectWare], personal communication, 1993).

Texas Instruments' *Voice Across America* project, for example, consists of gathering large numbers of samples from American speakers from all parts of the United States. Samples are for speech over the telephone. The resulting models can be used to develop sample-based vocabulary for applications and speech databases for subword modeling.

The need to accommodate a broader spectrum of variability requires the use of more complex calculations than are needed to create speaker-dependent models, but the calculations resemble those used to generate speaker-dependent models. Template-matching systems seek patterns of commonality by clustering the acoustic data for each word into groups of similar patterns. The center of each group (called the *centroid*) becomes the reference pattern for the type of pronunciation represented by that cluster. In HMM generation, acoustic data from all tokens for a word are pooled as if they were generated by a single speaker. Calculations are performed on the entire data set using Baum-Welch and/or other algorithms to construct a single HMM. Speech Systems, Inc. (SSI) uses a similar approach but augments the models with decision trees.

In 1991, Bolt Beranek and Newman (BBN) proposed another sampling methodology designed to reduce the time and cost of speaker-independent model creation. It entails the collection of a large amount of data from a small number of speakers. Calculation and model-creation proceed in three stages. The first stage is identical to the traditional approach: the pooled data for a word are used to create a single model. That model becomes a *code word* in a speaker-independent vector-quantization codebook (see chapter 2, section 2.2.2). In the second stage a speaker-dependent model is created for each speaker. Finally, one or more speaker-independent models are generated by averaging the acoustic parameters of the speaker-dependent HMM's. BBN reports that speaker-independent models created using this method perform well when compared with models generated using traditional sampling. Because the final model is created from averages rather than calculations on pooled data, it is easier to update the BBN approach with data from new speakers.

Voice Control Systems uses an entirely different approach to speaker-independent modeling for small, confusable vocabularies, such as spelling (see chapter 3, section 3.5.3). They remove features of confusable words from the target word. This is called *discriminative training*. Voice Control Systems uses it to obtain more accurate recognition for difficult word sets.

When it is done well, sampling produces good speaker-independent models. It is, however, labor-intensive and slows application development, making large-vocabulary model creation extremely difficult. This has prompted researchers to seek alternative methods for model generation. One, subword modeling, was introduced in chapter 3 (section 3.1.5) and is discussed further in the next section.

Rabiner & Juang (1993, chapter 5) provide a technical description of sampling techniques and issues. Wilpon & Rabiner (1985) describe a commonly-used clustering technique called K-means; Kubala & Schwartz (1991) present the BBN approach to sampling; and Meisel, et al. (1991) explain SSI's technology.

5.3.2 Subword Modeling

Subword modeling is designed for rapid, large-vocabulary construction (see chapter 3, sections 3.1.5 and 3.2). It facilitates vocabulary development for large vocabulary systems and was originally used exclusively by speaker-adaptive systems. The extension of subword modeling to speaker-independent systems offers rapid vocabulary development to these systems and allows the extension of speaker independence to applications requiring large vocabularies.

The initial creation of a subword modeling system is directed at

- Constructing a database of subwords
- Developing a technique for concatenating subwords to create word models
- Defining the form of the user input

These processes are long and labor intensive. The database contains all the subword elements of the system. The expected input is generally via the keyboard, but vendors have incorporated different spelling conventions into their systems. Some allow standard spelling while others expect a form of phonetic spelling. Typed spelling is easier for application developers (and users) to learn and use; but for English, the correspondence between spelling and pronunciation is unreliable. Phonetic spelling is more reliable but harder to learn. As a result, vendors have been slow to let word model creation tools leave their laboratories.

The basic elements of subword modeling were presented in chapter 3 (section 3.1.5). Subword modeling uses HMM's. Some vendors rely on existing spoken language corpora (see chapter 3, section 3.2.1) containing large numbers of samples from a range of speakers. Other technology developers collect their own samples. The preference for internal data collection depends upon the vendor and the speech environment. AT&T, for example, collected its own samples for its *FlexWord* subword modeling system that is designed for telephone-based applications.

> The subwords in *Conversant's FlexWord* were created from samples. We used a set of phonetically-balanced sentences created by MIT. Then we collected speech samples representing the entire United States (Kathy Breslin, Marketing Manager, AT&T *Conversant* System, AT&T Global Business, personal communication, 1994).

AT&T's *Conversant* was the first speaker-independent commercial product to offer subword modeling as a feature of telephone-based application development.

As the data for a subword modeling system are collected, they are segmented into subword units. Calculation and model creation steps are very similar to those described for sampling methodology. The resulting collection of subwords is placed in the database and tested. Once the subword database is complete, no further data collection is required unless the system is ported to new populations.

The final step of subword modeling is word model creation using the established input technique. The input is segmented into subword chunks, translated into acoustic correlates, matched with existing subword models, and reassembled as a complete word model (or baseform for speaker-adaptive systems). The model is stored in the system dictionary. Mark Mandel of Dragon Systems likens this process to using tinker toys. Jay Wilpon of AT&T Bell Laboratories compares it to accessing pronunciation codes in dictionaries.

Chin-Hui Lee, et al. (1993) and Huang & Lee (1993) describe triphone and subword modeling. Markowitz (1993a) compares subword modeling with sampling.

5.3.3 Neural Networks for Speaker-Independent Modeling

The ability of neural networks to perform complex classification of difficult data makes them ideal for discriminating among speakers and for generating speaker-independent models. Neural network developers have taken several approaches to speaker modeling. As with all neural network development, they require large numbers of tokens. Like BBN's sampling technique (see section 5.3.1), the tokens can be provided by a small number of speakers. Some developers have adapted existing speaker-dependent networks to speaker-independent recognition (notably the *TDNN*), but most researchers are creating new network models.

One approach is to design a prediction network using a multi-layer perceptron (MLP) or other feedforward architecture. These networks are trained to predict the acoustic parameters of an incoming speech vector based upon the parameters of preceding vectors. Called *neural prediction,* this approach is comparable to linear predictive coding (see chapter 2, section 2.2.2; also see chapter 6, section 6.4).

Some researchers train networks to categorize speakers into groups represented by clusters of reference speakers. Each new speaker is classified as an instance of one of the reference speaker clusters. Once that classification is accomplished, recognition proceeds by comparing the spoken input with the reference models of the selected cluster.

Iso & Watanabe (1990) have developed a neural prediction model; Nakamura & Akabene (1991) describe a clustering network; and Nakamura, et al. (1992) have constructed a very large *TDNN* for speaker-independent recognition.

SPEAKER ADAPTATION

Commercial applications of speaker adaptation were first applied to speaker-dependent models and used during the enrollment cycle. In 1988, Dragon Systems' *DragonDictate* demonstration system became the first commercial system to use on-the-fly adaptation for large-vocabulary recognition. It incorporated adaptation for the acoustic model of the speaker, the language model, and the background noise. Speaker adaptation has become a core technology for both speaker-dependent and speaker-independent modeling.

When referring to their systems, most vendors use the term *adaptation* to refer to the speaker-adaptation processes described in this chapter. Some vendors, such as Dragon Systems, extend the term to include adaptation of a system's internal language model (usually an N-gram model) and/or to the ability of a system to adjust to background noise.

5.4 SPEAKER ADAPTATION

We wanted our speech model to have the flexibility necessary for robust recognition across a range of speakers with widely varying vocal tract characteristics, yet we wanted speaker-dependent recognition rates (John Hampshire II & Alex Waibel, Carnegie Mellon University, "The *Meta-Pi* network: Connectionist rapid adaptation for high-performance multi-speaker phoneme recognition," 1990, p. 165).

Unlike the previous modeling methodologies, *speaker adaptation* is a means of modifying existing reference patterns rather than of creating new ones.

It must be clear that the models in *DragonDictate* are not the same as full speaker-independent models. *DragonDictate* is speaker-adaptive. That is, there is enough of a model of each word to be sufficiently speaker-independent for acceptable initial recognition, but they are immediately modified by adaptation to include the individual speaker's characteristics (Mark Mandel, Dragon Systems Inc., personal communication, 1993).

Such alterations enable recognition systems to process incoming patterns that differ from those used to derive the reference patterns. Another benefit of speaker adaptation is that the adaptation process can produce good recognition for a speaker using a small amount of speaker-dependent information.

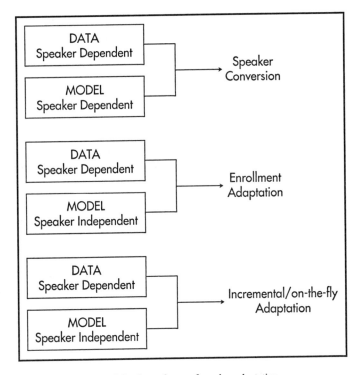

Figure 5.1   Some forms of speaker adaptation

With only 300 adaptation sentences, the error rate [of our adaptive system] was the same as that of the speaker-dependent system trained with 600 sentences. This shows that speaker-adaptive speech recognition utilizes training data more effectively than speaker-dependent speech recognition (Xuedong Huang & Kai-Fu Lee, Carnegie Mellon University [Huang is currently at Microsoft Corporation. Lee is currently at Apple Computer Corporation], "On speaker-independent, speaker-dependent, and speaker-adaptive speech recognition," 1993, p. 151).

Speaker adaptation can be accomplished in many ways. Figure 5.1 displays the most frequently used approaches.

RAPID ENROLLMENT

The first commercial system to utilize rapid enrollment was the *PE-100* of Speech Systems, Inc. SSI tried an experiment in 1986 to adapt the speaker-independent models in the *PE-100* dictionary. They later abandoned this technique in favor of separate male and female speaker-independent models. The large vocabulary dictation systems of IBM use it exclusively. Kurzweil AI and Philips Dictation Systems' toolkit combine rapid enrollment with on-the-fly adaptation.

Speaker conversion involves the shifting of speaker-dependent reference patterns for one person to speaker-dependent reference patterns for a second speaker. It generally functions at the word level. Enrollment adaptation uses data from an initial enrollment process (called *rapid enrollment*) to modify speaker-independent models, making them more like the speech of a particular speaker. Rapid enrollment generally involves having the user read a pre-determined text or provide other dictated input. It is generally done in a single session lasting one to two hours.

Another approach is to collect adaptation data *on-the-fly*. On-the-fly adaptation is accomplished by modifying reference models while the speaker is using the system. It was designed to enhance user acceptance by eliminating enrollment, although it can be combined with rapid enrollment to produce faster accuracy gains.

5.4.1 Template Adaptation

Speaker adaptation using templates is rare. It is performed on whole-word patterns and requires templates constructed using robust training (see chapter 2, section 2.3.1). Speaker conversion is accomplished using a small amount of data from the new speaker to modify code words in the vector quantization codebook. Enrollment or on-the-fly adaptation of speaker-independent reference templates clusters the acoustic data from the new speaker with that of the reference templates.

Scott Instruments (now part of Voice Control Systems, Inc.) used on-the-fly adaptation with its speaker-independent templates. Whenever a match was questioned or identified as incorrect by the speaker, the system added the new acoustic information to the correct reference model and subtracted it from the incorrect reference model.

Rabiner & Juang (1993, chapter 5) provide a detailed technical analysis of the spectrum of adaptation techniques. Smith, et al. (1990) describe Scott Instruments' approach to template adaptation.

5.4.2 HMM Adaptation

Speaker adaptation of HMM's can be applied to words, but it is most strongly identified with large-vocabulary, subword systems (see section 5.3.2). The use of speaker adaptation with subword models alters the triphones (or other subword units) that make up the reference model baseforms of an application or system. The process of adaptation of words or subwords is called *mapping*. The modifications are generally stored in a file and represent the model of a single speaker.

Two common approaches to HMM adaptation are vector quantization codebook adaptation and HMM acoustic-parameter adaptation. Vector quantization codebook adaptation entails the modification of code words in the vector quantization codebook (see chapter 2, section 2.2.2). The alterations make the acoustic patterns of the codewords resemble the speech of a specific talker. This is an attractive approach for speaker adaptation because the use of vector quantization codebooks reduces searching. The codebook representation also offers the possibility of effecting global pattern shifts based upon small quantities of data from a new speaker.

HMM acoustic-parameter adaptation involves the modification of the acoustic parameters of the HMM itself. These parameters are adjusted to make them more like the data provided by the new speaker.

Detailed technical descriptions of several approaches to adaptation can be found in Huang & Lee (1993), Rabiner & Juang (1993, chapter 5), and Schwartz, et al. (1987).

5.4.3. Neural Networks for Speaker Adaptation

Unlike other methodologies described for speaker adaptation, neural networks designed for speaker adaptation neither modify their internal reference models nor create permanent speaker-dependent models for new speakers. Instead, they use their internal reference models to classify the speech patterns of new users as members of an existing speaker reference-class or speaker cluster. The process is similar to that used by neural networks doing speaker-independent recognition (see section 5.3.3).

CMU's modular *TDNN* network has been used to design a variety of speaker-adaptive systems. CMU's *Meta-Pi* superstructure network, for example, is a variant of the *TDNN*. Its development was motivated by the need to extend the speaker-dependent *TDNN* to multi-speaker tasks. It links several speaker-dependent *TDNN* modules that work in parallel to classify the speech of a new speaker. After applying the *Meta-Pi* network to a speaker identified as MHT, Hampshire and Waibel reported:

> Indeed, the superstructure learns to model speaker MHT with a dynamic combination of *other* male speakers and, in doing so, still achieves a 99.9% recognition rate on the speech of MHT (John Hampshire II & Alex Waibel, Carnegie Mellon University, "The *Meta-Pi* network," 1990, p. 167).

Another group of researchers combined a speaker-dependent *TDNN* trained to do word recognition with another feedforward network trained to perform speaker-adaptation. The combination was found to improve the *TDNN*'s performance for new speakers, but it was still less accurate than a traditional speaker-dependent model for those speakers.

The speaker-cluster neural network (SCNN) is a hybrid MLP-HMM system that was constructed using a multi-stage development process. During the first stage of development, the MLP was trained to cluster speakers into two groups based upon sex-linked acoustic parameters. That network had two output nodes: one to express the probability the speaker was female and the other indicating the probability the speaker was male. Another network was constructed to classify speakers into one of several groups (called *clusters*).

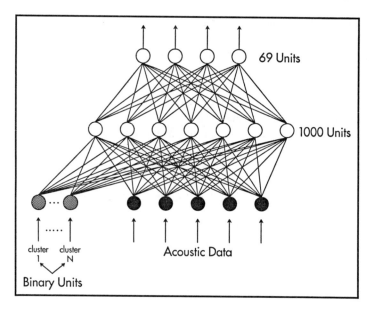

Figure 5.2   Speaker-Cluster Neural Network (SCNN) (Konig & Morgan, "Supervised and unsupervised clustering of the speaker space for connectionist speech recognition," Copyright 1993, IEEE)

The MLP network (shown in figure 5.2) performs speech recognition. It identifies a phone (a *phone* is an instance of phonemes, see chapter 2) from a sentence uttered by an unknown speaker. It uses the spoken input and the speaker-identifying parameter clusters defined in the previous experiments as its sources of data. Each output node expresses the probability that the data represent a specific phone.

The SCNN was found to improve recognition accuracy for new speakers but, like the *Meta-Pi* system, its accuracy did not approach that of traditional speaker-dependent models.

Hampshire & Waibel (1990) describe the *Meta-Pi* network and Fukuzawa, et al. (1992) provide a technical analysis of the *TDNN*-feedforward adaptation system. Konig & Morgan (1993) describe the *SCNN*.

5.5 THE SPEAKER-MODELING CONTINUUM

The speaker-modeling methodologies described in the Technology Focus are characterized by different technological approaches and goals. When viewed from the functional requirements of an application, the distinctions among them become less clear.

> It must be recognized that we are dealing with a continuum. The speaker-dependent approach can model groups of people as well as individuals . . . but the aims are dif-

ferent (Jeff Hill, Vice President of New Product Development, Voice Processing Corp., personal communication, 1993).

Speaker dependence, multi-speaker modeling, and speaker independence resemble points along a continuum, like the one displayed in figure 5.3. Recognition of input as the speech of a single individual and recognition of all speakers using a specific language represent the extremes of the continuum.

Speaker-dependent modeling should not be confused with *speaker verification*. Speaker verification, a component of security systems, has the role of verifying the claimed identity of a speaker rather than understanding what the speaker says. In contrast, the primary function of speaker-dependent modeling is to maximize recognition accuracy for the speech of the person who provided the samples. Speaker dependence should not be used as a security tool to prevent access to a system by unauthorized speakers.

Speaker-dependent word models created for one speaker can be used by other speakers of the same sex whose vocal characteristics are similar to the speaker whose voice was used to make the models. They will be less accurate for other speakers, but the overall accuracy can be enhanced by using highly differentiated sets of words. Similarly, multi-speaker models can be used by individuals who did not contribute samples during enrollment. Sometimes, when a speaker population is small and homogeneous a multi-speaker model may even be used as if it were designed for speaker-independent recognition. Such extensions of multi-speaker modeling must be done with care.

The placement of speaker-independent modeling in figure 5.3 is intended to emphasize the fact that speaker-independent models cannot be expected to operate flawlessly with the speech of people who do not come from the population from which the samples were drawn.

If you put Voice Control System's United Kingdom system into Northern Scotland the recognition for certain words would become less than optimum because of the dialect

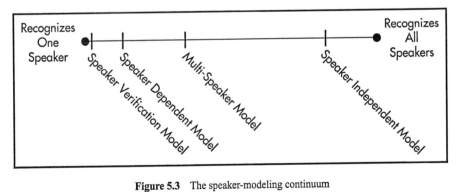

Figure 5.3   The speaker-modeling continuum

. . . You would want to retrain certain items using samples taken from the dialect region (Ed Tagg, Vice President of Engineering, Voice Control Systems [currently with ConnectWare], personal communication, 1993).

In the future, neural networks or comparable technologies might help break the barrier to universal recognition, but no existing commercial recognition system is capable of recognizing all speakers from every population. This is why most speaker-independent recognition applications include a backup procedure for speakers who cannot use the recognition system.

5.6 ISSUES IN SPEAKER-DEPENDENT MODELING

Typically, speaker-dependent systems can achieve better recognition performance than speaker-independent systems . . . However, this is achieved at the cost of a new enrollment session that has to be done for every new speaker (Hervé Bourlard, Faculté Polytechnique de Mons, Belgium and International Computer Science Institute of the University of California at Berkeley & Nelson Morgan, International Computer Science Institute, *Connectionist Speech Recognition: A Hybrid Approach,* 1994, p. 5).

The enrollment process constitutes a major source of concern in speaker-dependent modeling. It is the sole source of word model creation requiring every user to provide at least one spoken sample of each word in the application.

Users can be annoyed by the enrollment process, making it unsuitable for large vocabulary applications. Most speaker-dependent systems allow training to be done in small increments, but even this becomes unacceptable when the number of words in the application exceeds one hundred. It becomes unthinkable beyond two hundred words. Despite this, one of the first versions of Kurzweil AI's large vocabulary dictation system required users to train all seven thousand words in the system.

Even for small vocabulary applications the enrollment process must be planned carefully and designed to maximize the cooperation and interest of the users. It can, for example, be used as a means of familiarizing the users with the application and the speech recognition system.

Another issue associated with both speaker-dependent and speaker-adaptive systems is the loading and unloading of speaker models. Each time an authorized speaker begins to use a speaker-dependent system, the user's templates/word models must be loaded into memory. If speed is an issue, or if the application is characterized by frequent changes of speaker, requirements of model-loading may make speaker-dependent recognition unacceptable. Hospital emergency report generation in some environments, for example, involves interleaved contributions of several professionals. For such settings, the time required to unload the model of the previous speaker and load the new model can appear excessive, making speaker independence the only acceptable speech recognition option.

Since a speaker-dependent model is molded to the acoustic patterns of the person who has trained it, there may be a temptation to use it as a security device. If the acoustic patterns of an unauthorized individual are similar to those of the authorized speaker the speaker-dependent system is likely to function reasonably well with the new voice. A well-designed application with acoustically distinct words in its active vocabularies would be able to accurately recognize input from unauthorized speakers even when their voices only marginally resemble that of the individual who trained the system.

5.6.1 Accuracy in Speaker-Dependent Modeling

Enrollment may be annoying and labor intensive, but speaker-dependent technology is still more accurate than speaker-independent technology for word sets like digits. The potential confusion of "5" with "9" can occur with almost any speech recognition tool. If this error seems strange, it is helpful to note that telephone operators were trained to mark the distinction by saying "nigh-in" for "9" and military personnel are trained to say "niner." The ability of a recognition system to break enrollment into short sessions and to allow enrollment or retraining while the application is on-line can help reduce the negative effects of enrollment. To maintain high accuracy, these technical capabilities should be accompanied by both developing enthusiasm for the system among users and by carefully designing a reenrollment program.

The tailored word models of speaker-dependent systems can be very accurate, even in noisy speaking environments. The enrollment process itself enhances overall accuracy by acclimating users to the recognizer and the application. Accuracy is also improved when enrollment is done in the environment in which the application will be used. This enables the recognizer to distinguish between environmental noise and speech (see chapter 7).

The number of tokens required to achieve good accuracy depends upon the design of the recognition system, the vocabulary size, the presence of confusable words (see chapter 3, section 3.5.2), the accuracy requirements of the application, demands of the task, and the nature of the speaking environment (see chapter 7). In general, performance increases with additional training, particularly for sets of highly confusable vocabulary.

Accuracy may decline as a result of changes in a user's speech. These changes may represent normal shifts in the speaker's voice or in the environment. If, for example, speakers will use the system at different times in their work schedules, they may need to provide tokens when their voices are fresh, as well as when they are tired. In situations involving varying degrees of stress, tokens may be taken of both stressed and non-stressed speech (see chapter 7, section 7.2 and section 5.10.1).

Sometimes, performance of the task will change the way a person speaks. Climbing, lifting, and protective headgear are likely to alter the speech of users. In these cases, enrollment may be rendered useless if it is not done under the conditions of the task.

New users tend to speak to recognition systems in an overly careful manner. This practice disappears with acclimation to the system and may require collection of additional tokens.

The enrollment process itself fosters an unnatural style of speaking called the *recitation effect*. The recitation effect occurs when speakers use a flat, mechanical style. Word models created from recitation effect speech will be prone to error because they will differ from the style used when those words are spoken in the context of the application.

Reenrollment can be programmed into the maintenance of an application. To reduce possible user frustration, many speaker-dependent systems provide retraining tools to update, enhance, or correct individual word models while the application is running.

5.6.2 Adding Words in Speaker-Dependent Modeling

Most speaker-dependent recognizers, having no built-in vocabularies, allow application designers to select and define all necessary vocabulary. Each word that is created must be trained by all users. Some products signal the user that there are untrained items; other products do not. Generally, new vocabulary items are trained in the same way as the original application vocabulary (see chapter 3, section 3.4).

5.7 ISSUES IN MULTI-SPEAKER MODELING

Multi-speaker modeling is generally implemented for applications with small to mid-size vocabularies when it is neither possible nor desirable to load and unload speaker models. Multi-speaker modeling is particularly useful when the application is characterized by rapid shifting from one user to another. It is also useful for verbal sign-on modules of larger applications. A sign-on module might, for example, consist of entering a personal identification code. In many manufacturing applications sign-on codes consist of the person's name or employee number. Their function is to tell the system which speaker models to access. They are not suitable as security devices because multi-speaker models can easily be used by unauthorized individuals whose voices are similar to those of authorized people.

It is not advisable to use multi-speaker modeling for large vocabulary applications because the fine differentiations that must be made cannot be captured by a multi-speaker model. They require more sophisticated speaker-independent or speaker-adaptive modeling.

5.7.1 Accuracy in Multi-Speaker Modeling

Because speaker models are created from the voices of two or more individuals, the overall accuracy of multi-speaker systems can be acceptable but poorer than that of speaker-dependent recognition. This is due to expansion of variability in the recognition parameters for word models that cover more than one speaker and to the fact that the technology being used was designed to represent the voice characteristics of a single speaker. Accuracy is best when the speaker group is small and homogeneous; it is poorest when a multi-speaker model is used as if it were a speaker-independent model. Such use of multi-speaker modeling should be done with care.

5.7.2 Adding Words in Multi-Speaker Modeling

Once an application with multi-speaker modeling has been deployed, the addition of new vocabulary to the system can be problematic. It requires obtaining tokens for all new vocabulary from several speakers whose voices are encoded in the models. The application developer or system manager must make certain that a sufficient number of samples have been obtained for accurate recognition of newly-added words.

5.8 ISSUES IN SPEAKER-INDEPENDENT MODELING

Speaker-independent modeling is essential for applications designed to be accessed by populations of one-time users. Many telephone-based and kiosk applications fall into this category. Speaker independence also contributes to the acceptability of large vocabulary applications.

5.8.1 Accuracy in Speaker-Independent Modeling

Overall, speaker-independent models are less accurate than comparable well-designed speaker-dependent models. This is an understandable consequence of the degree of variability that must be captured by speaker-independent models.

5.8.1.1 Creating speaker-independent models through sampling.
Speaker-independent models created using sampling vary greatly in quality. When it is done well, the sampling approach can produce high-quality models. Differences in quality are a reflection of

- The number of samples used to create the models
- The representativeness of the samples with regard to the user population and speaking environment
- The quality of the algorithms used to generate the models

The number of tokens that must be collected to achieve a high degree of accuracy depends upon the

- Size and diversity of the expected speaker population
- Noise characteristics of the speaking environment
- Accuracy requirements of the application
- Characteristics of the vocabulary

Heterogeneous populations require more sampling than homogeneous populations. As indicated in section 5.5, speaker-independent models are not designed to be universal. They are constructed for particular user populations and specific speaking environments. Developers recognize these limitations and understand that when speaker-independent models constructed for one population are used with another population, accuracy will probably decline. This is especially likely when major dialect boundaries are crossed.

Noisy speaking environments and those with varying noise characteristics require additional sampling. Such sampling is designed to capture speech embedded in the expected noise of the environment or to identify noise patterns that need to be removed from input.

Confusable words and vocabulary items important for the operation of an application merit a larger sampling. Accurate recognition for multi-syllabic words, such as "Massachusetts," can be achieved with as few as fifty tokens if there are no similar words. In contrast, one thousand or more tokens per word may be required to develop models for sets of one-syllable words.

As with speaker-dependent enrollment, sampling for speaker-independent model development can suffer from the recitation effect. One method of obtaining more natural samples is to create a prototype system and collect samples from speakers while they are using the system. Another method is to use on-the-fly adaptation.

5.8.1.2 Creating speaker-independent models through subword modeling. Creation of speaker-independent vocabulary models using subword modeling is extremely fast, easy, and generally inexpensive when compared with sampling. They are also less accurate than word-level models.

> The main reason for the superiority of the word-based models is that they model the words at a much finer level of detail. The effects of context dependence and coarticulation are implicitly built into the models (Bahl, Lalit, et al., IBM Speech Recognition Group, "Acoustic Markov models used in the Tangora speech recognition system," 1988, p. 498).

Models produced by subword modeling are not only less finely tuned to the speech of the target population, they generally do not model the speaking environment as closely either. These limitations make it difficult to produce the high quality, speaker-independent models required for some applications. It is also why major vendors of subword modeling systems use speaker adaptation. Even systems using carefully designed speaker-independent subword models, like AT&T's *Conversant,* may rely on sample-based models for important or confusable word groups, such as digits.

> If the application calls primarily for digits we go with the whole word approach be-
> cause they are more accurate than *FlexWord.* For longer words it does not matter as
> much (Kathy Breslin, Marketing Manager, AT&T *Conversant* System, AT&T Global
> Business, personal communication, 1994).

A considerable amount of research is being directed towards the development of subword modeling techniques and tools. One of the outcomes of this work will be improved accuracy.

5.8.2 Adding Words in
Speaker-Independent Modeling

Speaker-independent systems contain vocabularies constructed from the analysis of large numbers of samples or from the melding of subwords. The built-in vocabulary of a system, however, may fail to contain needed application-specific terminology. To address that omission, all vendors offer custom vocabulary development tools. The forms of custom development were discussed in chapter 3 (sections 3.2 and 3.4). The following sections review some of that material, highlighting issues related to speaker modeling.

5.8.2.1 Sampling by application developers.   Some vendors offer modeling tools to application developers along with detailed instructions to guide the sampling process. These tools can be excellent, but sampling also requires careful initial design, a good understanding of the user population, effective data collection, and careful testing. All of these factors influence the quality of recognition. When sampling is done properly, the result is high quality recognition. Poorly designed or executed sampling procedures can be costly in terms of time as well as money. Even when vendors offer sampling and model generation tools to their customers, the best modeling is generally done by vendors of speaker-independent systems because they have experience with sample estimation and model generation.

In some instances, when the system is used primarily by a single speaker or a small number of speakers, models can be generated by the end users themselves. Voice Processing Corporation allows speaker-independent models to be added to its small vocabulary systems.

5.8.2.2 Subword modeling by application developers. When the vendor of a dictation system supplies a dictionary containing more than 100,000 words, most vocabulary requirements can be met by accessing the dictionary. Dictation products vary with regard to whether models of words added by users are speaker-dependent or speaker-independent. Philips Dictation Systems and IBM, for example, generate speaker-independent baseforms, although they differ greatly on how that is accomplished.

5.8.3 Modifiying the Models

As indicated in the discussion of the speaker model continuum (section 5.5), speaker-independent models cannot handle all speakers with every possible dialect (foreign and native) speaking in all environments. Whether they were generated from word samples or subwords, speaker-independent models reflect the data used to create them. Whenever dialect, the speaking environment, or the speech channel (microphone/telephone, see chapter 7) differ from those used to create the model, the model is likely to require modification.

Recognizing the need to adapt speaker models to an application, most vendors offering speaker-independent models also provide tools to application developers for tuning those models to the speech of the expected user population. Companies with models based upon word-level sampling offer sampling tools and instructions. Subword models can also be modified through the addition of new data. BBN's *HARK* system, for example, contains tools to modify the existing speaker models by adding new data. These tools generate a new set of models for the target application and do not make permanent changes to the original vendor-supplied models.

5.9 ISSUES IN SPEAKER ADAPTATION

One might argue that an ideal system is the one that begins with a speaker-independent system, and adapts to a speaker incrementally over time (Xuedong Huang & Kai-Fu Lee, Carnegie Mellon University [Huang is currently at Microsoft Corporation. Lee is currently at Apple Computer Corporation], "On speaker-independent, speaker-dependent, and speaker-adaptive speech recognition," 1993, p. 150).

The value of adaptation for an ideal system varies with its intended use. Adaptation most benefits those applications whose users will access the application repeatedly. It is particularly valuable for large vocabulary applications for which extensive enrollment would not be tolerated.

Adaptation during use can also help overcome the 'monotony' factor of training by data collected from subjects reciting a list of words and phrases (L. Smith, Brian Scott, L. Lin & J. Newell, Scott Instruments Corporation [currently Voice Control Systems, Inc.], "Template adaptation in a hypersphere word classifier," 1990, p. 565).

Speaker adaptation is inappropriate for applications that involve brief interaction with one-time users; and even when users access the application on a regular basis, the value of speaker adaptation must be assessed to determine the benefit of using a speaker-adaptive system rather than a speaker-independent system or no speech recognition system at all. Some large vocabulary applications, for example, may involve rapid shifting from one speaker to another in high-pressure situations when two- or three-minute delays can seem intolerable. Rapid enrollment may not seem "rapid" to users who must provide one or two hours of speech. As with speaker-dependent enrollment, some speakers experience frustration during this process. That is one reason why Philips offers speaker-independent models as part of its speech recognition toolkit.

Such irritations must be balanced against the greater accuracy of speaker-adaptive models as compared with speaker-independent models. They should also be compared with the greater efficiency of using a speech system instead of hand-written reporting or the cost savings and speed of using speech recognition rather than transcription of dictation.

5.9.1 Accuracy in Speaker Adaptation

The primary benefit of using speaker adaptation is the enhancement of accuracy resulting from modifications to acoustic features of existing reference models. Initial recognition quality may be poor for systems that rely upon on-the-fly adaptation, a process which can actually be viewed as a sophisticated variant of enrollment. In large vocabulary applications, speaker adaptation satisfies the detailed modeling required for fine discrimination among extensive numbers of word candidates.

5.9.2 Adding Words in Speaker Adaptation

The ability to add new words to a system or application depends entirely upon the technology used to create the speaker models. Large vocabulary systems containing speaker-independent baseforms generated through subword modeling contain large backup dictionaries. If a new word is not found in the dictionary, the items may be provided by the system vendor or by subword modeling techniques.

5.10 SPEAKER ISSUES

Stress, "lambs and goats," and acceptance are all speaker issues that will be discussed in the following sections.

5.10.1 Stress

Stress can be a function of the affect of the user, a by-product of the task, a reaction to an emergency situation, or a response to a noisy speaking environment. All forms of stress produce changes in speech. Those alterations include more rapid speech; more vocal effort used to speak; shallower breath support; tighter jaw positioning, causing different articulator positioning (see chapter 2, section 2.1); and eventual hoarseness of the voice. Changes such as these are noticeable and can have a strongly negative impact on recognition accuracy. In some instances recognition accuracy has declined 60 percent when reference models created in unstressed conditions were used with stressed speech.

Poor response by a recognition system is likely to increase stress and lead to greater deterioration of performance by the human and the recognizer. In most applications, if the initial speech input is not recognized properly, the recognition system will ask the user to repeat the input. Frequently, speakers will repeat the input as they would when communicating with human listeners who fail to understand: by using more clearly enunciated (and possibly, slower) speech. Since these patterns do not match the stored models, the recognizer's performance is likely to degrade further.

As mentioned in section 5.6.1, it is sometimes possible to perform training in the stressful environment. Since such training, however, is not always an option, researchers are developing methods of altering normal speech patterns to resemble stressed speech. This ongoing research has been complicated by the fact that the effects of stress vary across words and within sentences.

Chapter 7 (section 7.2) discusses the nature of stressed speech resulting from environmental noise. For additional information about speech patterns under stress consult Hansen (1993) and Bou-Ghazale & Hansen (1994).

5.10.2 Lambs and Goats

Some modeling problems appear to be linked to the speakers themselves. The speech of most people is easily modeled by one or more of the approaches described in the Technology Focus. In the speech recognition industry those speakers are called *lambs*. They are the delight of application developers.

Other speakers have voice patterns that are difficult for speech recognition systems to capture. These speakers are called *goats*. Speaker-dependent, speaker-adaptive, and multi-speaker modeling require additional training from them and in some cases will not succeed in creating a good set of models. When they use speaker-independent systems they may be forced to access the alternative input device or human backup mode provided by the system.

Although it is not clear why some speakers have difficulty, it is generally assumed that they have unusual vocal characteristics or are not cooperating. While one or both of these speaker-related causes may be the source of the problem, it is equally possible that

> poor recognition performance for a particular talker may result from an interaction between vocabulary, recognition device, and talker, and may not be entirely due to the talker alone (David Pisoni, Howard Nusbaum & Subrata Das. Speech Research Laboratory, Department of Psychology, Indiana University, "Automatic measurement of

speech recognition performance: A comparison of six speaker-dependent recognition devices," 1986, p. 18).

This position was supported by additional research for the European *ESPRIT* project *SAM* (an acronym for *Speech Assessment Methodology*) completed in 1992 (also, see chapter 8). The goal of *SAM* was to establish standard tests for speech recognition products using only standard hardware and software. Although there were a number of factors that affected the accuracy of the products that were tested in a pilot study, one of the most significant sources of variation in accuracy was the speaker. Interaction between the recognizer and the speaker accounted for more than 25 percent of the total variation.

When more than one or two speakers experience consistently poor recognition it is unlikely that the application designer has encountered a herd of goats. Flawed application design, an inappropriate recognition tool, or poor user cooperation (see section 5.10.3) are more likely causes.

5.10.3 Acceptance

Unlike many other modes of input, speech recognition is highly sensitive to the cooperation of the system users. Lack of acceptance may result from poor application design, low accuracy, or a mismatch between the flow of an application and the ways in which speakers understand a task.

The design of an application and the quality of recognition can be less important to the success of an application than the following user-acceptance factors:

- Perceived benefit of the system
- Participation in the system development
- Fear of the computer/technology
- Fear of change

In fact, the same application constructed with the same recognition product can succeed in one instance and fail in another because of the degree of cooperation of the system users.

When an application is designed for a specific population of repeat users, the user-acceptance factors defined above argue strongly for active participation of representatives of the speaker population in the design and testing of the application. The list also argues for effective, well-planned user orientation and training programs.

A striking example of the importance of user acceptance is provided by the financial industry. Two brokerage houses opted to introduce Verbex Voice Systems' *VoiceTrader* system which was named by *Banker's Monthly* as one of 1989's outstanding products serving the financial and banking industries. When Smith Barney Shearson elected to use *VoiceTrader,* they actively involved the traders in the process and added a feature to their application enabling users to do rapid, on-the-fly retraining whenever it was needed. Smith Barney reported overall speech recognition accuracy of 96 to 99 percent, regardless of the noise level in the trading room and changes in a trader's voice over the course of a day. This means that the system recognized the correct word or utterance 96 to 99 percent of the time. Another *VoiceTrader* customer, NatWest Markets Ltd. in London, described the opposite experience. Their system "fell to pieces" in the dealing room even after displaying 100 percent accuracy during testing and training. Misrecognitions and non-recognition were so prevalent that the users became disgusted with the technology and stopped using the system. NatWest admitted that a large component of the poor performance of the system was due to the "psychology" of the users who had not been prepared to view the *VoiceTrader* as an aid. Instead, they treated it as a threat and showed little willingness to provide good training or to institute retraining for problematic words.

When the user population consists of a large number of one-time users, the preceding list of user-acceptance factors argues for the implementation of a small prototype to assess user-response, speaker model issues, and overall interface design. Whatever the nature of the user population, a developer should

> never underestimate the ability of a user to fail to conform to *your* paradigm (Judith Tschirgi, Director Services and Speech Technology, AT&T Network Systems, personal communication, 1994).

6

THE FLOW OF SPEECH

INTRODUCTION

Vendors of speech recognition systems often market speech recognition as the natural human-computer interface. Naturalness connotes the ability to communicate with the recognition system using a normal and familiar style of speaking. Two facets of naturalness, large vocabulary and flexible grammar, were examined in chapters 3 and 4. Another critical component is the flow of speech itself. The term *speech flow* is not standard terminology in the speech recognition industry. It is used in this book because there is no generally accepted term that characterizes the set of options to be described in this chapter.

The flow of speech refers to how the user of a recognition system must speak:

Is • the • speaker • required • to • pause • between • words? or
Can the speech be uttered in a natural fashion?

It may seem strange that such questions need to be asked. Since we speak in sequences of individual words, it is easy to imagine that the acoustic representation of speech would also contain natural breaks between individual words, much like the spectrographic display of "do re me" in figure 6.0. Unfortunately, this is not the case. Acoustically, the words we say flow together, as shown in the spectrogram of figure 6.1 and, as we saw in chapter 2, the process of recognition is complicated by coarticulation effects and other distortions.

The issues embodied in these examples have guided the speech-flow options

Figure 6.0   Spectrogram of "do re mi" spoken with pauses

of commercial speech recognition systems. The Technology Focus begins with definitions of the three types of speech flow found in commercial systems:

- Discrete-word (also called *discrete utterance*)
- Connected-word
- Continuous speech

The greatest attention is given to continuous speech, including discussions of the problems of locating word boundaries and overcoming cross-word coarticulation effects.

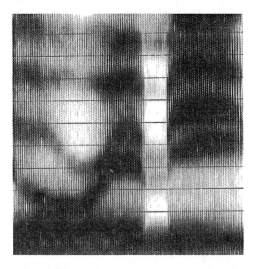

Figure 6.1   Spectrogram of "do re mi" spoken naturally without pauses

The Application Focus begins by addressing some of the myths surrounding continuous speech. Then it describes accuracy and ease-of-use issues associated with discrete, connected, and continuous speech. The sections on discrete and continuous speech conclude with techniques for evaluating recognition systems.

6.1 DISCRETE-WORD INPUT

In order to communicate with a *discrete-word* (also called *isolated word*) recognition system, a user must pause between words. The pauses serve two purposes:

- Preventing cross-word coarticulation from distorting the acoustic pattern of the word to be recognized
- Allowing the processor time to accomplish its analyses

The development of faster PC processors has made it possible to reduce the length of the pauses. Traditionally, the length of that pause was one-quarter of a second or more, but some vendors have been able to reduce this to one-tenth of a second. Whatever the duration of the pause, discrete-word recognition requires a clear beginning and termination for a word or phrase.

The features of recognition presented in preceding chapters, particularly the word modeling technologies presented in chapter 3, describe the basic elements of discrete-word recognition. Discrete-word recognition is used with templates and hidden Markov models (HMM's). When HMM's are used in discrete-word recognition systems the initial and final states of each HMM reference model may contain models of silence and/or background noise. The inclusion of these states facilitates identification of word boundaries.

Discrete-word input can be used with vocabularies of any size, with all forms of speaker modeling, and within any kind of speaking environment. It is currently required by virtually all dictation products.

6.2 CONNECTED-WORD INPUT

Connected-word speech (also called *connected speech*) is used to refer to two different types of speech flow. One of its meanings is synonymous with continuous speech; that sense of connected speech will be discussed in section 6.3.

The second meaning refers to a flow of speech requiring the speaker to insert a momentary hesitation between words. Until recently, these hesitations were required to last for at least fifty milliseconds, giving connected-word speech a staccato effect. Some vendors have been able to eliminate the pause but, like discrete-word recognition, connected-word speech relies on the pauses to eliminate cross-word coarticulation. Because of this, the staccato speaking style is still needed.

6.3 CONTINUOUS SPEECH

A speaker communicates with a *continuous speech* recognizer by speaking in a natural manner without unnatural pauses. Although such a natural speaking style is the goal of speech recognition, only a few products can analyze it. The principal challenges involved in recognizing continuous speech are

- The number of words in a block of input speech is generally unknown
- The locations where each word begins and ends are unknown
- Cross-word coarticulation effects blur word boundaries

These three issues function together to make continuous speech recognition extremely difficult.

> It is often difficult, if not impossible, to specify (i.e., find accurately and automatically) the word boundaries because of sound coarticulation. Thus, for example, the boundary between the digit 3 and the digit 8 in [the digit sequence 2 3 8] is fuzzy because the ending sound /i/ [iy] in 3 coarticulates strongly with the initial sound /e^y/ [ey] in 8 (Lawrence Rabiner & Biing-Hwang Juang, Senior Researchers, AT&T Bell Laboratories, *Fundamentals of Speech Recognition*, 1993, p. 392).

The first two issues listed above can be consolidated into the basic problem of locating word boundaries in a stream of speech, like that shown in figure 6.1. The last problem refers to the fact that neighboring phonemes affect each other even when they appear in different words.

6.3.1 Word Boundaries

Unlike discrete-word and connected-word input, continuous speech recognizers do not have clearly delineated words available for analysis. Instead, the recognition task has been expanded to include evaluation of competing hypotheses regarding the number of words in the utterance and their locations. At each digitized frame (see chapter 2, section 2.2.2) the recognition system must determine whether it has arrived at a word boundary. In figure 6.1, for example, the recognition system needs to decide whether the first word is "do," "door," or even "during." There is nothing in the signal itself to indicate the correct choice and there are numerous examples of speech patterns that cause confusion in human listeners. "Grey tape" for example, is similar to "great ape;" "an ice chest" can be almost identical to "a nice chest;" and the acoustic patterns of "How to wreck a nice beach" are very close to those of "How to recognize speech."

If all the words in a vocabulary are evaluated as potential word candidates at virtually every frame of input, the number of calculations required to accomplish continuous speech recognition could easily overwhelm a powerful PC, even for small vocabularies. Consequently, recognition systems have devised a number of techniques for reducing the number of word candidates and locating word boundaries. Some of them have already been described in the discussions of application structure (see chapter 4). Others are described in section 6.3.3.

6.3.2 Cross-Word Coarticulation Effects

There are two types of coarticulation effects (also called *cross-word coarticulation effects*) with which developers must contend: soft and hard. *Soft coarticulation effects* are similar to those discussed in chapter 2 (section 2.1.3). They are minor, predictable alterations often involving voicing (changing the *t* phoneme in the word "wait" to *d* in the sentence "Wait a minute."), or lip rounding (as for the *k* phoneme in the word "cool").

Hard coarticulation effects are more extreme. They generally entail deletion of individual phonemes (such as *t* at the end of "what" in "What time is it?"), alteration of phonemes (such as the blending of the final *d* of the word "did" and the initial *y* in "you" into *jh* in the phrase "Did you?"), or a combination of deletion and alteration (as when "What do you want?" becomes "wah ju wan?").

Coarticulation effects are greatest for function words like "the," "and," "do," and "to." Function words are typically one-syllable words spoken without emphasis (called *unstressed*). They are so strongly distorted by cross-word coarticulation they become unrecognizable. The most well-known examples are "wanna" and "gonna" which obliterate the function word "to," but all function words are vulnerable to distortion or deletion.

More information on hard and soft coarticulation effects can be found in Giachin, et al. (1990) and Rabiner & Juang (1993, chapter 8). Kai-Fu Lee, et al. (1990a) discuss function word distortion and how it was handled in CMU's *SPHINX* system.

6.3.3 Systems

Continuous speech systems differ in their handling of word boundary and coarticulation. The methods they use generally reflect the size of their vocabularies and the unit of analysis used for recognition (see chapter 3). The approaches can be generally grouped as

- Word-based (Small and Mid-size Vocabulary) Systems
- Subword/triphone (Large Vocabulary) Systems
- Acoustic-Phonetic (Large Vocabulary) Systems

Jelinek (1976) and Rabiner & Juang (1993) provide a technical engineering perspective and Kaisse (1985) offers a technical linguistic perspective on understanding the challenges of recognizing rapid, continuous speech.

6.3.3.1 Word-based (small and mid-size vocabulary) systems. One effective technique for locating word boundaries in small and mid-size systems is to use a structuring technique such as a grammar (see chapter 4). This is the approach used by most commercial recognition systems. A finite-state or word-pair grammar will specify the allowable word sequences of an application. Adjacent words can then be trained as units to obtain both hard and soft coarticulation patterns. As it proceeds through the input, a grammar identifies the starting point of the next unidentified word.

Several searching and evaluation approaches are used to organize the computational demands of continuous speech so that speech can be recognized on a PC within a reasonably short period of time:

- Two-level dynamic-programming matching
- Level building algorithm
- One-pass (one-stage) algorithm

The *two-level dynamic-programming matching* and the *level building algorithm* reduce computational demands by segmenting the search process into two steps, called *levels*. In each algorithm, the first level consists of selecting arbitrary frames from the input to use as test frames. These test frames are compared with every word-candidate. At the second level, the candidates with the best scores from the first level are pieced together to create a complete string of words. The *one-pass algorithm* performs the first and second steps together and then uses backtracking to obtain the best scores.

Rabiner & Juang (1993, chapter 7) provide detailed descriptions of the methods of handling word-boundary problems. The original formulations of the searching algorithms described in this section are in Sakoe (1979) for the two-level dynamic-programming matching, Myers & Rabiner (1981) for the level building algorithm, and Ney (1984) for the one-pass algorithm.

6.3.3.2 Subword/triphone (large vocabulary) systems. The problems facing continuous speech recognition are compounded when the number of word candidates that must be evaluated is large. The dearth of commercial, large-vocabulary, continuous-speech recognition systems is evidence that the problem has not been resolved satisfactorily.

As with word-based systems, finite-state grammars (or word pair grammars) (see chapter 4, section 4.2) can be used to restrict word choices. Unfortunately, deterministic grammars, such as finite-state and word pair grammars, have two important limitations for large vocabulary systems:

- They are too restrictive for some large vocabulary applications, particularly free-form dictation.
- If the active vocabulary exceeds ten thousand, the grammar has done little to minimize the challenge of continuous speech recognition.

Other methods are needed to allow users to dictate.

Large vocabulary systems are based upon subword units rather than entire words. Since the total number of subword units is far smaller than the number of words in a system, it would appear that the problems facing continuous speech recognition would also be lessened. Using this reasoning, some researchers added triphone models of cross-word coarticulation to their systems and included special models for function words. They found that

> when highly detailed (context dependent) speech units are used, including both intra-word and interword context dependent units, the complexity of the overall implementation often increases quadratically with the number of basic units . . . A full search implementation . . . is totally impractical, if not impossible (Roberto Pieraccini, Chin-Hui Lee, Egidio Giachin & Lawrence Rabiner, Researchers, AT&T Bell Laboratories, *Complexity reduction in a large vocabulary speech recognizer,* 1991, p. 729).

Unlike intra-word triphone models the number of inter-word (called *cross-word*) models explodes.

> there are 2381 within-word triphones in our 997-word task. But there are 7057 triphones when between-word triphones are also considered (Kai-Fu Lee, Hsiao-Wuen Hon, Mei-Yuh Hwang & Sanjoy Mahajan, Carnegie Mellon University [Lee is currently at Apple Computer Corporation], "Recent progress and future outlook of the *SPHINX* speech recognition system," 1990, p. 60).

The reason is that the acoustic information for one side of the cross-word triphone is unknown. A cross-word triphone for the end of words like "plain" and "stain," would contain acoustic information for the transition from the vowel to the final *n* in one state of the HMM; it would contain acoustic data for *n* in its second state; but it would have no guide for selecting acoustic material for the third state since a vast array of words can follow "plain" or "stain."

Some researchers have proposed methods for reducing the number of subword units. Such proposals adopt one of two major strategies:

- Use units other than triphones
- Use clusters of subword units

A number of subword units, such as *semiphones* and *fenones* are being used. These units are larger, smaller, or simply different from triphones. Semiphones (proposed by Doug Paul of MIT Lincoln Laboratory), for example, combine context-dependent triphones, context-independent phonemes, and *classical diphones* (classical diphone models begin at the center of one phoneme and end at the center of the next phoneme). Fenones are *subphonetic* (smaller than phoneme) units proposed by IBM and used in IBM's continuous-speech research, as well as in their discrete-word *Tangora* system. Like triphones, all these subword units are represented using HMM's.

Generalized triphone modeling (developed at CMU) for both intra- and inter-word contexts is the most popular clustering technique. A generalized triphone is created by clustering and merging acoustic data from contexts for a single phoneme. The acoustic contexts *s, th,* and *f,* for example, might be among those collapsed into a generalized triphone for the vowel *aa* (as in "sock"). Although the resulting triphones are more generic, CMU researchers have found that recognition accuracy is not diminished when the models are well-trained (see chapter 3, section 3.1.5).

Multi-stage searching, such as the N-best algorithm (see chapter 3, section 3.2.2, and the historical note in 3.2.2), can minimize the growth in complexity for systems with cross-word triphone models in the following way:

- *Stage 1:* The best sequence of words is determined using intra-word triphone models only.
- *Stage 2:* The results of stage 1 are reevaluated using cross-word triphone models only.

Efficient searching and evaluation techniques rely on good models. As with the development of all triphone models, it is difficult to obtain a large enough sample of each cross-word coarticulation effect to construct a good model. Fortunately, less data intensive approaches can be used to handle some cross-word coarticulation effects. Soft cross-word coarticulation effects are similar to intra-word coarticulation patterns, making it possible to use existing triphone models to represent them. Most hard cross-word coarticulation effects can be predicted from their linguistic environments. Some researchers have constructed cross-word triphone models using linguistic rules to account for them.

Paul (1991) describes Lincoln Laboratory's semiphones. See Bahl, et al. (1988) for information on fenones. Kai-Fu Lee, et al. (1990b) explain generalized triphones. See Schwartz, et al. (1992) for descriptions of how Bolt Beranek and Newman (BBN) uses the N-best paradigm in its *BYBLOS* system to handle cross-word coarticulation. Consult Kai-Fu Lee, et al. (1990b) for more information on the use of generalized triphones for cross-word coarticulation. Using information provided by Oshika, et al. (1975), both Giachin, et al. (1990) and Rabiner & Juang (1993, chapter 8) delineate rules governing cross-word coarticulation.

6.3.3.3 Acoustic-phonetic (large vocabulary) systems. Acoustic-phonetic models are generally constructed from context-independent phoneme models (see chapter 3, section 3.1.4). Since the number of phonemes in a language is generally small and fixed, acoustic-phonetic systems do not suffer from the growth of units of representation that plagues triphone systems.

The major problem facing acoustic-phonetic systems is the absence of contextual information. Some researchers address this problem by constructing special subword models to handle silence and hard cross-word coarticulation. Like developers of triphone systems, they risk creating an explosion of models.

Speech Systems, Inc. (SSI) captures the intra- and cross-word coarticulation effects by combining a finite-state grammar with two-stage phonetic processing. In the first stage, a decision tree is used to form segments based upon broad phonetic classification. In the second stage, this stream of segments is encoded via another decision tree and used as input to phonetic HMM's.

Other researchers introduce statistical information about context into the phoneme models themselves.

> The phoneme units are not explicitly conditioned on the neighboring phonemes . . . However, to some extent, the context dependency will be modeled implicitly by incorporating context information into the acoustic vector (Hermann Ney, University of Technology, Aachen, Germany & Andreas Noll, Founder, Aspect GMbH, "Acoustic-phonetic modeling in the SPICOS system," 1994, p. 312).

Such systems might be described as *semi-context-dependent* systems. Meisel, et al. (1991) provide additional information on SSI systems. Fissore, et al. (1989) describe a system with special models for cross-word coarticulation. Ney & Noll (1994) describe a semi-context-dependent system.

6.4 NEURAL NETWORKS

> Extending the classification capabilities of connectionist networks to continuous speech recognition is an important research direction in speech recognition (Patrick Haffner, CNET Lannion A TSS/RCP, and Michael Franzini & Alex Waibel, Carnegie Mellon University, "Integrating time alignment and neural networks for high performance continuous speech recognition," 1991, p. 105).

In order to design neural networks capable of performing high-quality continuous speech recognition, a developer must be able to exploit the excellent classification capabilities of neural networks while compensating for their inherent weakness in handling time alignment (see chapter 2, section 2.5).

The most popular approach to continuous speech recognition is hybrid system design. It has also been the most successful because it melds the classification capabilities of neural networks with the superior time alignment of conventional techniques such as HMM's and dynamic time warping (see chapter 2, section 2.3.1).

> Solving a real-world problem almost always requires the crafting of a heterogeneous system . . . This is at least partly because the structure of hard problems themselves is typically heterogeneous . . . ASR [automatic speech recognition] is no exception (Hervé Bourlard, Faculté Polytechnique de Mons, Belgium and International Com-

puter Science Institute of the University of California at Berkeley & Nelson Morgan, International Computer Science Institute, *Connectionist Speech Recognition: A Hybrid Approach,* 1994, pp. 3–4).

Some hybrids use the neural network as a post-processor for an HMM-based system, but a growing number are using a network as the primary recognition component or as the first stage of a two-step recognition process. CMU's multi-state *TDNN* (*MS-TDNN*) is an example of such a network-based hybrid. The *MS-TDNN* is a hybrid version of their *TDNN* system (see chapter 2, section 2.5). It was designed to enable the *TDNN* to move from discrete-word recognition to continuous speech. The adjusted outputs of the *TDNN* modules are transmitted to a dynamic time warping matrix for temporal alignment. When the *MS-TDNN* performed very well on initial tests with continuous-speech databases containing up to four thousand words, testing was expanded to larger vocabularies.

Other hybrid systems use a multi-layer perceptron (MLP) network to perform signal prediction for an HMM. The function of the neural network is to anticipate acoustic patterns rather than to classify them. CMU's *Linked Predictive Neural Network* (*LPNN*) system is one example. It contains a feedforward network that uses data from previous speech slices to predict feature values of succeeding frames. When the next segment of speech is received, the *LPNN* scores and corrects its own performance. The output of the *LPNN* is sent to a dynamic time warping algorithm for time normalization.

Levin's *Hidden Control Neural Network* (*HCNN*), shown in figure 6.2 is another example of a hybrid prediction system. Unlike most other hybrids, the *HCNN* receives input from three separate sources:

• Preprocessed, digitized speech sample vectors

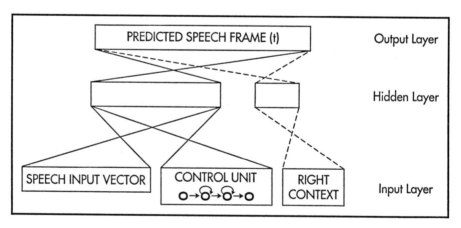

Figure 6.2 Levin's Hidden Control Neural Network (adapted from Petek & Tebelskis, "Context-dependent hidden control neural network architecture for continuous speech recognition," Copyright 1992, IEEE

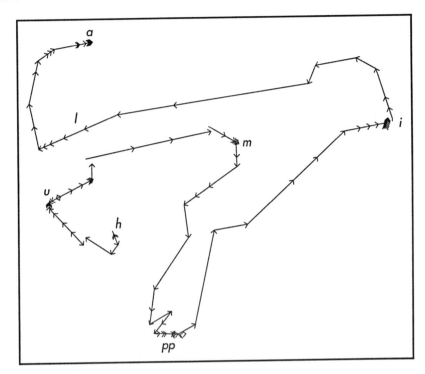

Figure 6.3 Kohonen's Phonotopic map (from Kohonen, "The *neural* phonetic typewriter," Copyright 1988, IEEE)

- An independent control unit
- Contextual units

The control unit handles temporal variation without modifying the network's other parameters and its structure parallels that of an HMM. The network in figure 6.2 is *right-context dependent* because the contextual units provide acoustic information about the phoneme to the right of the current segment. This network could also be configured to include the left context as well.

One of the most unusual hybrid systems is Kohonen's *Neural Phonetic Typewriter*. It combines two network architectures: a *Learning Vector Quantization* (LVQ) network and a *self-organizing map* (SOM). The self-organizing component generates *phonotopic* maps, such as the one shown for the Finnish word *humppila* in figure 6.3. The neural phonetic typewriter has a linguistic grammar that converts the output of the network into an orthographic transcription. It can handle a one thousand word vocabulary in near real time with a reported accuracy of 98 percent.

The book by Bourlard & Morgan (1994) and the paper by Morgan & Bourlard (1995) provide technical descriptions of neural networks used for continuous-speech recognition. Haffner & Waibel (1992) describe *MS-TDNN*. Tebelskis, et al. (1991) discuss the *LPNN*, Levin (1990) describes the *HCNN*, and Kohonen (1988) explains the neural phonetic typewriter.

6.5 SELECTING THE SPEECH FLOW

The speech flow of a recognition application is often the most noticeable feature of the system. Too often, developers reject all but continuous-speech systems. This is unfortunate for a number of reasons:

- Continuous speech is not necessary for some types of applications and application designs.
- Speech flow may be a less important factor than other features, such as vocabulary size or flexibility.
- For some applications, discrete-word recognition may be the only choice available.

Most equipment command-and-control systems are naturally oriented towards short bursts of speech. Both discrete and continuous systems are appropriate for such application types. To eliminate all but continuous-speech systems would dramatically reduce available price and performance options, as well as other important features offered by some discrete-word recognition products. These include excellent application interface development tools of products like Kurzweil AI's *VoiceMed* systems, the on-the-fly language model adaptation of Dragon Systems' *DragonDictate,* and the chip-level recognition offered by Voice Control Systems, Inc.

6.5.1 Continuous Speech vs. Free-Form, Spontaneous Speech

Continuous speech is often confused with free-form speech. Free-form, spontaneous speech refers to the communication humans enjoy with each other, selecting whatever topics, style of speech, and vocabulary they wish.

Continuous speech recognition by computer is far more restrictive. It supports speech without pauses between words, but it imposes constraints on the topic of discussion, style of speech, and/or other facets of communication. Acceptable options are determined by other system features:

- The size and nature of the vocabulary (chapter 3)
- The nature of the grammar (chapter 4)
- The nature or structure of the application (chapters 8 & 9)

Virtually all commercial continuous speech recognition systems place rigid constraints on the vocabulary and structure available to speakers. Some continuous-speech recognition systems still offer fewer than one hundred words. Although increases in PC computing power have enabled vocabularies of applications to exceed ten thousand words, most continuous-speech systems specify a maximum branching factor. Most commercial continuous-speech products rely on rigid, finite-state, or word pair grammars. A structured medical dictation system using such a grammar might, for example, limit input about a patient's blood pressure to the following patterns:

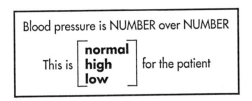

Figure 6.4   Sample of structured input for medical dictation application

Depending upon the recognition product, these sentences might be entered with a discrete or continuous speech flow. Although the sentences in figure 6.4 are reasonable for the topic, they allow no deviation. A physician cannot say:

The patient's blood pressure is NUMBER over NUMBER today. This is entirely within the normal range for this patient.

Anything that diverges from the patterns shown in the figure is unacceptable.

N-gram modeling (see chapter 4, section 4.3.1) allows a much closer approximation to free-form speech. Virtually all commercial dictation systems using N-gram models require discrete-word input because the combination of continuous speech with a large vocabulary and free-form input results in enormous computational requirements (see section 6.7.1 and chapter 10, section 10.1). Philips Dictation Systems' *SpeechMagic,* the first commercial continuous-speech dictation product using N-gram models, has side-stepped the problem of slow response by invoking the recognition process after a user has finished dictating.

6.5.2 Continuous Speech vs. Intelligence

The desire for continuous speech, coupled with confusion between free-form speech and continuous speech, has bred a second misunderstanding about the requirements of human communication. When one person understands the spoken language of another person, she/he is applying more than acoustic and statistical knowledge to the task. A wide range of knowledge and information is involved, including:

- The auditory stream of speech

- Sentence structure
- Word-meaning, including synonyms and antonyms
- The subject
- Knowledge about the speaker

Existing commercial recognition systems have only information on the auditory stream of speech combined with some elements of sentence structure available to them. Even the combination of continuous speech, large vocabulary, and free-form structure cannot enable systems to achieve human-like performance. That requires at least a battery of spoken language analysis tools comparable to those listed above. It is, however, important to remember that even after using these and other tools, humans still misunderstand each other. Without understanding human limitations, it can be easy (albeit erroneous) to expect that once speech technology becomes capable of accessing all the analytical tools in the list it will perform without error.

6.6 DISCRETE-WORD AND CONNECTED-WORD SPEECH

Discrete and connected speech recognizers expect clear word boundaries and do not tolerate cross-word coarticulation. Connected speech is generally used as an option within discrete-word recognition systems. It is often limited to well-defined vocabulary subsets, usually digits (zero through nine). When used in this way, connected speech facilitates input of the designated vocabulary in repetitive data entry applications. Spoken entry of long strings of digits, for example, becomes faster and less tedious; however, they must still be articulated clearly.

6.6.1 Accuracy

The use of pauses (or *staccato speech*) is a benefit as well as a limitation. It enhances recognition accuracy by identifying the boundaries of each word.

At the same time, pausing makes discrete-word and connected-word systems more vulnerable to insertion errors (see chapter 2, section 2.6.2) resulting from sudden, unexpected noise, such as the ringing of a nearby telephone or loud background speech. These problems cannot be eliminated but they can be minimized through the development of more sophisticated recognition algorithms combined with

- High-quality, directional microphones
- Good modeling of the speaking environment (see chapter 7)
- Good speaker modeling
- High acceptance thresholds
- Easy-to-use error correction techniques

One effective method of error correction is to include one or more words, such as "Oops," "backup" or "scratch that" that will cause the system to back up. These words instruct the system to remove the most recent recognition decision. Error correction strategies are often combined with verification techniques that allow users to review the most recent set of recognized words. Many recognition products allow the design of verification using digitized or synthesized speech output of the items recognized.

Since pausing between words is not a natural way of speaking, discrete-word and connected-word applications that are accessed by one-time users must control the flow of speech of those users. This is an issue facing most telephone applications. Input of digit sequences over the telephone can be paced through the use of beeps between digits to prevent users from speaking too quickly. The *script* (see chapter 4, introduction) may direct the user to say single words or to pause between words. If the likelihood of extraneous speech is high, word-spotting (see chapter 4, section 4.5) may be used to locate target vocabulary embedded in extraneous speech.

6.6.2 Ease-of-Use

The obtrusiveness of pausing depends upon the nature of the application and upon the speaker. In many applications it is not an impediment. When the user's responses are limited to single words, for example, the pauses go unnoticed. Most equipment command-and-control applications and many data entry applications can be structured so that they consist primarily of short utterances (see chapters 8 and 9).

If an application seeks single word responses, but it is likely users will embed desired vocabulary in continuous speech, word spotting can be used. In such applications, word spotting

> is a kind of generalization of an isolated word recognition system in which the user is not constrained to pronounce the words in isolation; this leads to more user-friendly systems (Hervé Bourlard, Faculté Polytechnique de Mons, Belgium and International Computer Science Institute of the University of California at Berkeley, & Nelson Morgan, International Computer Science Institute, *Connectionist Speech Recognition: A Hybrid Approach,* 1994, p. 5).

Currently, the use of word-spotting works best when the set of target words is small and the level of confusability is low. Recent research at SRI suggests these limitations may be unnecessary. They found significant increases in word spotting accuracy when they modeled a large number of non-keywords, as well as the word-spotting keywords. These findings may also serve to increase the size and flexibility of word spotting applications in the future when they become more robust.

In general, it is the pausing combined with the perceived slowness of discrete-word systems that is the source of the greatest annoyance to users. Speakers who experience the most frustration are those who use speech recognition for dictation. The irritation is especially pronounced among speakers who are accustomed to rapidly dictating a report that is corrected and transcribed by someone else. They perceive the use of discrete-word speech as making their work more difficult. When the motivation of a speaker to use a dictation system is high, required pauses become less of an obstacle.

Consult chapters 8 and 9 for more information on different types of recognition applications. Weintraub (1993) contains information on SRI's research.

6.6.3 Performance Evaluation

One critical evaluation metric is the willingness of the user population to adapt to the requirements of discrete-word speech. The level of acceptance depends upon the

- Type of users involved
- Nature of the application
- Design of the application
- Preparation/participation of the users in the application design

Some groups of users, notably physicians and senior executives, exhibit less patience with discrete-word speech than other users. Since that impatience is not universal within these groups, the acceptance of discrete-word speech must be weighed against other objectives of using speech recognition systems for such populations.

The use of discrete-word speech for high-pressure, high-speed applications, such as stock trading, may produce resistance if the speakers believe the discrete speech flow is interfering with their ability to perform other functions. That perception may also reflect a response to poor application design, resistance to change, discomfort with any speech system or new technology, or even inadequate training. All of these issues need to be considered.

Performance scoring should include tabulation of

- Correct recognitions
- Deletions
- Insertions
- Substitutions

A more detailed analysis can include comparison of different types of errors and problems linked to specific vocabulary items or groups. Chapter 8 (section 8.5) discusses product and application evaluation in greater detail.

6.7 CONTINUOUS SPEECH IN APPLICATIONS

People think that if you can have 50,000 words, why not continuous speech? It is an order of magnitude more difficult (Chuck Bunting, Regional Sales Manager, Kurzweil Applied Intelligence [currently with Interactive Systems], personal communication, 1994).

The challenge defined by Bunting can be exemplified by a single utterance:

Jeet?

If it is not yet clear what this means, imagine that it is noontime and you are getting hungry. Then imagine someone appearing before you and asking "Jeet?" This extreme distortion of "Did you eat?" is not as uncommon as one might imagine. You might have even responded with:

No. Skweet!

or

Ahminuheet later.

Other examples, including "Wanna," "gonna," and "doncha," have become commonplace. They are not noticeable to humans because we generally use the context of the situation or discussion to eliminate most potential confusions. When these tools fail, confusion or misunderstanding results. The humor of the song "Mairzy Doats," for example, is predicated on forcing listeners to understand distorted speech without the aid of context.

Commercial speech recognition products live in the world of "Mairzy Doats:" they have very little context to help them interpret what a user is saying and no intelligence to enable them to construct a context. As in the song, the use of discrete-word speech flow helps comprehension but, unlike people listening to "Mairzy Doats," speech recognition systems are incapable of appreciating any humor that might be part of their situation.

6.7.1 Accuracy in Commercial Systems

Existing commercial systems rely heavily on external methods of enhancing accuracy and facilitating error correction. Systems based upon input of short commands or data utilize some of the same techniques found in discrete and connected-word systems.

When the utterances are longer and more complex, the choice of error correction strongly affects the system's ease-of-use and overall acceptability. The difficulty achieving high-quality continuous speech recognition for large vocabularies is a major reason why most of these systems have not left the research laboratory. Philips Dictation Systems' *SpeechMagic* tools avoid some of these problems by performing the recognition after the dictation has been completed. This simply means that the time spent correcting recognition errors and identifying missing vocabulary is performed at a later time and, perhaps, by someone other than the person who dictated the material.

The accuracy of continuous speech systems can be impaired by non-communication speech, such as "Uh," self-corrections, and interjections. When such errors and extraneous speech are expected to be frequent, word-spotting can be used. In other cases, the user's familiarity with an application or highly structured prompting can minimize non-communication speech. Wayne Ward of CMU has found that creating models of some of these speech phenomena increases accuracy in free-form, continuous speech research systems. For more information on Ward's work in this area consult Ward (1991) and chapter 7 (section 7.1.4).

6.7.2 Ease-of-Use in Commercial Systems

As with discrete and connected speech, the flexibility of a system's grammar and the quality of its error correction strategies can have a direct impact on the ease-of-use of a system. Most users will not be willing to repeat entire utterances, especially if there is time pressure or stress linked to the task.

Some dictation systems provide visual feedback of the recognized items on a PC display and allow a combination of spoken, keyboard, and mouse corrections. These tools are designed to replace transcriptionists. Unlike human transcriptionists, such systems have difficulty responding to common commands, such as

Delete that last paragraph.
Change the first sentence to read . . .
Get the address from the file.

Users of dictation systems who are also familiar with standard dictation devices are likely to discover the value of transcriptionists in correcting speaker errors and in improving the overall quality of the dictation. On the other hand, these systems offer dramatic reductions in the overall cost and turnaround time of transcriptions. Systems that do not perform the recognition during the dictation are the most user friendly for the person doing the dictation, but can be less cost effective if another person must be paid to do the editing.

6.7.3 Performance Evaluation in
Commercial Systems

It is much more difficult to evaluate the performance of a continuous-speech recognition system than to assess discrete-word systems. A simple count of total errors, even if it is grouped by type of error, is likely to present a false picture. If an erroneous word-end location occurs early in an utterance it can produce a domino-effect of misrecognitions. The best guides for product and application assessment are the needs and priorities of the application itself.

> Selection of the most appropriate scoring method involves consideration of the relevant application, and particularly the manner of verification and correction by the speaker (David Pallett, National Institute of Standards and Technology, "Performance assessment of automatic speech recognizers," 1985, p. 380).

The issues related to performance evaluation are presented in greater detail in chapter 8.

7

THE SPEAKING ENVIRONMENT

INTRODUCTION

A speech recognition system is expected to function properly in the environment of its target application. That environment can range from a quiet, personal office to a factory, loading dock, or automobile. As speech recognition applications increase in number and diversity, they are being required to overcome the challenges of a growing assortment of adverse speaking environments.

> We can't design speech recognition systems that work only in the quiet, controlled environment of a laboratory. In real-world situations, there will be multiple voices and background noise—street sounds, music or the hum of an air conditioner—to contend with (Pat Russo, President, AT&T Global Business Communications Systems, Keynote speech at *Advanced Speech Applications and Technologies Conference* '94).

The ability of a recognition system to perform accurately under adverse conditions is called *robustness*. Robustness is critical to the success of an application because if users must struggle with a recognizer to get it to respond, they will not use it.

The Technology Focus begins with a classification of the types of noise that affect the performance of recognition systems and ways in which the speaking environment impinges upon the speech recognition process, including the response of the speaker to background noise. It examines technologies that are used to reduce or eliminate the negative effects of noise (called *noise reduction* techniques) and research directed at enhancing the speech signal itself (called *speech enhancement*). The Application Focus reexamines the impact of various types of noise on accuracy and describes how an application developer can minimize their negative effects.

7.1 WHAT IS NOISE?

Sounds that are transmitted to a recognition system but are not part of the meaningful input signal are noise. There are four basic kinds of noise that affect speech recognition systems:

- Background noise
- Channel noise
- Speech noise, such as lip smacks
- Non-communication vocalizations, such as "Uh"

Each plays a role in challenging the accuracy of a recognition system (see figure 7.1).

Figure 7.1 Types of noise

Background noise refers to the noise produced at the location where speech is being input to a recognition system. Channel noise is generated by the speech input devices that carry the speech to the recognizer. Speech noise and non-communication vocalizations represent some of the speaker's contributions to the adverse recognition environment. Other speaker factors were discussed in chapter 5.

Speech input that contains background noise and/or channel noise is called *corrupted* or *noisy speech*. Speech that contains little or no background noise is called *clean speech*. Clean speech may also refer to a speech signal containing background and channel noise that matches the noise in the reference models of the recognition system.

A similar set of definitions exists for the concept of *adverse environment*. An adverse environment can be characterized by one or more of the following:

- A great deal of noise
- Unknown noise properties
- Noise that is not encoded in the reference patterns of the recognition system

The third type of adverse environment refers to the ability of recognition systems to overcome the negative effects of some types of noise by capturing it during model development or enrollment.

Characteristics of the speaking environment having the greatest impact on the performance of a speech recognition device are the

- Nature of the background noise (background speech, machinery, etc.)
- Variability in the noise
- Loudness of the noise
- Type of speech channel used (telephone vs. microphone)
- Quality of the speech channel

Added to these environmental characteristics are the speaker's response to noise (called the *Lombard effect*). All of these factors must be considered when a recognition product or application is being designed.

7.1.1 Signal-to-Noise Ratio

One of the ways to assess the potential impact of noise on recognition accuracy is to calculate the *signal-to-noise ratio* (*SNR*) of the input. SNR measures the power of the speech component of input compared with the power of the noise. Because of the ability of some microphones to screen background input, SNR for a speech system is measured both in terms of the microphone response as well as the speaking environment. It is generally calculated using decibels (dB) (see chapter 2). Higher SNR's represent stronger speech signals with respect to ambient/background noise. A quiet laboratory or private office might, for example, have an SNR of 45 dB. A factory or subway can have an SNR of less than 5 dB.

SNR has a strong bearing on the accuracy of a speech system. Findings reported for research and fielded applications clearly show that recognition accuracy declines with decreases in the SNR. Unfortunately, most real-world environments have relatively poor SNR's.

> While laboratory signal-to-noise ratios may reach 90 dB (although 50 dB would be more typical), measurements of speech levels in a variety of natural environments show an average signal-to-noise ratio of only 4.8 dB. Clearly . . . much of our present laboratory-based knowledge about speech perception may not apply to communication in more typical settings (Thomas Carrell, Northwestern University, "Acoustical cues to auditory object formation in sentences," 1992, manuscript p. 2).

Consequently, the analyses of the SNR and other noise characteristics of an application are fundamental components of the design of that application.

7.1.2 Background Noise

> The whole area of acoustics has been ignored in the speech recognition industry. People have just been concerned with the signal showing up at the recognizer. But you get all kinds of noise and extraneous signals that greatly diminish the ability of the recognizer to perform (Bill Porter, General Manager, AT&T Intelligent Acoustics Systems, personal communication, 1995).

Background noise is part of the surrounding speaking environment and it enters the input device along with the speech. It can include other voices, machinery noise, and sounds resulting from human activity (such as opening of file drawers and walking). Because most background noise is superimposed upon the speech input, it is often called *additive* or *ambient* noise. It can occur at any frequency or range of frequencies, including those critical for speech.

Background noise is most often described using

- Signal-to-Noise ratio
- Variability
- Power spectrum

Variability refers to the consistency of the noise patterns. Environments characterized by intermittent noise (such as ringing telephones), are more challenging to recognition systems than the steady roar of machinery. This is true even when the consistent noise is extremely loud because consistent noise patterns are more easily identified and screened from the input or captured and included in the reference models of a recognition system. Highly variable and intermittent noises elude capture and, consequently, are more difficult for the recognition system to identify and eliminate.

The *power spectrum* describes the frequency range where any sound exhibits its greatest intensity. Noise reduction and speech enhancement techniques are more difficult when the power spectrum of noise falls within the power spectrum of speech. Fortunately, the acoustic patterns of most background noise, even intermittent noise, change more slowly than speech patterns. This contrast makes it possible to distinguish non-speech background noise from the speech to be analyzed. When the background noise consists of speech, however, this type of discrimination is not possible. As a result, intermittent background speech noise, including radios and televisions, constitute the most difficult environment for speech recognition systems.

Not all background noise is additive. Any room or other enclosed speaking environment produces reverberation. Reverberation in rooms represents a significant design challenge for speech recognition in consumer products, in automobiles, and over speaker phones. The acoustics of enclosed speaking environments cause them to behave like a resonating chamber (see chapter 2, section 2.1.2.3). They alter the power spectrum by amplifying some frequencies while damping others. This is called *signal distortion*. Many disparate factors influence the reverberation time, including the size and shape of the speaking environment, construction materials, furniture, the type of microphone used, and the speaker's distance from the microphone.

A second damaging effect of reverberation time is that it prolongs individual sounds, causing them to repeatedly enter the microphone. We hear this effect as echoes.

> When you create a speech signal you want the power of the signal to be strong momentarily and to decay quickly. Reverberation slows the dissipation of the signal power in the room and makes it hard for a recognition system to know what it is getting (Chris Welsh, Acoustical Engineer, AT&T Intelligent Acoustics Systems, personal communication, 1995).

The most desirable speaking environment is one that has no reverberation (called *anechoic*). Since anechoic speaking environments are almost non-existent, particularly for hands-free speech recognition, application developers must always be prepared to resolve reverberation problems.

7.1.3 Channel Noise

Channel noise refers to the effect of the speech input device (called the *speech channel*) on the spoken input. The functions of the speech channel are to transform sound waves into analog electrical signals (that is, act as a transducer) and to transmit those signals. There are two primary channels used for speech recognition:

- Microphones
- Telephones

When they convert the input signal, they introduce patterns of signal distortion. The distortion is a by-product of the acoustic response patterns and capabilities of the input device. It is produced before the speech is processed by the recognition system. The channel also contributes its own additive noise to the signal, usually electrical noise.

The impact of the channel on recognition accuracy is significant. For speaker-independent systems, it even outweighs the effects of speaker variability (see chapter 5). Designers of speaker-independent systems for use over the telephone are careful to collect speech samples over telephone networks that will be used by the application. To accommodate different channel noise conditions, technology developers create separate sets of models for land line and for cellular telephones.

7.1.3.1 Microphones.

Each brand and model of microphone produces a unique configuration of distortion and additive electronic noise. Since it is extremely difficult to remove the microphone noise characteristics from the signal, they are generally encoded in the reference models of an application or system. As figure 7.2 illustrates, when the microphone used with a deployed system is different from that used for model development or enrollment, the effect on recognition accuracy is strong and deleterious.

Rabiner & Juang (1993, chapter 5) describe one instance involving a large vocabulary system which experienced a drop in accuracy from 85 percent to below 19 percent as a result of changing microphones.

Microphones also vary in quality and type. *Omnidirectional* microphones have comparatively uniform pickup patterns. In contrast, *directional* microphones (also called *differential* microphones) are designed to respond to sound from a sin-

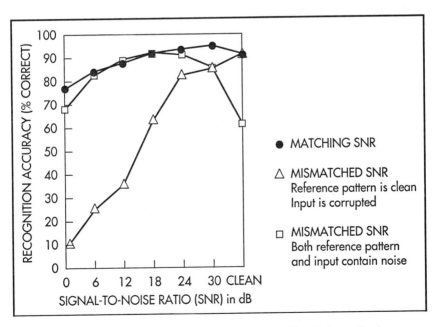

Figure 7.2   Effects of mismatching microphones (from Rabiner & Juang, *Fundamentals of Speech Recognition,* Copyright 1993, Prentice Hall)

gle direction (called *unidirectional* microphones) or from two specific directions (called *bidirectional* microphones). Because they can isolate sound sources based upon location, directional microphones are better for speech recognition than *omnidirectional* microphones. Directional microphones differ in their range of sensitivity (called the size of the *beam*). Some are sensitive to sounds emanating from a relatively broad space, while others have a pencil-thin beam.

Noise-canceling microphones are preferred in high-noise environments because they are resistant to sound coming from distant sources. They are generally constructed from bidirectional microphones or a pair of unidirectional microphones: one facing towards the speech source and one towards the environment. Frequency patterns input by the "environment" microphone are removed from the speech input before processing. This process improves the SNR as well.

Close-talking microphones are designed to be placed near or against a sound source, such as a speaker's mouth, and are typically found in microphone headsets. They are constructed to respond primarily to sounds generated from that source. The design and positioning of close-talking microphones eliminates the negative effects of reverberation and enhances the SNR. When close-talking microphones are unacceptable, as in kiosks and other *far field* applications, narrow-beam directional microphones or arrays of directional microphones can be used to cover the required speaking space.

One extensive experiment performed at IBM is especially useful for understanding the relationship between microphone type and noise. The researchers compared five types of microphones:

- Hand held noise-canceling
- Close-talking head mounted
- Stand mounted
- Unidirectional tie-clip
- Omnidirectional tie-clip

in five background noise conditions:

- Cafeteria during lunch (speech and other intermittent noise)
- Computer room (consistent machinery and fan noise)
- Secretary's office (intermittent noise in a generally quiet environment)
- Photocopy area (loud, repetitive machine noise)
- Quiet office (SNR benchmark for quiet environments)

In all cases there was a strong relationship between SNR and recognition accuracy. Directional microphones were less sensitive to background noise of all types. Noise-canceling microphones were particularly resistant to sound coming from background sources and performed well in high-noise environments (cafeteria and photocopy room). The close-talking headset microphone also performed very well.

Like Rabiner & Juang, the IBM researchers found that it is not advisable to train with one microphone and use another in the field. Accuracy in all environments was adversely affected by changing microphones.

For more information on the IBM research consult Das, et al. (1993). Also see Rabiner & Juang (1993, chapter 5).

7.1.3.2 Telephone channel.

Speech recognition applications designed for use over the telephone must accommodate noise generated by microphones in the telephone handset. If the recognition system is on the telephone network rather than in the handset, the system must also address noise in the telephone network.

Three types of microphones are used in standard telephone equipment:

- Electret speaker phone
- Carbon button handset
- Electret handset

These classes of microphones vary in the amount of reverberation captured from the environment and in their patterns of distortion. Speaker phones are particularly difficult for both recognition systems and humans. Fluctuating distance and location of the speaker in relation to a speaker phone reduce the power of the speech signal at the microphone, contributing to poor SNR's. Speaker phone input is also vulnerable to reverberation. Speakers make recognition over speaker phones even more difficult when they turn away from the phone while speaking or when they change the volume of their speech to use a speaker phone.

Electret and carbon button microphones are far less difficult for recognition systems. Both are used as close-talking devices in telephone handsets. As figure 7.3 shows, they are not at all similar in their frequency response patterns.

Electret microphones predominate in the United States, while telephones in most other countries employ carbon button microphones. Electret microphones provide much more balance in their response pattern than carbon button microphones. Carbon button microphones also exhibit poor response for the second- and third-formant frequency range (1500–2000 Hz) and for the high frequency noise patterns that help identify voiceless fricatives (see chapter 2, section 2.1). As with standard microphones, both electret and carbon button microphones vary greatly in quality and in the algorithms used to transduce input signals. Furthermore, every handset model contributes its own distortion and additive noise.

The telephone network adds more distortion to the signal. In addition to additive noise, switching and other network operations attenuate signal frequencies below 100 Hz and above 3100 Hz. Both human listeners and speech recognition devices must focus their processing activities on the frequency range of 100 to 3100 Hz. That range is called the *telephone bandwidth*.

The nature and patterns of additive noise and distortion vary from network

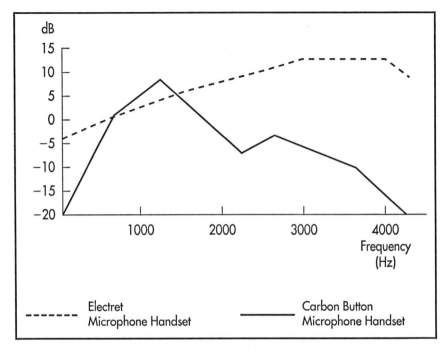

Figure 7.3 Comparison of electret and carbon button microphones (from Foster &
Schalk, *Speech Recognition,* Copyright 1993, Peter Foster and Dr. Thomas Schalk)

to network. They are largely by-products of the type, quality, and maintenance of
the equipment.

Network noise can be systematic or random. *Systematic noise* is a permanent
feature of a telephone network. Each switch contributes its own noise characteristics to the patterns. Although it varies from network to network and telephone carrier to carrier, the systematic noise of a network is consistent and predictable. This
is particularly true of land-line networks.

> Knowing the channel, we can predict what is going to occur. The pulse may *always* be
> distorted in a certain way. Given frequencies will *always* have a certain minimum
> phase delay (James Martin, Chairman, James Martin Associates, *Telecommunications
> and the Computer,* 1990, p. 640).

Random noise is unpredictable. Its additive components include electronic
white noise hiss, crosstalk, atmospheric noise, crackles, and pops. These can produce sudden, momentary shifts in SNR or even render the channel unusable. Random sources of distortion include loss or surge in signal amplitude, echo, and
changes in phase.

The noise characteristics of a land-line telephone network are challenging, but the systematic noise and distortion of those networks (and some random noise characteristics) can be encoded in word models. Typically, however, a single telephone communication is routed through more than one network, making it necessary to model the characteristics of several networks.

Speech recognition over cellular networks represents an even greater challenge. Variability in transmission is greater than for land-line networks and is compounded by the transmission power of the telephone, cell boundaries, high levels of background noise, and reverberation. Handling of channel and background noise has demanded extensive data collection. Texas Instruments' *Voice Across America* project, for example, collected large numbers of samples representing both telephone network and handset characteristics from speakers all over the United States. These network effects are eliminated when the speech recognition is embedded in the cellular telephone handset rather than on the network.

Foster & Schalk (1993), Martin (1990), and Rabiner & Juang (1993, chapter 5) provide additional information about the telephone channel.

7.1.4 Non-Communication Speech Noise

The act of speaking produces sounds that must be processed by a recognition system as non-communication input. Such speech noise includes lip smacks, air puffs, clearing of the throat, and tongue clicks. Some, notably a lip smack at the start of an utterance, are predictable and can be ignored by the system or modeled as special words or *garbage models*. Such non-communicative utterances characterize normal, spontaneous speech:

> spontaneous speech contains mid-utterance corrections and verbal edits, out-of-vocabulary words, meta level comments, dysfluencies, ungrammatical constructions and partial utterances . . . It is very difficult to generate rules that provide good coverage of the word sequences people produce when speaking spontaneously (Wayne Ward & Sheryl Young, Carnegie Mellon University, "Flexible use of semantic constraints in speech recognition," 1993, p. 49).

Speakers hesitate, stutter, correct errors in the middle of words ("It's yell—Uh! No! blue."), and fill pauses with non-communication sounds like "Uh" (see chapter 6, section 6.7.1). These patterns are beginning to be modeled, but are still poorly understood. Acoustically-based speech recognition systems, such as the commercial recognition systems of today, will be able to handle some of these phenomena; but true robustness with regard to them will come only with the development of commercial spoken language understanding systems (see chapter 4, section 4.4). Spoken language understanding systems use knowledge about speaker goals, conversational structure, and other cognitive-linguistic resources to process speech.

Wayne Ward of CMU is actively researching non-communicative speech behavior in continuous speech. Consult Ward (1991) and Ward & Young (1993) for additional information.

THE LOMBARD EFFECT

The *Lombard effect* (also called *Lombard speech*) describes the changes that occur to speech when a speaker attempts to make her/himself heard over noise. The characteristics of Lombard speech were first described by a French physician, E. Lombard, in 1911 and published in a journal for specialists in eye, ear, nose, and throat disorders.

Beginning in the 1950's, researchers interested in human-to-human communication began examining the effects of increased vocal effort (such as shouting), one facet of the Lombard effect, on intelligibility of speech. Some of this work served as the basis for understanding the impact of the Lombard effect on the accuracy of speech recognition devices.

For more information on the Lombard effect, consult Lombard's (1911) original paper in *Ann. Maladies Oreille, Larynx, Nez, Pharynx* (in French), Gardner (1966), Pickett (1956), and Rostolland & Parant (1973).

7.2 SPEAKER RESPONSE TO BACKGROUND NOISE

Even if the effects of microphone, channel, and noise are removed; the effects of stress and Lombard effect will contribute significantly to loss in recognition performance (John H.L. Hansen, Robust Speech Processing Laboratory, Duke University, personal communication, 1994).

Like recognition systems, speakers are not indifferent to stress and background noise. Stress produces emotional and physical responses that affect the way a person speaks. Noise interferes with a person's attempt to communicate. Even small increases in noise of less than 10 dB produce changes in the way people speak. These changes are magnified as the background noise becomes louder. Some of the speech and acoustic features affected by a speaker's attempt to overcome the noise include

- Increased vocal effort
- Greater duration of words due to increased vowel length
- Shifts in formant locations for vowels
- Increased formant amplitudes
- Deletion of some word-final consonants

These behaviors are called *Lombard speech* or the *Lombard effect*. The Lombard effect makes speech easier to hear and understand when the listener is another human. In contrast, it has a strongly negative impact on the accuracy of recognition systems and can produce declines in accuracy of up to 25 percent.

Existing commercial speech recognition systems are not able to automatically adapt to the acoustic effects of Lombard speech. One reason is that there is disagreement regarding the nature and consistency of the acoustic changes listed above. Some researchers have discovered intra- and inter-speaker variability in the patterns of Lombard speech.

> For some parameters [that we tested] there are significant differences between male and female speakers and that the variability of some phonemes can be very dependent on the context (Jean-Claude Junqua & Yolande Anglade, C.R.I.N./I.N.R.I.A. Vandoeuvre les Nancy, France, "Acoustic and perceptual studies of Lombard speech," 1990, p. 844).

Most researchers, however, have encountered more overall consistency in the shifting acoustic patterns of Lombard speech. Differences between the findings of these two groups of researchers may be due both to the specific parameters they have examined and the size and diversity of the populations used for testing.

Additional alterations of speech due to stress have been found to exacerbate the effects of noise. These are less well studied and understood.

For more information about Lombard speech consult papers by John H.L. Hansen (1993), Hansen & Bria (1990 & 1992), Stanton, et al. (1989), and Junqua & Anglade (1990). The papers by Hansen and Hansen & Bria also describe stressed speech.

7.3 AUDITORY MODELS

The goal of auditory modeling is to enable a recognition device to screen noise from the input signal in the same way humans do. Auditory modeling offers the promise of being able to develop more efficient, robust, and accurate systems for speech produced in noisy environments. At this time there are no commercial speech recognition systems based upon auditory modeling.

Some features of auditory modeling, such as the mel scale (see chapter 2, section 2.1.4), have already become standard components of research and commercial recognition systems. The use of these and other features are being extended in a wide range of research systems. Researchers at Duke University have developed a dual-channel, noise-reduction filtering algorithm based upon mel scale parameters. It has performed well in tests of speech produced in white noise and in noisy aircraft cockpits.

Research systems using other properties of mammalian auditory processing are being developed in laboratories. Cheng and O'Shaughnessy of INRS-Telecommunications of Canada have developed additive noise-reduction algorithms based upon *lateral inhibition* behavior of the human auditory system. Lateral inhibition is the ability to separate sounds from two distinct sound sources. The algorithms are designed to handle different types of additive noise when the SNR is below 5 dB and, unlike most conventional approaches, they require no special non-speech detectors.

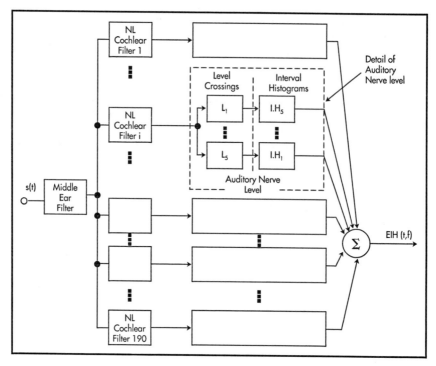

Figure 7.4 The Ensemble Interval Histogram (EIH) model (from Ghitza, "Auditory models and human performance in tasks related to speech coding and speech recognition," Copyright 1994, IEEE)

Ghitza's *Ensemble Interval Histogram (EIH)* system, shown in figure 7.4, focuses on the firing patterns of the auditory nerve.

The *EIH* is one of the more complex auditory modeling systems. It performs speech coding using models of most of the peripheral auditory system. Its *middle ear filter* removes frequencies below 1000 Hz (a *high pass filter*) while its *cochlear filters* are constructed to mimic the behavior of structures in the inner ear. The activity of the level crossings and the internal histograms represent the combined activity of individual fibers of the auditory nerve. In recent experiments, the *EIH* coder discriminated diphones (see chapter 6, section 6.3.3.2) more like a human than conventional coding systems.

The systems described in this section integrate known behaviors of the peripheral auditory system (mainly the cochlea and the auditory nerve) into speech recognition systems. The developers admit that known behaviors constitute a small segment of human auditory capabilities. Recent discoveries by speech perception researchers have revealed how complex human auditory processing is. One feature of perception, auditory object formation (see chapter 2, section 2.1.4), enables humans to extract the speech of a single voice from a noisy background. Auditory object formation is achieved, in part, by the ability of the human auditory processing system to *hear* some frequencies within a wide range of frequencies as if they were one frequency because they vary together (called *co-modulation*). Once they are fully understood, processes like auditory object formation will provide tremendous improvements in the ability of speech recognition systems to function in noise.

Detailed descriptions of the auditory modeling approaches described in this section can be found in Ghitza (1994), Cheng & O'Shaughnessy (1991), and Nandkumar & Hansen (1992). Carrell (to appear), Carrell & Opie (1992), and Darwin (1981) describe their research on auditory object formation and co-modulation.

7.4 NEURAL NETWORKS

The majority of neural networks designed to handle noise accomplish their goal by mapping noise-corrupted input to clean speech. Recognition is performed on the output of these networks by separate speech recognition devices. Most of these networks operate on discrete-word input. The *Noise Removing Network (NRN)* shown in figure 7.5 is one example. It is a recurrent network trained using backpropagation. The *NRN* maps noise-corrupted speech to clean speech and sends its output to a *TDNN* network (see chapter 2, section 2.5).

Researchers at the Interpreting Telephony Research Laboratories of the Advanced Telecommunications Research Institute of Japan (ATR) and Professor Helge Sorensen of the University of Aalborg in Denmark have developed feedforward noise-reduction networks. Like the *NRN*, these networks convert noisy input to clean speech and are designed to work in conjunction with existing recognition sys-

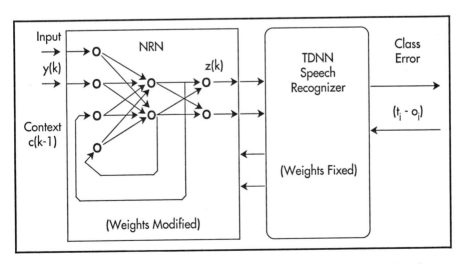

Figure 7.5   The Noise Removing Network (NRN) (from Moon & Hwang, "Coordinated training of noise removing networks," Copyright 1993, IEEE)

tems. Sorensen's network uses an auditory model to preprocess input to the network. When Sorensen tested this design as a front end for a standard recognition system, recognition accuracy improved by up to 65 percent.

The *Selectively Trained Neural Network (STNN)* is the result of a French-American collaboration. Unlike the networks described above, it performs word-level recognition on alphabetic spelling (see chapter 3, section 3.5.3) in clean, in noise-corrupted, and in Lombard speech. It is selectively trained to locate a phonetic *reference point* within the discrete-word input and to perform a fine discrimination analysis. The *STNN* is a feedforward, backpropagation network.

Researchers at Wright Air Force Base have developed a hybrid neural network and cochlear model system for speech enhancement. It mimics the two-channel (called *binaural*) speech analysis done by the human auditory processing system.

> The goal is to improve recognition of degraded speech over the monaural [single channel] case by modeling certain known aspects of the binaural auditory system (Martin DeSimio & Timothy Anderson, Wright Patterson AFB, "Phoneme recognition with binaural cochlear models and the stereausis representation," 1993, p. I-521).

The first two stages of the system do two-channel filtering, time delays, intensity differences, and other auditory-model analyses as part of the analog-to-digital conversion process. Stage three uses auditory modeling to recombine the signals and then feeds the results into a self-organizing map (SOM). The SOM performs speaker-independent phoneme recognition. Initial testing with this model significantly reduced deletion and insertion errors but increased substitution errors.

Moon & Hwang (1993) describe the *NRN*. Sorensen (1991) and Ohkura & Sugiyama (1991) describe their feedforward noise-reduction networks, and Anglade, et al. (1993) describe the *STNN*. DeSimio & Anderson (1993) provide a detailed description of the Wright Patterson cochlear model.

7.5 ASSESSMENT

In order to handle background noise, it is critical to understand the types and characteristics of the noise involved. This is accomplished through application assessment. That assessment needs to be applied to conditions in all environments to which the application will be ported. Assessment consists of an analysis of the noise in the expected speaker environment. The principal parameters of the assessment are the

- Nature of the background noise (speech, machinery, etc.)
- Variability in the background and channel noise
- Loudness of the background and channel noise
- Type of speech channel used (telephone vs. microphone)
- Quality of the speech channel

Environments with high degrees of noise and low SNR's (see section 7.1) will adversely affect recognition accuracy. Those settings, however, may not represent the most challenging speaking environments. Environments containing a great deal of reverberation or variable noise, particularly telephone rings and loud voices, will exhibit higher error rates than speaking environments characterized by machinery roar. Erratic noise is difficult to sample and is more likely to produce the noise mismatches that degrade accuracy (see figure 7.2). Quiet settings which have occasional bursts of noise can cause more problems than settings with loud, persistent noise because the system may not have the proper information to screen out the noise. Background speech is the most difficult form of noise to process. It competes directly with the primary speech signal using the same frequency range and comparable patterns of frequency variation.

Whenever possible, noise types, sources, direction, amount of reverberation, and distance of the background noise of an application should be identified. This information provides a means of assessing the appropriateness of an application for speech recognition.

Recognition products should be thoroughly tested within the application environment. If a speaker-dependent recognizer is to be used, testing should be based upon models trained in the expected noise environment. Typically, settings which are less noisy (such as quiet offices) generally require the fewest training samples, especially if the recognition is to be done using high quality, directional microphones. Noisy environments, like factory floors, require more tokens and must also include sampling of the background noise. The noise immunity of a quiet environment can be enhanced by providing some training in noise. If there is a possibility that speech noise might occur, providing some training in a noisy environment (such as a cafeteria) can help improve the recognizer's accuracy. High reverberation may need to be addressed through the use of close-talking microphones (such as headset microphones), narrow-beam directional microphones, or microphone arrays.

7.6 TECHNIQUES FOR DESIGNING ROBUST SPEECH SYSTEMS

Robustness describes the ability of a speech recognition system or application to function in a variety of environments. The importance of robustness is growing as a by-product of the desire to use speech recognition in a wider range of environments, however

> Though much research has been devoted to extending isolated-word systems to continuous speech recognition versions, there has been limited progress in addressing noise, stress and Lombard effect (John H.L. Hansen, Robust Speech Processing Laboratory, Duke University, personal communication, 1994).

Many approaches focus on additive noise and rely on knowledge about the spectral and intensity patterns of that noise. Generally, information about additive noise is captured through *noise tracking* techniques, usually applied automatically by the speech recognition system during non-speaking periods. The effort to eliminate the negative impact of background, channel, and speaker noise is directed at increasing the intelligibility of speech. When it involves the identification, reduction, or removal of noise from the signal it is called *noise reduction*. The most successful and commonly used techniques are

- Training
- Preprocessing
- Noise cancellation

When the focus is on improving the quality of the speech signal itself the process is called *speech enhancement,* although the term "speech enhancement" is sometimes used to refer to noise reduction/elimination as well.

These techniques, combined with proper microphone selection and placement, can greatly enhance the accuracy and robustness of most applications. Research on noise reduction and speech enhancement is continuing, although most speech enhancement still remains in the laboratory. Commercial microphone technology is improving steadily and is helping to move speech recognition into harsher speaking environments. None of these approaches, particularly when applied to single-microphone systems, is comparable to the noise reduction and speech enhancement capabilities of human beings.

> We have had millions of years of evolution to help us deal with sound and reverberation. Computers do not have these capabilities. So many things that sound clear to us sound garbled to a computer. With computers you must reinvent the way humans process sound (Bill Porter, General Manager, AT&T Intelligent Acoustics Systems, personal communication, 1995).

Until computers learn to handle noise as well as humans can, the responsibility for addressing noise and noise-induced issues will continue to lie with the application designer.

7.6.1 Training

If the expected background noise is known and if there are a small number of distinct noise conditions, it is possible to train the reference models in the expected noise as well as in quiet conditions. This process (called *multi-style training*) allows the noise to be interpreted as part of the normal signal. It is a standard technique for developing speaker-dependent applications and is used to develop speaker-independent models for telephone-based systems as well. Multi-style training works very well in environments with consistent noise patterns; but when variable or undetermined noise conditions are present, sampling and enrollment can become lengthy and difficult.

A more effective approach for variable noise conditions involves developing noise immunity as a part of the creation of reference models.

The focus is on developing likelihood measures which are robust to the effects of noise rather than trying to remove the noise from the degraded speech (Beth Carlson & Mark Clements, Georgia Institute of Technology, "Speech recognition in noise using a projection-based likelihood measure for mixture density HMM's," 1992, p. 237).

Some researchers have found that simply adding ambient noise to models of clean speech will increase robustness. Other researchers are modifying the algorithms that generate those models.

Consult Ohkura, et al. (1991) for robustness evaluations of two training algorithms. Carlson & Clements (1992) describe other robustness measures. Das, et al. (1993) describe an IBM study recommending the inclusion of noise in reference models (also see section 7.1.3.1).

7.6.2 Preprocessing

Our goal is to understand and eliminate variance in the speech signal due to the environmental changes and thus ultimately avoid the need for extensive training of the recognizer in different environments (Hynek Hermansky of US West and Nelson Morgan & Hans-Gunter Hirsch of International Computer Science Institute, "Recognition of speech in additive and convolutional noise based on RASTA spectral processing," 1993, p. 83).

Preprocessing techniques remove additive noise from the signal before it is digitized. The most commonly used preprocessing approach is *signal filtering*. The function of filters is to restrict the frequencies that can pass through them. *Low pass filters* only allow frequencies lower than a designated frequency (or frequency range) to pass through, *high pass filters* restrict frequencies to those above a specified frequency (or frequency range), and *band pass filters* restrict all but a specified range of frequencies. High pass and well-designed band pass filters have proven the most successful for speech recognition systems. Some filters are based upon the linear (Hertz) scale, but a growing number are being designed using the mel scale (see chapter 2, section 2.1.4) or a logarithmic scale.

Hermansky, et al., (1993) Hansen & Applebaum (1993), and Hansen & Arslan (1995) describe specific preprocessing implementations.

7.6.3 Noise Cancellation

Noise cancellation removes or attenuates the frequencies associated with noise. It can be accomplished in a variety of ways. The most commonly used approaches are spectral *subtraction* and *masking*. As its name implies, spectral subtraction removes the frequencies of noise from the signal. When the noise covers a wide range of frequencies, including critical speech frequencies, masking techniques, which adjust the power of those frequencies to match the speech signal more closely, have proven more effective. Spectral subtraction and masking use information gathered from noise tracking to estimate the power spectrum of additive noise and to cancel it from the signal. They are often accomplished using two or more microphone sensors, which may be located on the same microphone or may be deployed as part of a microphone array.

Some noise cancellation algorithms designed for telephone systems reduce or remove noise from the *side tone* of the handset. The side tone is part of the voice feedback circuitry of the telephone that allows the speaker to hear her/his own voice. By attenuating noise in the side tone, these algorithms reduce the Lombard effect. Noise canceling microphones are excellent for high noise environments (see section 7.1.3.1) because they work to eliminate noise at the point of input.

Technical descriptions of noise canceling techniques are provided by Klatt (1976) and Rabiner & Juang (1993, chapter 5).

7.6.4 Microphones

The microphone that is selected for an application must satisfy the needs of the recognition systems, of the speaking environment, of the application, and of the users. The microphones generally used for speech recognition are high quality *directional, noise canceling, close-talking* microphones. Directional microphones reduce the harmful effects of background noise because they are most sensitive to sound emanating from a specific direction, such as the speaker. Noise cancellation eliminates frequencies of background noise from the signal. (For more information on microphone types see section 7.1.3.1).

The quality of the microphone must increase with the distance from the speaker's mouth, especially in noisy environments containing a lot of background speech. For that reason, vendors of many recognition products prefer close-talking microphones. Close-talking microphones are designed to focus on very close sound sources. They are suitable when speakers will be positioning the microphone very near or against their mouths. Such microphones can be configured as telephone-like handsets, headset microphones, or they may be suspended in front of the speaker's mouth.

The proper placement of close-talking microphones is critical for accurate recognition. Placement against the side of the mouth rather than directly in front of the mouth captures the necessary spectral patterns without the excess noise created by release of stop consonants (such as *p,t,k*). Positioning at the side of the mouth also minimizes the effect of non-communication speech noise and is less likely to result in moisture build-up on the microphone. Even with proper positioning of the microphone, most close-talking microphones need screens to prevent distortion created by saying stop consonants and fricatives and to reduce moisture build-up. Unfortunately, maintaining correct microphone positioning is difficult. Bad habits may develop even when speakers have been trained to position microphones properly. Microphone positioning on headsets is adjustable rather than fixed, making it easy for the microphone to be moved by users. Users tend to move the microphone towards the center of the mouth or down and away from the mouth. Similar problems occur with boom microphones.

Handheld microphones perform well when there is little background speech. Microphones on a stand, embedded in equipment, or worn on clothing (tie-clip microphones) must be carefully tested before an application is deployed because they must compensate for changing distances, nearby clothing or machine noise, and reductions in speech signal power that can occur when the user faces away from the microphone.

Close-talking microphones are inappropriate for *far field* applications, such as kiosks, and can be rejected by users as uncomfortable, difficult to use, or intrusive. A close-talking microphone can be replaced by a noise-canceling directional microphone with a tight beam or with a microphone array. The *Alice's Interactive Wonderland* kiosk at Epcot Center in Disney World is an example of the successful deployment of a microphone array in a noisy, reverberant speaking environment. The linear array of microphones, designed by AT&T and shown in figure 7.6, is embedded in the ceiling of the kiosk above a small sofa where the speakers sit. Speakers interact with animated figures that ask them questions. Their responses are recognized using a word spotting (see chapter 4, section 4.5) recognizer in a PC. The mi-

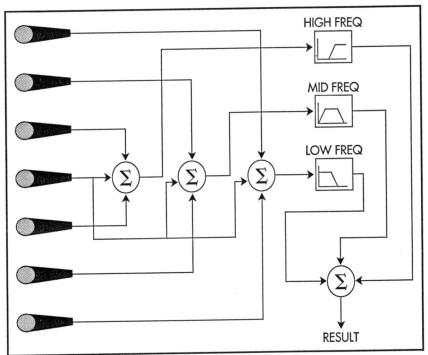

Figure 7.6 Schematic representation of AT&T's image derived linear array microphone system used in *Alice's Interactive Wonderland* kiosk (figure provided by AT&T Intelligent Acoustics Systems)

crophone array creates a three-dimensional area of maximum acoustic sensitivity (sometimes referred to as the *sweet spot*) surrounding the couch. Its shape is comparable to that of a flat-bottomed paper cup. The phased microphone input shown in figure 7.6 adjusts the input to account for differences in the time the speech arrives at each pair of microphones. The input is passed through several filters (shown at the right of the figure) before being sent to the preprocessor. The linear array configuration shown in figure 7.6 was carefully designed for the acoustics of the kiosk. It has made the system impervious to sounds emanating from outside the sweet spot, such as the noise from neighboring exhibits, and contributes to the high accuracy (better than 95 percent) of the recognition system.

Some recognition systems can use *push-to-talk* microphones. These microphones require the user to depress a button or foot pedal during speech. Push-to-talk is characteristic of many hand-held microphones but can be used with all other microphone configurations, including headsets. They enhance accuracy in high noise environments by signaling the recognizer when speech is being input. Systems using push-to-talk may also be structured to allow users to pause in the middle of an utterance without signaling the end of the utterance. Push-to-talk buttons are less useful for hands-free applications, unless a foot pedal can be safely used. If a push-to-talk approach is selected, users should be trained in the proper timing of button and speech. In particular, they need to be taught to be certain to press the button immediately before beginning to speak, rather than as they start talking, and to release the button after the utterance is completely finished, rather than as they are finishing.

A software technique similar to push-to-talk for variable or high-noise environments is to use *keywords* like "Computer" or "Input." The keywords signal incoming speech and allow the system to stop listening during periods of non-speech.

The gain control of a microphone is another application consideration. In some systems, gain control is automatic; other systems allow users to adjust the control. Automatic gain control is usually preferable. One danger of manual gain control regulation is that it may be more a reflection of the user's response to loud background noise or recognition errors than a requirement of the recognition system. Gain settings that are too high can generate distortion. An automatic system assumes responsibility for calculating the proper gain setting. This can be based upon enrollment data, the initial input, or an average over all speakers. Selection of the best method of gain control depends upon the requirements of the application. Consistent, high-noise environments and applications in settings demanding soft-spoken input are easier for automatic gain control systems than applications in variable environments. In all cases, the gain control methodology should be tested as part of product evaluation.

The quality of microphones and noise canceling microphone technology has been improving steadily. Microphone manufacturers, such as Gentex, offer directional microphones designed for lightweight headsets and for mounting on computer monitors. These microphones are also designed to be less sensitive to humidity and electromagnetic interference. The availability of higher quality microphones is increasing as their prices decline and as interest in audio input to computers grows. Microphones suitable for speech recognition, for example, are being offered as standard hardware for personal computers.

The undesirable distortion associated with speakerphones has spawned *echo-cancellation* software to reduce the barrel-like quality of speaker phones and on long-distance telephone communication. It can also be used to provide a cleaner signal to a speech recognition system.

7.7 HANDLING CHANNEL NOISE

One of the issues facing speech recognition application and system developers is the nature and quality of the input device used for recognition. The quantity and frequencies of the noise generated by the input channel, its frequency response characteristics, and the presence of more than one channel, affect the quality of recognition.

7.7.1 Microphone Quality

Microphones vary greatly in quality as well as in function. All applications require good quality directional microphones, but even a high-quality microphone may be poorly matched to a specific recognition system. To minimize incompatibility, some vendors provide or recommend specific types of microphones for their products. Whether the microphone provided by the vendor or another is used for an application, it is not advisable to train with one microphone and use another when the application has been deployed. This practice will adversely affect accuracy, even in good speaking conditions (see section 7.1.3.1 and figure 7.2).

7.7.2 Telephones

Construction of telephone applications is particularly demanding (also see chapter 8). Variations in telephone quality, carrier characteristics, and transmission type are compounded by telephone hiss that can render words like *six* almost incomprehensible. In view of the nastiness of the telephone channel, it is not surprising to find vendors collecting more than ten thousand tokens to develop digit models for continuous speech.

In the United States, the quality of the telephone networks is comparatively uniform. Differences are largely due to the characteristics distinguishing cellular, land-line, and satellite usage. Unless the recognition is embedded in the telephone, the quality of the telephone represents a second layer of variability. A telephone costing less than ten dollars will respond very differently than one that costs over one hundred dollars. This difference is due to the quality of the components and algorithms found in the two telephones.

Applications designed for use outside of the United States must be done with care. The greatest source of difficulty arises from the idiosyncratic behavior of national telephone network systems. Some of these networks are characterized by high levels of noise and poor transmission quality. Network characteristics may also vary dramatically within and across countries. Most telephones outside of the United States use carbon button microphones which contribute a considerable amount of additive noise and signal distortion (see section 7.1.3.2).

7.8 HANDLING NON-COMMUNICATION SPEECH NOISE

Concern over the effects of non-communication speech noise has surfaced accompanying the appearance of free-form dictation systems. It will grow as free-form, continuous speech systems appear and are used with different populations of users. It is an issue facing systems of all sizes and functions, particularly those using continuous speech. Recognition errors resulting from identifying non-speech communication as valid responses can throw the recognizer out of synchronization with the application software.

Non-communication speech noise, such as "Uh" and lip smacks, is harder to screen than channel and background noise. Some of it is poorly understood, especially self-correction behavior, such as

"The number is 555-12 No! 555-2134."

Other non-communicative speech behavior can be addressed today. Proper microphone placement, primarily close-talking microphones, can attenuate the effects of some speech noise, particularly the puffs of air associated with certain speech sounds. Well-designed applications, good reference models, and the acclimation of users to an application all help to reduce recognition errors linked to non-communication speech input. Reference models can be created for frequent forms of non-communication speech, such as utterance-initial lip smacks and filled pauses, like "Uh." Creating models of pause fillers enhances the robustness of continuous speech systems in particular (see chapter 6, sections 6.3 and 6.7). Backup and other error correction mechanisms can help users extract the system from incorrect paths. Visual feedback from video screens or auditory confirmation of input can help users to correct errors as well. Designing speech-aware systems (see chapter 2, section 2.8) contributes greatly to application robustness by reducing the possibility that the speech interface will lose synchronization with the other application software.

7.9 HANDLING LOMBARD SPEECH

It is imperative that speech researchers focus on improved speech modeling schemes in order to better address the range of dynamic articulatory movements which occur when speakers are under stress (including Lombard effect) (John H.L. Hansen, Robust Speech Processing Laboratory, Duke University, personal communication, 1993).

Little attention has been given to attenuating the impact of Lombard speech on recognition accuracy. The most frequently applied technique for attenuating Lombard speech is multi-style training that produces speaker-dependent models containing both Lombard and non-Lombard speech. This approach works best if the vocabulary is relatively small, the noise conditions are uniform, and the speakers are cooperative. Since the characteristics of Lombard speech have been found to vary with the noise conditions, changeable or undetermined noise conditions make multi-style training difficult to accomplish. Variable stress conditions accompanying noise (see chapter 6, section 6.7.2) complicate training even more.

Rather than training on multiple speech conditions, it is more desirable to develop recognition algorithms that use only normal speech for training and implicitly account for the speech variation due to speaker workload and stress (Bill Stanton, U.S. Air Force Academy, and Leah Jamieson & George Allen, Purdue University, "Robust recognition of loud and Lombard speech in the fighter cockpit environment," 1989, p. 675).

This speech enhancement (see chapter 7 Introduction, and sections 7.1.2 and 7.4) technique is applied during preprocessing (see chapter 2, section 2.2 and its subsections). It makes the input appear more like the speaker-dependent reference models for normal speech stored in the system. Tests using this approach under controlled noise conditions improved recognition accuracy for Lombard speech by up to 42 percent. Another approach, designed for speaker-independent systems, removes acoustic features most affected by Lombard effect for speaker-independent models. The *STNN* being developed in France represents another approach to handling Lombard speech (see section 7.4).

As yet, these techniques have been tested on small groups of speakers under controlled conditions. Assessment of their effectiveness in handling Lombard speech requires considerably more testing on diverse populations of speakers talking under varying noise conditions. One step in that direction is the *ICARUS* system of Duke University. *ICARUS* exploits the power of IBM's *Mwave* digital signal processing technology to perform extensive preprocessing (see chapter 2, section 2.2 and its subsections) of the input signal in real time. The preprocessing consists of constrained iterative speech enhancement and stress compensation algorithms that Duke researchers John Hansen and Douglas Cairns found to be effective in improving accuracy for Lombard and stressed speech. The use of commercial, real-time technology moves the research on Lombard and stressed speech closer to the conditions that will be encountered in real applications.

Additional technical information on this topic can be found in Hansen (1993), Hansen & Applebaum (1990), Hansen & Bria (1990 and 1992), Hanson & Applebaum (1990), Junqua & Anglade (1990), and Stanton, et al. (1989). Hansen's work includes the design of dynamic algorithms to handle Lombard speech. Hansen and other researchers have also been examining ways to handle a combination of Lombard speech, stress, and background noise.

7.10 SPEECH RECOGNITION IN HARSH ENVIRONMENTS

Speech recognition in vehicles or for consumer products and services is difficult. These adverse environments will be discussed in the following sections.

SPEECH RECOGNITION IN VEHICLES

Automotive manufacturers and speech recognition system developers have worked on car telephone dialing systems and environmental control applications (voice control of non-critical operations, such as opening windows and turning on the heater) since the first half of the 1980's, in anticipation of state-level legislation requiring hands-free operation of telephones and other systems. Environmental control systems have not yet emerged from the laboratory.

The first commercial cellular car telephone dialing system was implemented by Voice Control Systems in 1986. Consumer awareness of the technology did not begin to grow until the 1990's with the widespread use of car telephones and the appearance of speech recognition systems in other environments.

7.10.1 Vehicles

Vehicles are highly desirable environments for speech recognition applications because the driver's eyes should remain on the road as much as possible and, ideally, both hands should remain on the steering wheel. Vehicles also represent one of the most adverse environments for speech recognition. Depending upon the vehicle, as well as the roadway, traffic patterns, and external weather conditions, the background noise level can be extremely high and is likely to contain the full range of ambient noise types:

- Relatively consistent machine noise from the engine can be combined with intermittent machine noise of other vehicles and with the sounds of activities within the cab of the vehicle.
- The SNR of wind, engine, and tire noises vary with external conditions, such as window aperture and speed.
- The power spectrum of the background noise ranges from very low frequencies (engine noise) through the speech spectrum and into high frequencies (wind and tire).
- Operation of the radio adds music, background speech, and an almost infinite variety of sound patterns, including white noise hiss.
- The configuration of vehicle cabs makes the environment prone to high levels of reverberation.

The speaker's voice is also highly variable. Changeable background noise levels account for a portion of speech variability as Lombard speech. Stress, strong emotions, eating, head position, and fatigue are additional components. The range of variation can be extreme for commercial truckers or sales representatives who may drive eight or more hours in a day.

Careful human factors design is a challenging, but critical, component of application development for this environment. Cellular telephone voice dialing systems have been successful when users hold the telephone handset. Hands-free voice-dialing and environmental control systems for voice management of windows, radios, and heat/air-conditioning represent far greater challenges. Directional microphones embedded in a telephone handset, microphone arrays, and headsets have been tested. Both truck and automobile drivers reject headsets, leaving surface-mounted microphones as the only viable option. Some developers have employed a push-to-talk button to signal incoming speech (see section 7.7.1). Some systems use microphone arrays and sophisticated filtering techniques to compensate for variable head positioning and ambient noise. None of these systems has been able to hurdle the constellation of noise factors, speaker factors, human factors, and user acceptance obstacles that face speech recognition use for tasks other than voice dialing of car telephones.

7.10.2 Consumer Products and Services

The attributes that make hands-free speech recognition in vehicles difficult extend to many other types of applications. Among them are consumer products and services.

Consumer services at kiosks face challenges that are comparable to those addressed by AT&T in the *Alice's Interactive Wonderland* (section 7.6.4). Some applications can use a linear microphone array. Telephone-like handsets and tight-beam microphones are better suited to other walk-up services, such as automatic teller machines (ATM's). Similarly, a drive-up service at a bank or fast-food restaurant requires a directional microphone with a tight beam capable of capturing the speech of the customer without also inputing engine and tailpipe noise. This technology is also under design at AT&T's Intelligent Acoustics Systems.

Developers of portable consumer products must also design for variability of background noise, durability and damage resistance, small size, and very low price overheads.

Consumer products and services promise to be one of the most lucrative industries for speech recognition. Success in this arena will insure widespread acceptance of speech recognition. In order to succeed, however, the problems presented by the speaking environment will need to be solved.

7.11 DESIGNING FOR MULTIPLE ENVIRONMENTS

If an application is to be used in more than a single targeted speaking environment or if the speaker is expected to be mobile, recognition products should be tested in every potential environment.

Tokens collected from one environment cannot be expected to function well in environments with different background (or channel) noise characteristics. Existing models should be tested and updated with data from the new environments. This approach is a standard operating procedure for developers of speaker-independent recognition systems. Vendors who develop applications for both cellular and rotary telephones, for example, collect separate sets of tokens for each of these environments.

On-the-fly adaptation (see chapter 5, section 5.4) can assist in the porting of an application from one environment to another but should not be used as a policy if the characteristics of the new environment are known. Modeling the new environment before deployment produces greater accuracy more quickly.

Consumer products represent a special case of multiple-environment systems. They are likely to be used in a wide range of settings with unknown noise characteristics. The use of speech in such products is new and many facets of the challenge are in the process of being discovered.

8

APPLICATION TYPES

INTRODUCTION

What is the value of speech recognition? It is totally dependent upon the application you are using (Larry Dooling, President and CEO of Verbex Voice Systems, personal communication, *Advanced Speech Applications and Technologies '95,* April 5, 1995).

Most speech recognition applications are constructed to perform one or more of the following functions:

- Data entry
- Command-and-control
- Information Access
- Dictation

Each of these functions has a unique constellation of

- Speech requirements
- Human factors requirements
- Typical examples

Among the most important, yet the most often ignored, are the human factors of an application. Like all human-interface technologies, the success of a speech recognition application hinges on acceptance by the people who will use it. Speech recognition faces a greater challenge because users and developers often approach it with unrealistic expectations. For these reasons, the chapter begins with an examination of the *Star Trek* Model, a set of unrealistic expectations about speech recognition that can threaten the success of any application. That discussion is followed by an overview of other human factors issues. A detailed examination of the four major functions ensues, and the chapter concludes with a discussion of product and application assessment.

8.1 THE STAR TREK MODEL

The *Star Trek* Model of speech recognition is based upon the futuristic communication systems used in *Star Trek* movies, books, and television programs. Those advanced, artificially-intelligent devices are capable of verbal interaction comparable to that of a human being.

Problems arise when developers and users forget that the *Star Trek* speech recognition systems are images of the future. Users become excited about the possibility of entering the realm of science fiction, but that excitement disintegrates into frustration and anger when the speech recognition of the 1990's fails to perform as magnificently as the fictional communication devices of the 23rd century. Addressing unrealistic user expectations of this sort is a vital facet of the planning of an application.

> Before our users experienced speech recognition, we set their expectations so that they understand where the technology is today, and what can be expected now. Many users expect voice input and output like in "Star Trek."—they expect to do natural speech dictation without errors. It is dangerous to lead them into that path (Janet Ho, Vice President of Engineering, KorTeam International & Gabriel Groner, President, Insight Solutions, "Speech recognition in a hospital bedside charting system," 1994, p. 47).

The primary reason users turn to the *Star Trek* Model is that it is the only model for speech recognition that they have. The speech recognition technology of the 1990's is still unfamiliar and lacks a standardized interaction paradigm.

> The mass market will be waiting for that paradigm to advance to the point where when you walk up to your PC or workstation and there is a microphone there you say, "I know how to use this. I know how it works with this new application. Even though I have never used this application before." (Michael Krasner, Manager of the Speech Group, BBN, Industry Leaders Panel, *Advanced Speech Applications and Technologies Conference '94*).

The design of such a standard is a goal of the industry, but some of its principles are grounded in basic human factors guidelines (see section 8.2). Until a standard paradigm is established and widely-accepted, the *Star Trek* Model will persist. Developers who attach speech recognition to their systems as a means of exploiting the aura of *Star Trek* will likely produce poorly designed and badly integrated systems, as the following example illustrates.

> Company X had an advanced office automation system. They added speech recognition as a secondary interface to their product thinking it would emphasize the product's high-tech nature. They selected the technology of an established company whose speaker-dependent speech recognition technology had been successfully deployed in a broad range of applications and speaking environments. They implemented the speech on an input device that could be held close to the mouth or mounted on the user's PC, but they did no testing to determine how the speech would be used. A reporter who reviewed the system praised the product but found the speech unusable, labeling speech recognition as an unreliable, immature technology. The company agreed and, taking no responsibility for the failure of the speech interface to work properly, was relieved that the reviewer had pointed out that the speech was provided by another company.

Had Company X developers understood the nature of speech technology and done human factors testing to see how the speech interface would be used, they would have identified the source of the problem. Users of this speaker-dependent system enrolled their vocabulary while holding the microphone within an inch of their mouths; but they used the system with the microphone mounted on the PC, almost two feet away! In most cases, a difference of less than two feet would have little impact on the ability of humans (or *Star Trek* communication devices) to understand speech. Unfortunately, the microphone and speech recognition technology of the 1990's perceives marked differences in the voice signal and in the background noise as the microphone moves away from the speaker's mouth. Deteriorations of the primary speech signal have a fatal impact on the accuracy of a speech recognition system.

Another error made by Company X was the spirit of *Not-Invented-Here*. Company X forgot that most people do not partition their evaluation of a product between features developed by the manufacturer versus components acquired from other companies. Poor performance by any feature, particularly the user-interface, degrades the perception of the product as a whole.

Speech recognition must offer benefits beyond simple novelty.

> There are good and bad reasons for using speech technology in your human interface. It is critical that you know why you are using speech, and that you can express the reasons explicitly (Bruce Balentine, Human Factors Specialist, Scott Instruments [currently Voice Control Systems, Inc.], *Goodlistener Cookbook*, 1992, p. 47).

This demands understanding of the technology, of the task which the application is designed to perform, and of the people who will use that application.

8.2 HUMAN FACTORS

Speech recognition can make an application or product more usable, useful, and natural. It can offer hands-free operation, greater control over the personal environment for people with visual and motor impairments, simultaneous control of multiple pieces of equipment, cost savings, and greater efficiency. Given these and other benefits

> it is reasonable to ask why speech is not more widely used in practice . . . One obvious answer is that the technology has not yet advanced to the stage where adequate performance for mass applications is available at a competitive cost. Another possibility, however, is that even present capabilities in speech technology are not being appropriately exploited because of lack of understanding of the requirements of a successful speech interface (Bob Damper & Graham Leedham, "Human factors," 1992, p. 261).

That lack of understanding derives from several sources, including

- Unfamiliarity with the technology on the part of developers
- Unfamiliarity with the technology on the part of system users
- Rapid changes occurring in commercial speech recognition technology
- Use of speech recognition in new types of systems, such as consumer products

Taken together, these points can make application development a challenge. Developers new to speech recognition can benefit from lessons learned by others, keeping in mind that

> Every time you introduce a new technology to people, you cannot predict their response. The only thing you can predict is that they will do something unpredictable (Judith Tschirgi, Director Services and Speech Technology, AT&T Network Systems, personal communication, 1994).

The temptation is to focus primarily on engineering issues or to view human factors concerns as unrelated to other facets of design.

> However, even "simple" human factors decisions usually involve trade-offs. Second, even "trivial" mistakes are cumulative. As callers experience additional problems or frustrations, they will quickly abandon any use of the system unless they are driven to use it (Martha Lindeman, President, Users First, "How to design 'caller friendly' applications," 1993, p. 16).

Good human factors design will enhance the likelihood of success of a system and will reduce the cost of modifying a system once it has been deployed.

There are many ways to conceptualize human factors design. They all include understanding

- The power, limitations, and nature of speech recognition technology
- The goals and structure of the task
- The people who will use the system

Most of this book has been devoted to the first point. The other two are closely intertwined. Entire books have been written about these two points and other human factors issues. The following sections do not attempt to cover the entire domain. They offer some guidelines and points to consider.

Consult Balentine (1992) Lindeman (1993), Schwab, et al. (1995), and chapter 4, section 4.9.4 of this book for additional information about human factors design.

8.2.1 Understanding the Task

The objectives of a task are built into the systems created to accomplish it. They are reflected in the way a system is structured, the organization of sub-tasks, the input/output modalities, and communication with people who access the system. Facets of the way the system is conceptualized are translated into design specifications and details of implementation.

The task's goals define basic elements of the human interface, including the

- Information the system will obtain from a user
- Information to be given to the user
- Options available to users at different points in the interaction and their priority
- Proper positioning of the input device
- Types of error handling
- Interface modalities

These and other facets of the task are refined and elaborated upon using knowledge about the people who will use the system. Changes, in turn, are tested to verify that they promote the speedy and efficient satisfaction of the goals of the task.

> At first we used a bright and sunny voice to give the prompts because we thought it would be nicer and more like a human. The callers responded by chatting. As a result we have made our prompts less friendly and more focused to encourage callers to say the target words (Robert Perdue, Supervisor, AT&T Bell Laboratories, personal communication, 1994).

Two elements of understanding a task are to determine whether speech recognition is appropriate for the task and, if so, what form it must assume. Generally, tasks requiring an individual to attend to auditory input are not good candidates for speech recognition. One example of such a task is air-traffic control communications. Air-traffic control is a high-stress job requiring careful attention to multiple, simultaneous conversations over a noisy channel. As such, the training of air-traffic controllers is an ideal candidate for speech recognition, but paradoxically, the task itself is not. There are several speech recognition systems for training air-traffic controllers. The only system designed for actual air-traffic control communications was developed by BBN. The approach they employed, gisting, (see chapter 4, section 4.5.2) is the only one that is suitable for the task because gisting is non-intrusive. It identifies and extracts important pieces of information from air-traffic control communication without interfering with those dialogues. The participants are unaware of its presence. The benefits of utilizing such an approach are that the needed information is gathered in a timely fashion and that the job of the air-traffic controller is eased somewhat by eliminating the need to recall and document communications.

In another instance, UMECorp is developing a brokerage application which allows a broker speaking with a client to simultaneously communicate with a speech recognition system. Normally, speech recognition would very likely interfere with broker-client communication; the planned system, however, is designed to allow the client to listen while the broker places the client's trades.

8.2.2 Understanding the Users

I would emphasize having to watch real users . . . using your product. It sometimes can be a very enlightening and sometimes a very painful experience to watch people stumbling. People don't read user manuals. They don't select help. They won't even try to understand what the menu items are. People expect to be able to just install software and use it perfectly (Ray Kurzweil, Founder and Chairman of Kurzweil Applied Intelligence Inc., Leader's Panel on "Money-making opportunities in speech recognition," *Advanced Speech Applications and Technologies Conference '95*).

8.2.2.1 Who is the user?   Users differ in many ways, including personal characteristics, task-related attributes, and experience with the system. Personal characteristics, such as sensory, motor, and linguistic capabilities, help define the interface, no matter what task is involved. People with upper-body motor paralysis, for example, require hands-free systems, with implementation being defined by the nature and extent of the impairment. Other groups of users may need bilingual or multi-lingual speech interfaces.

Some task-related characteristics are by-products of performing the task. Auditory and visual acuity as well as manual dexterity can be affected by personal protective equipment. Similarly, protective headgear can muffle or otherwise distort speech. Users' speech characteristics are also affected by environmental noise, stress, and physical activities, such as lifting, that are part of the task.

When speech recognition is applied to an existing task, there are two ways to conceptualize its design. Both of these are governed by the nature of the users. If the users are experienced with the task, the vocabulary and language patterns associated with performing that task must be incorporated into the system. If, on the other hand, the users are unfamiliar with the task and do not wish to become knowledgeable, it is not appropriate to organize the application around the language and vocabulary of experts.

An example of the second group of users are those who choose to use a voice-driven remote-control system to program VCR's. Such people are likely to be ignorant about VCR programming and may see speech input as a way to avoid learning it. For populations of users in this group, the language and vocabulary needs of a successful application must reflect the language patterns and the expectations of naive users. Similarly, when a new task is created or being converted from another modality, new patterns of behavior may need to be identified, defined, and tested. One example is when manual operation of equipment is replaced by voice command. Another is the replacement of the mouse with voice for navigation of graphical user interfaces (GUI's). The GUI menus are likely to foster speech patterns like "file, open," but people may prefer more grammatical forms, such as "open a file" or "open file X."

The design of help modules, error correction procedures, prompts, and instructions are all affected by the anticipated range of users' familiarity with the system or comparable systems. Systems may need to contain two or more sets of interaction techniques to accommodate such differences in user knowledge and experience. People who use a system repeatedly may require the incorporation of *power user* techniques. *Barge-in* is one power user technique that is found in telephone applications. It allows users to respond before a prompt has ended. In contrast, design for populations of individuals who will unexpectedly encounter the system or who will use it only on rare occasions may need to minimize user confusion and misunderstanding. One method is to provide longer prompts containing detailed explanation.

Lack of experience with computer applications in general can either make speech more attractive or make an application with speech seem even stranger. Some groups of users are uncomfortable with new technology and do not wish to "talk to a machine." This is compounded by what Judith Tschirgi of AT&T calls *technophobia*. Some people can become easily frustrated with a machine seemingly intent on forcing them to do something they do not want to do. When technophobia is ignored, the users resist adjusting to the application.

> In our situation, I think the users were rather scared of the system. They were sort of treating it tentatively with kid gloves, whereas one has to be relaxed and fluid (Steve Rogers, Manager of Systems and Technology, NatWest Markets Ltd., Quoted by Teresa Yraslorza in Merrill Lynch, "Special Supplement: Voice recognition," 1993, p. 10).

8.2.2.2 What do users want or need?

People who access a speech recognition interface generally have a clearly defined goal they wish to accomplish. Goals can be as diverse as getting information about a bank account, placing a telephone call, completing a quality-audit inspection, or dictating a report. In every case, speech is incidental to the completion of the objective.

Speech can be viewed favorably when users perceive that it makes accomplishment of the task easier, better, or faster. User satisfaction goes beyond the simple requirements of the task itself. It has environmental, personal, and social components that threaten or enhance user acceptance of the application, including the following examples:

> Inspectors on a factory production line must complete their inspections in the time allotted by the movement of the production line. Using speech may reduce the stress related to identifying and documenting product defects in that short timespan.
>
> Callers who encounter a speech recognition system may become irritated when they are greeted by a machine rather than a human being.
>
> People speaking to a speech recognition system in an ATM may be too embarrassed to be seen talking to a machine.

Users have equipment configuration preferences as well as needs. They may object to wearing headsets or they may want screen displays that contain facsimiles of the forms they are completing. Discovering and satisfying these choices enhance acceptance of the application.

Some user needs conflict with the goals of the application. Some physicians who have been accustomed to the work of transcriptionists, for example, complain about the need to edit their own dictation rather than leaving the editing for someone else. Their discomfort conflicts with the needs of hospitals which have implemented the systems as ways to speed reports to payer agencies and to reduce administrative costs.

Sometimes the needs or limitations of speech recognition technology itself interfere with attainment of the user's goals.

> In asking for a credit card number we found that the system worked best for short digit strings, so we asked the callers to put in their numbers in groups of four digits. Many people did not know what the word "digit" meant. When we changed it to "number" people became confused because "number" can equal a single "digit" or the entire string of digits. So they wanted to know if they were to enter the entire string of digits four times (Robert Perdue, Supervisor, AT&T Bell Laboratories, personal communication, 1994).

In most instances, the needs of the users should be satisfied through careful design and testing.

8.2.3 Iterative Design and Testing

> Careful design and iterative testing of user-system interaction are required to realize the full potential of using speech for an interface style that is perceived as more natural and intuitive (Gerhard Deffner of Texas Instruments, Linda Jo Black of Sprint and Mark Ollmann of Texas Instruments, "Wizard of Oz market testing of spoken commands interface style," 1994, p. 124).

The use of *iterative design and testing* enables a developer to break an application into its component parts then assess the technological and human factors needs for each component. Some elements of iterative design can be performed using pilot or prototype systems. Prototypes are useful, for example, for observing how people interact with a system.

Another commonly used technique is *Wizard of Oz* testing. Inspired by the clever illusions created by the title character in the book and movie called *The Wizard of Oz,* human factors professionals have used this approach as a means of studying users' behavior when confronted with various types of interfaces and interface designs. Wizard of Oz tests (see section 8.3.3.4) simulate the expected interaction between a human and a recognition system performing a designated task. They help gather data regarding the vocabulary, speech patterns, and overall responses of users to a planned application or design component. They reduce the time needed to develop sets of alternative designs and can be a valuable part of iterative design and testing.

An excellent description of iterative human factors design and the use of Wizard of Oz testing is found in Deffner, et al.'s (1994) description of the development of the Sprint *Voice FONCARD* system.

8.2.4 Opening New Vistas

Recent commercial success has resulted in the use of speech recognition in a broader range of applications being used by a wider spectrum of people. These expanding horizons are stimulating increasingly diverse human-factors questions. Some of them will revise current assumptions and others will require novel solutions.

Until recently, for example, telephone applications could not process a caller's response until the prompt for that response had ended. The responses themselves had to be limited to the words specified by the prompt. These two limitations hampered the success of telephone-based recognition systems. The development of barge-in and *word spotting* (see chapter 4, sections 4.5 and 4.8) transformed the telephone into one of the most popular platforms for speech recognition.

The human-factors design features that will be needed for the systems of the future are, of course, unknown. Some discoveries will no doubt debunk assumptions that have been carried to speech from other modalities, such as touch-tone *interactive voice-response* (IVR) systems. Others will be the fruits of careful exploration of new vistas. Boitet & Loken-Kim (1993) discuss human-factors considerations for one new vista, speech-to-speech translation.

8.3 APPLICATIONS

Since the conclusion of the 1980's, there has been an explosion in the number and type of speech recognition applications being developed. In most instances, the technology is being used to accomplish one or more of the four basic functions shown in figure 8.1.

Function Name	Function Definition	Examples
Command-and-Control	Verbal control of equipment or software programs	Programming a VCR Controlling a wheelchair Navigating Windows
Data Entry	Voice Input of well-defined pieces of data into software programs	Performing a quality audit Completing a form Entering an order
Data Access/ Information Retrieval	Database query and other requests that search a database or other file for a specific piece of information	Banking by phone Getting directions Dialing a telephone (e.g., "call Mom")
Dictation	Creation of letters, reports and other documents	Dictating a letter Dictating a structured medical report

Figure 8.1   Application Functions

Command-and-control involves verbal control of any type of equipment. Command-and-control applications range from manipulating heavy mining equipment to navigating Microsoft *Windows*. *Data entry* uses speech to supply data to databases, quality audit systems, and other software. Before the end of the 1980's, most data entry applications were developed for manufacturing and military environments. Since then, its use has expanded dramatically and includes form completion, bedside charting in hospitals, and appointment scheduling. *Data access,* the newest speech recognition function, is most often used in telephone applications. *Dictation* systems convert the stream of speech into text for letters, reports, and other documents. Each of these functions is described below in terms of

- Design requirements
- Speaking environment
- Human factors
- Application examples

The examples were selected to illustrate points that are discussed in the other sections. They should not be construed as recommendations for specific products.

It is important to note that many applications use more than one of the functions listed in figure 8.1. *Windows* application interfaces are, for example, primarily command-and-control systems designed to manipulate menus and other objects in the Windows environment. Most of them are also capable of data entry and at least one has dictation capabilities. Similarly, dictation applications generally include a small list of command-and-control vocabulary to navigate the system. As consumer familiarity with speech recognition grows and as commercial applications become more diverse, the combination of functions within a single application will become more commonplace. For application developers, this will entail balancing several sets of speech, environment, and human factors issues.

8.3.1 Command-and-Control

Command-and-control of equipment involves the manipulation of computers, heavy machinery, and other machinery by voice. Battle management applications for military tanks, ships, and fighter jets were among the earliest research command-and-control applications developed. The first commercial command-and-control applications tended to be for manufacturing equipment control. More recently, command-and-control applications have migrated to other industries. The most widely known examples are for placing long-distance telephone calls in telecommunications and for controlling software, such as *Windows* and applications running under *Windows*. Applications in other industries include control of

• *Architecture*	Utilities in *smart* buildings
• *Automotive*	Windows, heaters, and other ancillary systems Car telephones
• *Consumer Products*	Toys, personal digital assistants (PDA's), VCR's
• *Design*	Screens and menus of computer-aided design (CAD) systems
• *Manufacturing*	Heavy equipment Manufacturing process control
• *Healthcare*	Radio microscopes in operating theaters
• *Military*	Map displays in airplane cockpits
• *Mining*	Heavy mining equipment in dangerous environments
• *Office Automation*	Form-completion software
• *People with Disabilities*	Wheelchairs, beds, and other equipment
• *Space Exploration*	TV monitors for robot repair-arms on the space shuttle
• *Telecommunications*	Dialing a telephone

Voice command-and-control is frequently used to operate support systems so that the user's hands are free to manipulate the primary equipment without interruption. This ability to maintain visual and manual focus on the primary task improves productivity, accuracy, and safety. During operation of a computer-aided design (CAD) system, for example, a designer can continue using the CAD design tool while issuing screen and menu navigation commands by voice. Military pilots can access visual displays, such as map readings, without moving their hands from the controls; and automobile drivers can dial car telephones while keeping their hands on the steering wheel and their eyes on the road.

Speech interfaces to computer software systems, such as Microsoft *Windows* or executive information systems (EIS), are often designed to enable computer novices to become productive more quickly. When applied to the operation of equipment in the individual's personal environment, speech allows people with severe physical disabilities to reduce their reliance on others.

8.3.1.1 Design issues of command-and-control.
1. Vocabulary size and selection

The vocabulary demands and structural complexity of command-and-control systems parallel the complexity of the equipment to be controlled. In many cases, the vocabulary size ranges from ten to fifty words. This limited vocabulary reflects the fact that there are usually a finite number of operations that a single piece of machinery can perform. Voice Powered Technology's *VCR Voice* product, for example, requires a vocabulary of fewer than seventy words to program VCR's. At the other end of the spectrum are military aircraft cockpits with their complicated array of flight control, battle management, and other sophisticated electronics. These cockpits have become so complex that researchers working on speech in the cockpit applications have estimated the vocabulary to range from 1,300 to 5,000 words. Vocabulary design for software application interfaces falls between these two extremes with multi-tasking systems and multi-featured applications requiring larger vocabularies.

One of the most difficult and tedious facets of designing a speech application is the identification of the application vocabulary. A partial solution has been developed for command-and-control of computer programs. Products such as Verbex' *Listen for Windows* contain tools capable of examining the code of a piece of software and extracting the vocabulary needed to control its screens and menus. Some *Windows* command-and-control products also offer tools allowing end users to create individual vocabulary items or personalized lists.

Outside the realm of graphically-oriented software, vocabulary development for command-and-control applications can be tricky. Most equipment control is performed manually through largely non-verbal activities. The application designer must identify simple verbal correlates to the manual operations. When the task is poorly understood by the user, as for example in programming VCR's, vocabulary and language structure design demand a human factors focus.

2. Translation (see chapter 3, section 3.3.2)

Since the verbal commands must be communicated to a piece of equipment, the translation is rarely text. Typically, it is a digital code or an electronic signal. The set of command signals that are meaningful to the equipment must be identified and the recognizer must convert the spoken input into a form that, at minimum, can be transformed quickly and efficiently into the correct signal pattern.

3. Language structure

The structure of a command-and-control application is defined by the equipment and is generally highly structured and filled with error-correction procedures. *Finite-state grammars* (see chapter 4, sections 4.2 and 4.6) or equivalent systems can control the sequencing of operations to insure that they correspond to the requirements of the machinery.

Keyword spotting is most often used for telephone applications. Unlike most command-and-control applications, telephone-based systems typically do not have experienced users. Their users tend to be large populations of one-time users whose responses to a speech recognition system are likely to be unpredictable. From the perspective of the users there appears to be no structure; keyword spotting permits callers to speak spontaneously, as long as they use one of the expected keywords.

Performance characteristics of some equipment present special communication challenges. One of the most difficult is the expression of movement. When the equipment is a PC or another device that allows multiple, simultaneous communication modalities, speech can be combined with other devices to provide a complete equipment control package. This multimedia approach allows each input modality to be used in ways that are suitable to its capabilities. In cases where speech is the sole command modality, it must accomplish all command-and-control tasks in a simple, natural fashion. Some developers have exploited the vagueness of language to overcome this problem.

In 1987, RCA designed a prototype system using voice control of cameras that monitor robot repair-arms of the NASA space shuttle. Their system contained vague, but effective, spatial modifiers like "a little" and "pan left" to control the extent and nature of camera movement. The translation for an expression like "a little" was a clearly-specified degree of camera movement, but the language was more natural for the astronauts than stating a numerical quantity.

4. Speaker model

In many command-and-control applications, the user population consists of one person or a small group of individuals. As a result, speaker-dependent recognition is often used to enhance accuracy and to help acclimate users to the system's vocabulary and grammar.

Speaker dependence can be counter-productive for applications designed for ease of use. This is particularly true for computer application interfaces. These systems are likely to possess larger vocabularies that would be annoying to train. The demands of enrollment frustrate the goal to make computer use simpler, faster, and easier. Realization of these linguistic and human factors features of computer application interfaces has caused some vendors to select speaker-adaptive or speaker-independent modeling.

Telephone applications generally use speaker-independent technology. Until 1993, that meant that the vocabularies of those systems needed to remain small (see chapter 5, sections 5.3.1 and 5.8.2). The introduction of subword modeling has freed these applications from such constrictive vocabulary, but the recognition accuracy for words created using subword modeling is still poorer than for words created from large numbers of samples. As a result, vocabulary must be selected carefully to avoid confusable words.

5. Speech flow

Most command-and-control systems are characterized by short bursts of speech representing a single command. This allows the use of discrete-word recognition or continuous speech recognition. Other factors, such as robustness in noise, play a significant role in the selection of speech flow.

In telephone applications, users input continuous speech but the recognition is of individual words and short phrases.

8.3.1.2 Speaking environment of command-and-control. Many
command-and-control applications are characterized by high noise. Noise characteristics vary greatly with the application:

- A dialing system for car telephones must contend with a noisy input channel, automobile noise, reverberation, radios, road noise, and the Lombard effect produced by the noisy environment.

- A toy with speech recognition is likely to be bombarded with the background voices and sounds of children at play. It may even contribute its own voice and machine noises to the environment. The speaker is likely to be inattentive to microphone placement as well.

- A piece of equipment in a factory will be surrounded by the roar of other equipment. The environment may also contribute intermittent crashes and shouted conversations among co-workers.

Despite such poor speaking environments for many command-and-control applications, accuracy is a priority. Products must be tested to ascertain they will perform well in their designated environments. They must also possess adequate error correction procedures when they fail to overcome the noise.

8.3.1.3 Human factors of command-and-control. Many people who
use command-and-control applications view speech recognition as a facet of the machine they are operating. For them, the role of speech is to translate verbal commands directly into action. There is often little tolerance of error and no patience for slow throughput or inefficiency.

Command-and-control systems must be simple and easy to use and must possess vocabulary that is easy to remember and access. Environment control systems for people with disabilities require tailoring to the needs of each individual. For people with severe speech problems this may require careful selection of vocabulary to enhance word differentiation within the capabilities of the individual. It may be necessary to incorporate more extensive enrollment, although the sessions may need to be very short. Systems may need to adapt to slower production of words and the presence of pauses within words. This may mean that the definition of word boundaries needs to include longer silences.

Speech command-and-control may be used as an argument for downsizing: If a single individual can control more machinery through the use of speech, it is unnecessary to retain a large staff for the task. Implementing such staff reductions in favor of automation should be done with attention to human factors considerations, such as safety and the number of operations a single worker will be asked to perform.

8.3.1.4 Examples of command-and-control.   The following examples represent three different types of command-and-control applications. The AT&T and NASA systems illustrate the importance of careful testing, even for simple applications containing seemingly clear instructions. Additional examples of command-and-control systems are described in chapter 9. They include computer software interfaces (section 9.1), systems for people with disabilities (section 9.4), call management (section 9.6.3), and consumer products (section 9.8).

1. Long distance calling. AT&T

One of the goals of using speech recognition for traditional operator-assisted services is to offer a high level of service 24-hours a day that is cost-effective for both peak and low calling periods. To assess the human factors challenge of implementing such a system for long distance calls, AT&T Bell Laboratories identified four calling conditions and one escape condition. To minimize errors, the call conditions were assigned acoustically distinct caller response words/phrases:

CALLING CONDITION	CALLER RESPONSE
collect	collect
calling card	calling card
third-party billing	third number
person-to-person	person
operator	operator

The list of options was introduced with a simple prompt, "This is AT&T. Please say. . . " The initial design used speaker-independent, discrete-word recognition. It was subjected to a field test consisting of approximately seventy-five thousand calls. They found that

> It is extremely difficult, if not impossible, to get real-world subscribers to such a service to speak only the allowable input words (Jay Wilpon, Lawrence Rabiner, Chin-Hui Lee & E.R. Goldman, Researchers, AT&T Bell Laboratories, "Automatic recognition of keywords in unconstrained speech using hidden Markov models," 1990, p. 1870).

In fact, only 65 percent of all callers followed the specified protocol. Almost 20 percent of the callers added extraneous speech to their responses (e.g., "I want to make a collect call, please."). The dilemma embodied in the outcome of the Bell Laboratories' study was whether to abandon one-time user applications or create an impossibly complex grammar for a simple task. Recognizing that the use of extraneous speech would be a common and unavoidable problem facing applications designed for telephones, they decided to implement the system using keyword spotting. The final system, the *Voice Recognition Call Processing (VRCP)* contains models of the keywords, silence, transmission noises, and extraneous speech. Non-keyword models were originally constructed from speech taken from the field tests, making certain that frequently used extraneous speech was adequately represented. More recently, the models of extraneous speech were recreated using detailed, higher order acoustic analysis of generic speech patterns taken from speech databases.

The *VRCP* system is also referenced in chapters 4 (section 4.5) and 9 (section 9.2.1), and described in Wilpon & Rabiner (1985). Another telecommunications command-and-control system is described by Lennig (1989).

2. Voice control for people with disabilities. Montefiore Hospital

The *Voice Activated Robotic Retrofit System (VARRS)* is a prototype that enables a bed-bound individual to control bed position by voice. The system was designed to be used by elderly, vision-impaired, or paralyzed individuals who are unable to use manual controls.

> The inability of these patients to perform simple readjustments of the head or foot positions of the bed causes feelings of decreased independence and unnecessarily burdens the nursing staff and ancillary personnel (Marc Liang, MD & Krishna Narayanan, MD, Montefiore Hospital, "The application of voice recognition to robotic positioning of a hospital bed," 1989, p. 31).

VARRS contains a small vocabulary including one password, two bed-part words (head and foot), five directional terms (up, down, tilt, backward, and forward) and three programmed bed positions (television, eating, and reading). Human factors considerations prompted the use of speaker-dependent training and a password as a means of preventing the bed from responding to other voices. The bed responds only to the voice of the patient issuing commands that are immediately preceded by a special password. There is also a fail-safe command that stops bed movement within one-thousandth of a second after it is issued. The fail-safe command was included as a backup measure in the event of misrecognition.

Since the *VARRS* system was designed, other controls for hospital beds have been developed. One of them, Hill-Rom's *Enhancemate*, is described in chapter 9 (section 9.4.2).

3. Control of closed circuit television cameras. NASA Jet Propulsion Laboratory

Voice control of equipment on space-borne vehicles enables astronauts to perform multiple complex operations simultaneously. One such operation is the control of the closed circuit television cameras that monitor the operation of the space shuttle's robot repair-arms. A single astronaut must operate the repair-arms and the cameras simultaneously. The Jet Propulsion Laboratory and Lockheed designed a voice system, called the *VCS*, to do command-and-control of the closed circuit cameras. It flew in a field test on the *Orbiter Discovery* shuttle in October, 1990.

Thirty-three of the forty-one command words selected for the speech system parallel the switch control functions of the manually-operated camera-control unit. They select and operate cameras, activate video recording by a camera, and store the cameras. The remaining words are log-in identifications and special speed and distance commands, such as "more," "too much," and "easy." The speed and distance vocabulary added flexibility to the control of spatial movement and gave the astronauts a means of compensating for recognition errors. Speaker-dependent recognition was used and carefully trained during several pre-flight sessions. Training was done in an environment that simulated the noise conditions of the shuttle so that the speaker models would contain the proper background noise (see chapter 7, section 7.6.1).

> Throughout the training session, the primary objectives were to familiarize the crew members with the technology and operation of the *VCS* and to extract a good set of templates that would be used in flight (George Salazar, Project manager, NASA Lyndon B. Johnson Space Center & Marc Sommers, Project Engineer, Lockheed Engineering & Sciences Company, "Space shuttle voice recognition flight experiment," 1991, p. 14).

Training was followed by three separate simulated flight tests designed to correct recognition errors and upgrade problem templates. Prior to the field test on the shuttle, recognition performed at or near one hundred percent for each of the astronauts. Recognition during the flight revealed a need to incorporate automatic gain control into the VCS to compensate for variability in the loudness of the input.

A similar system was developed at GE/RCA's Advanced Technology Laboratory and is described in Hackenberg (1987) and mentioned in section 8.3.1.2.

8.3.2 Data Entry

Data entry by speech involves verbal input of data directly to computer systems that process the data. Until the end of the 1980's, data entry applications were the staple of commercial speech recognition systems. Most early applications were created for branches of the military, factories, and warehouses. All of these customers were attracted to speech recognition because it allows hands-free data input.

Towards the end of the 1980's, the use of speech recognition as a data entry tool began to expand to other industries and functions:

• *Construction*	Entering data about the site
• *Dentistry*	Recording routine examinations
• *Education*	Multimedia computer-aided instruction
• *Engineering Design*	Entering manufacturing materials requirements
• *Finance*	Entering securities trades
• *Government*	Meter readers collecting meter data
	Forest rangers examining trees
• *Healthcare*	Patients scheduling appointments
	Bedside charting
	Pharmacists entering prescriptions
	Laboratory technicians analyzing slides and samples
• *Hotels/Motels*	Employee check-in for time-and-attendance recording
• *Insurance*	Inspecting damaged property
• *Office systems*	Forms completion
• *Package Delivery*	Sorting packages
• *Retail*	Documenting information on returned merchandise
• *Telephone Repair*	Personnel atop telephone poles checking phone lines

Data entry by voice has been called the *hands-busy, eyes-busy* function because it allows workers to continue to perform manual tasks while they verbally enter the data.

Because it takes a significant amount of time for an operator to take his or her eyes away from the microscope and refocus to record data on paper, the use of voice recognition can increase throughput considerably. It also decreases the incidence of eye-strain and headaches among operators (Rick Cook, Staff Writer, *Managing Automation*, "Voice recognition: Time for another look?" 1990).

Speech recognition is the only input modality that allows users to keep their eyes, hands, and minds on the tasks they are performing while they are entering data.

In manufacturing and warehousing applications, speech can be combined with other technologies to capture information these technologies miss. The hands-free nature of speech recognition does not interfere with the use of manually-operated devices required by other forms of data input. Bar coding, for example, is the most efficient means of capturing coded information about an item. It cannot record situational information, such as the condition of the materials when they arrive at a receiving dock, where they were sent within a facility, or the type of palette used to ship them. Combining speech recognition with bar coding makes it possible to gather such information, and even facilitates the generation of bar codes for items lacking them.

8.3.2.1 Design issues of data entry.

1. Vocabulary size and selection

Traditional data entry applications were characterized by vocabularies of fewer than fifty words. With the recent growth in the vocabulary capabilities of speech recognition technology, developers have discovered that tasks involving small-vocabulary input constitute only one segment of potential data-entry applications.

In most cases, vocabulary requirements include standard items (digits, *yes, no, cancel*) and application-specific terminology. Often, the largest portion of the vocabulary is unique to a single application. Consequently, most products with built-in dictionaries will not satisfy the vocabulary needs of the application. These are the conditions that argue for selection of a product with vocabulary-development tools.

2. Translation (see chapter 3, section 3.3.2)

Data entry applications often have special translation requirements. Frequently, the desired output of recognition is not a standard textual representation of the words that have been input. A database of defects, for example, may represent the phrase "scratched paint" as the code F435. Eastman Kodak's steam trap maintenance system (see section 8.3.2.4) exemplifies some of the problems that might occur when a speech system must communicate directly with mainframe software.

Single words or phrases may be used to replace complex keyboard commands, to consolidate sequences of mouse clicks into a single word or phrase, or to standardize spelling. Such concerns may even be the driving forces behind the creation of a voice-activated system. One American truck manufacturer, for example, could not perform accurate quality control analysis on production line defects because keypunched data contained variable spellings for identical defects. Although the same front-brake defect might be discovered in a series of trucks, it might be entered as "front brakes," "fr brks," "brakes, front," and "fr. brk" causing the statistical analysis to identify four distinct types of defect. Speech recognition, touch screen, and mouse input all eliminated this problem by maintaining a one-to-one correspondence between input and translation. Speech recognition is the only one of those technologies that does not become extremely cumbersome as the vocabulary increases.

3. Language structure

Most data entry applications are highly structured and are best represented using finite-state grammars or an equivalent. The use of structure provides two benefits that are important in most data entry applications: enhanced accuracy and speedier processing. These benefits derive from reducing perplexity (see chapter 4, sections 4.1 and 4.10). Accuracy and speed both increase as the number of words in the active vocabulary declines. Accuracy also improves as the words in an active vocabulary become more differentiated.

4. Speaker model

For small vocabulary data entry applications there is a speaker-modeling trade-off between accuracy and ease of use. Speaker-dependent modeling, which tunes recognition to the speech patterns of each user, enhances accuracy. Enrollment can be annoying, even when it is be partitioned into several sessions. Speaker-independent models are easy to use but are less accurate because they are not tuned to the speaker and may not contain adequate representation of the speaking environment.

As the vocabularies of these applications grow, it becomes more difficult to entice users into extensive enrollment programs. Speaker-independent systems and speaker adaptive systems with *on-the-fly* adaptation can be substituted when field testing demonstrates they are capable of performing acceptably well in the speaking environment.

5. Speech flow

As with command-and-control systems, data entry applications are characterized by short bursts of speech. The choice between continuous speech and discrete-word recognition depends largely upon other factors, such as the noise in the environment. As a group, continuous speech systems tend to have better noise immunity than discrete-word systems. The quality varies greatly with the product, vocabulary, users, and environment (also see item 5. of section 8.3.1.1).

8.3.2.2 Speaking environment of data entry.

Many data entry application environments are harsh. They contain physical irritants (such as dirt, temperature extremes, accidents, and vibration) that are capable of destroying computing equipment. One manufacturer whose employees refused to use plastic-covered keyboards, was forced to replace its equipment every two to three months.

These conditions argue for the use of factory-hardened equipment or radio-frequency transmission. Radio-frequency transmission allows the computer hardware to be placed in a safer, cleaner area. It also affords greater mobility to users who may need to move around objects during inspection or analysis. Radio-frequency transmission, however, may encounter interference from other transmission frequencies in the environment.

Some products are designed specifically for high-noise speaking environments. They contain special noise-handling algorithms. Although the ability of speaker-independent models to handle noise is increasing, many of the products designed for high-noise and high-stress environments are speaker-dependent. Speaker-dependent technology is more accurate in high noise because they can model the speaker, the background noise, and the Lombard effect more closely.

All products should be tested in the targeted application environment to assess their ability to perform under the anticipated noise conditions. This is particularly important in high-noise environments and for portable systems. Applications requiring portable/wearable systems generally involve a broader variety of speaking environments, including the outdoors.

8.3.2.3 Human factors of data entry. The people who use traditional data entry applications on manufacturing production lines, in warehouses, and on receiving docks are rarely experienced computer users. They may be uncomfortable with computing equipment. Acceptance can be increased by formulating an interface that possesses familiar components. If, for example, the task involves completion of a familiar form, user comfort can be enhanced by designing the screen to resemble the form. This type of presentation emphasizes the goal of the data entry task. Similarly, a quality audit or production line inspection application can be structured to conform to familiar forms, even when the items on the form are replaced by prompts spoken to the user.

Defining the use of the application and the role of speech recognition in terms of the goals of the task helps establish a positive attitude prior to implementation of the system. If that preparation comes from supervisors and other members of their group, the users' acceptance of the system will probably be greater. Participation of members of the user population in the design of the application helps to address human factors, user acceptance, and task completion issues. Users, for example, may prefer a specific microphone configuration or may have well-established task-operation patterns.

Many data entry applications require speech prompting to the user through speech synthesis or digitized recorded speech. The functions of the prompting are to request specific pieces of data and to verify recognized input. The quality and pitch of those prompts needs to be clearly differentiated from the background noise and must be acceptable to the users. Their verbosity and rate of speech need to match the demands of the task and the experience of the user with the system. Production lines may demand a quick pace, but bedside charting may not. If there are both novice and expert users, two or more interface levels reflecting the skills of the different groups of users may need to be created. The KorTeam bedside charting system is an example of a system with multiple interfaces.

Applications using screen output need to provide clear visual prompts adapted to the lighting, distance between the user and the screen, and other visual factors of the speaking environment. Screens structured like forms should highlight the current position clearly and offer easy navigation tools for error correction or revision.

In manufacturing and warehousing applications, users are often mobile. They cannot be tethered to a piece of equipment unless it is carried on their person. It may also be necessary to incorporate the microphone into face or head protection equipment.

8.3.2.4 Examples of data entry.   These examples illustrate the diversity of data entry applications. Additional data entry applications are discussed in chapter 9. They include systems for manufacturing (section 9.5) and finance (section 9.7).

1. Steam trap maintenance. Eastman Kodak Company

Steam traps are components of steam heating systems. They help drain condensed water out of the heating system and trap steam so that energy is not wasted. When a steam trap fails, it allows condensation to build and reduces heating efficiency. In a factory, the steam traps must be kept fully operational or they will result in lost production.

Eastman Kodak implemented speech recognition in its steam trap maintenance process:

> Mechanics worked in teams. Typically, one mechanic did all of the testing while the other recorded the results and helped with moving the equipment. Frequently, ladders or lifts are required to reach the traps.
>
> The primary purpose of introducing handheld voice computers is to allow the mechanics to work independently without pencil and paper. The voice data input allows mechanics to have their hands free to use their equipment while entering data. Another major benefit is eliminating the clerical key punching work (Lonnie Rood & John Lewis, Eastman Kodak Company, "Integrated voice data system for central steam trap maintenance," 1991, p. 94).

In short, they sought better utilization of personnel, hands-free data entry, and speedy updating of maintenance databases.

To address these issues they implemented a wearable speech recognition system and moved quickly from design to implementation. The system satisfied the stated goals. It also allowed maintenance workers freedom of movement, while its digitized voice prompts eliminated the need to consult a screen during data entry. As a result, data became eyes-free as well as hands-free.

Kodak encountered several problems that are typical of manufacturing applications. Background noise ranged from minimal to extremely loud and forced several microphone modifications after the system had been fielded. Wires linking the headset with the speech unit were too fragile for the manufacturing environment, forcing the maintenance engineers themselves to develop protective covers for the wiring. The maintenance engineers were uncomfortable with computers and several user-interface modifications were made to increase their comfort level. Finally, the mainframe database used to store the maintenance data was not designed to accept PC input. To resolve the last problem the designers implemented a software "robot" to read the PC speech file and generate simulated keyboard input to the mainframe.

2. Bedside charting. KorTeam International

There is growing pressure on the healthcare industry to improve documentation of patient treatment and to provide that documentation more expeditiously. This has stimulated a trend towards greater automation in the industry as a whole. Using survey and other marketing research techniques, KorTeam International determined that one means of satisfying some demands for better documentation was to design a computerized bedside charting system. The healthcare professionals they surveyed agreed but recommended that such a system be hands-free. They wished to minimize intrusion into the hands-busy, eyes-busy patient examination procedures and caregiving processes. The only solution was to use speech recognition.

Before selecting a product, KorTeam created a list of requirements based upon

- The requirements of the bedside charting task
- Characteristics of the users
- The conditions under which medical professionals would be operating the system

They also investigated the requirements for microphone selection, taking into consideration personal preference, response, and unobtrusiveness. The user interface they developed is menu-driven and runs on a PC under Microsoft *Windows*. It displays an image of the form being completed. The use of the actual form images required the development of special tools to add, delete, or change forms, because forms need to be modified periodically by the users. The interface was designed to meet the needs of four groups of users who are defined by experience with computers and experience in healthcare. Their careful design plan has lengthened the time between the conception of the application and its implementation as the *ChartWell* bedside charting system. At the same time, it has already enhanced user comfort with and acceptance of the system and has increased the likelihood the application will be a success.

3. Worker's Compensation reserving. Navistar International

Reserving is a means of maintaining a balance of funds that will adequately cover the costs of a company's Worker's Compensation claims. It entails a complex estimate based upon the factors of each claim. After eighteen years, Navistar's Worker's Compensation reserving expert was going to retire and no one could replace him.

The solution was to develop an artificial intelligence system (called an *expert system*) that would encode the decision-making logic used by the reserving expert. Speech recognition was included in the design because clerks who would use the expert system expressed discomfort with using a PC. They found speech to be more natural and comfortable than other input modalities. To facilitate ease of use, vocabulary development and user-interface design became a standard component of the expert system's knowledge gathering sessions.

A prototype of the speech-controlled *Worker's Compensation Reserving Advisor* was tested with the expert and the system users. Experiencing the prototype eased users' discomfort and allowed them to offer suggestions, such as including a simple voice-driven password system. They confirmed the accuracy of the system, the appropriateness of the vocabulary, and the importance of the speech interface:

I wouldn't use it without the speech (Ray Skarzynski, Manager, Worker's Compensation Department, Navistar International, personal communication, 1988).

8.3.3 Data Access

Data access (also called *information retrieval* and *information access*) is a relatively new function of speech recognition. Its purpose is to retrieve information from an on-line source, usually a database. The role of speech is to instruct the application regarding the data to be accessed. The earliest implementations were telephone banking applications that extended existing touch-tone applications to callers with rotary-dial telephones.

The number of data access applications is growing rapidly and now includes

• *Automotive*	Navigation tools for metropolitan areas
• *Banking*	Owners accessing personal bank account information
• *Consumer Products*	Use of personal data assistants (PDA's)
• *Customer Service*	Placing orders over the telephone
• *Equipment Repair*	Personnel accessing repair data in manuals
• *Finance*	Brokers accessing financial market data
• *Law*	Researching cases using on-line legal databases
• *Law Enforcement*	Highway police accessing driver's license database
• *Office systems*	Computer-telephone integration
• *Not-For-Profit*	Providing announcements and information to members
• *Retail*	Supplying payroll information to store managers
• *Telecommunications*	Accessing directory assistance Dialing telephones by naming the party to be called
• *Tourism*	Tourists browsing databases describing travel options

One popular data access application is voice activated dialing using the name of the person to be called. Unlike command-and-control dialing which converts the digits of the telephone number into telecommunications signals, dial-by-name expects users to enter a pre-defined name or other identifier (e.g., "call office"). The process is:

1. The speech is recognized by a speech recognition system
2. The recognized pattern is looked-up in a database table
3. The telephone number associated with the spoken pattern is accessed
4. The number is dialed

Most data access applications have simple objectives: dial a telephone; report bank account status; display a single piece of information. Newer applications, such as Amerigon's *AudioNav* (see chapter 9, section 9.8) and West Publishing's *LawTalk for WESTLAW* (see section 9.6.2) expect more complex interactions involving larger vocabularies.

Speech recognition is a way of extending existing touch-tone data-access telephone services to customers with rotary dial telephones. It is particularly useful in rural areas of the United States and overseas. As with the touch-tone services, the speech recognition system can provide services 24-hours a day.

8.3.3.1 Design issues of data access.

1. Vocabulary size and selection

Most existing data access applications have small vocabularies consisting of a few, highly differentiated keywords. The vocabulary requirements of data access applications will grow as these applications incorporate more extensive access of information from large databases and as they expand into full-text information retrieval. Even a relatively simple database query, like

List all the bolts for which our warehouse inventory count is less than 500

requires vocabulary covering the names of accessible database fields and for the contents of those fields. Applications of this sort are difficult to develop, but they are extremely useful for organizations whose employees need to access data but do not wish to learn how to construct database queries using Standard Query Language (SQL). The use of large vocabulary speech input to formulate natural queries makes it possible for professionals unfamiliar with SQL or Boolean query formulation to access the necessary information when they need it.

2. Translation

A primary objective of some data access systems is to replace complex or obscure patterns of keyboard keystrokes with a more natural form of input. The following SQL code corresponds to the verbal query "List all the bolts with a warehouse inventory of less than 500:"

```
SELECT TABLE1 ITEM_NUMBER, TABLE2 OH_BALANCE FROM MATERIALS_TABLE
TABLE1,    WAREHOUSE_TABLE    TABLE2    WHERE    TABLE1.ITEM_NUMBER =
TABLE2.ITEM_NUMBER    AND    TABLE2.OH_BALANCE    <    500    AND
TABLE1.ITEM_TYPE = 'BOLT'
```

Compare the following requests for a quarterly history of the Coca Cola Company as they are made to a widely-used trading-floor information system:

KEYBOARD	SPEECH
ko 83 q	Coca Cola history

In each instance speech eliminates the need for users to learn a potentially confusing data access system.

3. Language structure

Voice activated dialing and other data access applications that are designed to be used by a small group of people are implemented using finite-state grammars (see chapter 4, sections 4.2 and 4.6) or their equivalents. Telephone applications with large populations of one-time users rely on keyword spotting (see chapter 4, sections 4.5 and 4.8). In many cases these applications assume the prompt-and-response patterns characteristic of interactive voice response (IVR) systems. The user supplies a single word or phrase in response to a list of options (see section 8.3.5).

A statistical language model (see chapter 4, section 4.3) is needed for full-text information retrieval. The *LawTalk for WESTLAW* system uses the bigram model of *DragonDictate* combined with *WIN*, West's natural language query system. *WIN* analyzes the recognized input and converts it into SQL queries.

4. Speaker model

The selection of a speaker model depends upon the nature and size of the user population. Systems designed for widespread use incorporate speaker-independent technology (see section 8.3.5). A voice dialing system embedded in a single telephone or linked to the telephones of a single household are speaker-dependent. The use of speaker-dependent technology increases the accuracy of the system and allows the users to personalize the system by creating personal dial-by-name speed-dialing entries. The large vocabulary *LawTalk for WESTLAW* system is speaker adaptive because the people who will use the system will use it repeatedly. Speaker adaptation enhances accuracy by tailoring the recognition to the voice of a user. This facilitates discrimination among large numbers of word candidates.

5. Speech flow

The speech flow most suitable for data access is continuous speech used in conjunction with word spotting. Continuous or discrete-word recognition can be used, if the user population is not likely to utter extraneous speech.

8.3.3.2 Speaking environment of data access. The most common speaking environment is the public telephone. The use of the telephone for speech recognition applications is discussed in section 8.3.5.

Desktop applications usually presume an office environment. Offices are characterized by intermittent noise (such as a ringing telephone) and background speech (see chapter 7, section 7.1.2). In contrast, consumer products have ill-defined speaking environments, but their design should presume the worst: both loud, erratic noise and background speech (see chapter 7, section 7.6). Amerigon's *AudioNav* is designed for one of the worst speaking environments: the automobile (see chapter 7, section 7.10).

8.3.3.3 Human factors of data access. Since many data access applications are created for the telephone, the human factors issues correspond to those for other telephone applications (see section 8.3.5). Human factors issues for consumer product applications are still poorly understood. Car navigation and other systems designed to provide directions need to conform to accepted dialogue patterns and rituals of the task. This includes the manner in which instructions are provided, the handling of human errors, and the formulation of instructions to make them more easily understood.

8.3.3.4 Examples of data access.   The following are examples of typical data access systems. The Sprint/Texas Instruments application illustrates the use of Wizard of Oz (see section 8.2.3) testing in an iterative design approach. Other data access systems are described in chapter 9. They include products for manufacturing (see section 9.5), law (see section 9.6.2), and consumer products (see section 9.8).

1. Banking by telephone. National Westminster Bank P.I.C. London, England
The ease and convenience of using the telephone has produced an expanding home banking industry. The widespread use of touch-tone dialing technology fostered the growth of telephone banking, but touch-tone penetration in countries outside North America remains low. Overseas, the convenience of telephone banking depends on speech recognition.

National Westminster Bank's *ActionLine* typifies these applications. Its primary goal was customer convenience. Functionally, *ActionLine* combines command-and-control for funds transfer with data access of account information.

The system requires a hardware network configuration consisting of

- Several PC-based speech systems
- A host database containing account information
- A backup telephone located at a help desk

Each speech system is capable of simultaneously handling up to sixteen incoming calls. The host contains the needed account information and can respond to the user's fund transfer commands. The help desk provides a human backup for the system. All equipment is connected to a bank-internal digital network.

Human factors considerations ranged from identifying the type of customer who would be interested in using the system to details of interface design: selection of the kind of voice to be used in the prompts, the wording and length of prompts and re-prompts, and determining how a machine could communicate bad news about an account.

> We would have to learn to use a machine to tell a customer in an acceptable manner that he or she was overdrawn, or worse, that he or she was not entering valid data . . . For example, it is perfectly acceptable for one human to say "pardon" to another, but it is not particularly acceptable for machines to deal with the same situation in that way (Geoff Hammond, Information Technology Manager, Telephone Banking Project, National Westminster Bank, "Deploying speech technology in telephone banking services," 1990, p. 31).

Pilot testing was done at a single site with bank customers matching the profile of expected system users. Then the final system was deployed. Since its initial implementation, *ActionLine* has realized the expected convenience benefit for customers and has reduced costs by replacing handling of paper documents with cheaper electronic processing.

2. Voice dialing. Sprint & Texas Instruments

The Sprint *Voice FONCARD* (also see chapter 9, section 9.2.2) was originally designed as a means of reducing calling card fraud, but it evolved into an attractive service option for its subscribers.

> The initial interest in the technology was a way of building a security device that would help eliminate fraud. Upfront verification is important to us, but what we have learned is that security may not be the biggest focus for this technology. It is ease of use (Tommye Wealand, Director, Strategic Planning Research, Sprint, personal communication, 1994).

Such a system needed to combine speaker verification, speech recognition, and increased functionality based upon speech input. Several years of work were devoted to defining and developing a suitable design.

The design process was based upon iterative development and testing. A core component of that process was focused Wizard of Oz testing (see section 8.2.3). Facets of the interface, such as password input, were tested independently with callers using public telephone lines. This testing determined, for example, that callers liked the voice dialing by name (such as "Call my accountant") and that ease of use was greatly enhanced when passwords consisted of familiar numbers or word patterns. Further testing led the developers to shorten the interaction by consolidating *speaker verification* (see chapter 5, section 5.5) with speaker-independent digit recognition, optimization of prompts, and acceptance of both touch-tone and speech input.

> Both from a traditional human factors perspective and from a market research perspective, this may seem rather laborious and requiring a lot of effort. But given that ease of use has become an important determinant of market success, there was a need to optimize our research methodology. Thorough testing of this kind has been one of the factors contributing to the positive customer response to *Voice FONCARD* (Gerhard Deffner of Texas Instruments, Linda Jo Black of Sprint, & Mark Ollmann of Texas Instruments, "Wizard of Oz market testing of spoken command interface style," 1994, p. 128).

8.3.4 Dictation

One of the ultimate goals of speech recognition is to create a human-like listening typewriter. Technological advances in the late 1980's brought that goal closer to reality with the emergence of commercial, large vocabulary dictation products. The developers of these products have identified two major classes of users:

- Business, healthcare, and legal professionals with extensive document-generation needs

- People with disabilities who have professional and/or personal dictation needs

The use of speech recognition for report generation speeds the movement of information to organizations and computer systems that need it. This is particularly important in healthcare, where the faster documentation is submitted to insurance companies, Medicare, Medicaid, and patients, the faster payment is received.

In the legal profession, computer-based document creation systems (called *document assembly*) have existed for several years. They are recognized as an easy, efficient method of generating standard documents, such as wills and certain types of contracts. Structured dictation of reports is an extension of this capability. The use of macro-like *trigger words* (also see chapter 9, section 9.6.1) that cause large blocks of text to be placed in a document is much faster than typing the entire document word by word. This benefit can be extended to general business functions and some highly regulated industries that need to submit periodic reports to various government agencies.

Professionals with repetitive stress syndrome (RSI), motor-disabilities, and visual impairments view speech recognition as a means of liberating them from dependence on other people. Hands-free dictation allows them to create business and personal documents. Dictation systems are used to a lesser extent by hearing impaired people to follow courtroom proceedings and other primarily oral activities. Janet Baker (1994) provides additional information on dictation.

8.3.4.1 Design issues of dictation.
1. Vocabulary size and selection
The vocabulary of a dictation application can be partitioned into four types:

- Resident vocabulary
- User vocabulary
- Dictionary
- Active vocabulary

The *resident vocabulary* is the vocabulary that is loaded with an application. It contains all the words in that application. The *user vocabulary* may be distinct from the resident vocabulary of an application or it may be a component of it. Some products allow users to create new words that become a part of the application's resident vocabulary. These words can be accessed by additional users without further processing. Different products, however, store user-defined words in an individual user's file. Other speakers wanting to use these words must either define them for their own speaker files or import them. The *dictionary* is a backup resource for developers and/or application users. It is not loaded when an application is loaded, but it can be accessed when the developer and/or the user wishes to add a new word to the resident vocabulary. Most products will indicate whether a newly-defined entry is already in the backup dictionary. When a word is added to the application from the backup dictionary, it is as a speaker-independent dictionary baseform. The *active vocabulary* is a feature of the runtime operation of the system. It is the list of words that can occur next and is defined by the language model of the system. Chapter 3 describes all these terms in greater detail.

Effective dictation requires a very large, expandable vocabulary. In theory, the larger the resident vocabulary of an application the less likely the system is to encounter an unknown word. In reality, it is the appropriateness of the vocabulary that is critical. Whether the maximum resident vocabulary is twenty thousand or sixty thousand words, it must contain the words and phrases that are needed for the application. This is an important feature of an application because incorrect guesses for unknown words constitute the most frequent error produced by dictation systems. Methods for expanding the resident vocabulary vary with each product but generally require spelled input (typed or spoken). One of the goals of research in large vocabulary design is to automate the process of adding new words, but there are still no commercial systems that can automatically generate new vocabulary from spoken input alone. Until there are such systems, the responsibility of identifying and modeling the words and language of the application domain will continue to rest with the product designer or the application developer. Users will tolerate only a limited role in this area.

2. Translation

The translation of the spoken input is almost always converted to text. Most dictation systems allow the creation of trigger words that behave like macros. A trigger word can cause the generation of large blocks of formatted text and is part of the design of most report generation applications.

Most systems also contain a small set of command-and-control words that are used to navigate within the system or document and to perform common functions, such as adding new words. The character, number, and translations of these words are product dependent.

3. Language structure

Dictation systems require the highest degree of flexibility in their language structure; without it, free-form input is not possible. Therefore, finite-state grammars and other restricted methods of structuring are inappropriate. The most successful approach is statistical language modeling (see chapter 4, section 4.3). Finite-state grammars and comparable structures, however, are employed in *structured dictation*. Structured dictation (also called *report generation*) is replete with multiple choice and sentence completion items. In many ways structured dictation is more typical of data entry than of dictation. A good example of structured dictation is Kurzweil AI's *VoiceRAD* system (see chapter 9, section 9.6.1).

Some product designers have exploited the fact that language models are statistical in nature. They have included the ability to change models by exposing them to large quantities of text that contain language patterns that are typical of the documents which the system will be generating.

4. Speaker model

The ideal speaker model for a dictation system is speaker-independent. This requires a level of precision that is not yet available in speaker-independent models for very large vocabulary systems. Commercial products that offer speaker-independent models, such as Philips Dictation System's toolkit, clearly identify these models as secondary options and partition the models into male and female (or high-voice and low-voice) models.

Commercial dictation systems utilize *speaker adaptation* (see chapter 5, section 5.4). Speaker adaptation tunes the speaker-independent baseforms in the system to the idiosyncratic acoustics patterns of each user. These modifications can be achieved in a number of ways, but the most common are *rapid enrollment* and *on-the-fly* speaker adaptation (see chapter 5, section 5.4). Depending upon the system, words defined by individual users may remain speaker-dependent and be stored in the file of the speaker who created them, or they may be recast as baseforms and become part of the general resident vocabulary of the application.

People with impairments affecting speech, such as ALS, myasthenia gravis, or muscular dystrophy, are likely to have difficulty with dictation systems. Their speech patterns may be inconsistent and the pauses between words may be too long. On-the-fly speaker adaptation is helpful, but word differentiation by the speaker may not be sufficient for a dictation system to function properly.

5. Speech flow

Continuous speech is the most desirable speech flow for dictation and it is the goal towards which vendors of dictation systems are moving. In 1994, Philips Dictation Systems introduced the first commercial, continuous-speech dictation system. It is a toolkit for application developers.

Discrete-word recognition systems force the user to insert a momentary pause between words. These pauses eliminate two problems that contribute to the difficulty of continuous speech recognition: coarticulation effects and locating word boundaries (see chapter 6, sections 6.3.1 and 6.3.2). The result is greater speed and accuracy with less computing power. The shift from discrete-word recognition to continuous speech will be a by-product of the implementation of more powerful chips in PC's.

8.3.4.2 Speaking environment of dictation.   Many dictation systems are used in relatively quiet offices and laboratories. The background noise levels in these environments is low but consists primarily of background speech and intermittent noise (see chapter 7, section 7.1.2).

Dictation systems have been used with variable success in more difficult environments, notably hospital emergency rooms. Emergency rooms offer a tremendous challenge to any recognition system, because they can be quiet or filled with loud voices and noises and the stress on speakers can be very high. The emergency room, however, is characteristic of the speaking environments of future dictation systems as they begin to be embedded in consumer products.

8.3.4.3 Human factors of dictation.   A major source of difficulty derives from the erroneous expectation that dictation with speech recognition will be comparable to using a human transcriptionist. Dictation systems currently represent the most advanced form of commercial speech recognition technology, but they do not perform like human listeners or skilled transcriptionists. An application will fail if users are allowed to retain unrealistic expectations about its capabilities. Consequently, matching the tool and the application design to the user population is critical for the success of the application.

Speakers who are accustomed to rapidly dictating a report that is corrected and transcribed by someone else consider speech recognition an imposition that makes their work more difficult. They chafe at having to adjust to

- Expending time for rapid enrollment
- Pausing between words when they speak
- Verifying the accuracy of the recognized text
- Performing editing functions normally provided by transcriptionists

Systems that can be structured to permit a second person to edit the dictation may be more satisfactory, if they do not defeat the benefits of reducing administrative costs and speeding information to needed recipients.

Many users find discrete-word input annoying and unnatural, even when the pause is momentary. For these users, pausing is a stumbling block to acceptance. Others, including many people with disabilities who use these systems, find pausing between words to be a minor encumbrance compared with the benefits gained from using a speech recognition system (see section 5.3).

In dictation applications that involve more than one contributor, such as the creation of emergency-room reports, the loading and unloading of user models can be seen as demanding too much time. If a dictation system is desirable for other reasons, a developer can structure the application to allow contributions from different people to be generated independently and assembled later.

Dictation systems must possess user-friendly tools to validate recognition, correct errors, add words, and navigate the document. Most commercial products now offer these tools and have made them hands-free. The need for hands-free dictation is crucial to the usefulness of systems for people with disabilities. Companies who view people with disabilities as an important market have created hands-free products and more systems are adding these tools and features.

8.3.4.4 Examples of dictation.   The two systems described below represent different design and implementation strategies. Some facets of existing systems, such as *DragonDictate's* discrete-word recognition, will ultimately be superseded by more advanced technology, such as continuous speech recognition.

Most features depicted here represent design decisions based upon implementation goals.

1. DragonDictate. Dragon Systems

DragonDictate is designed for runtime generation of dictated documents. Adaptation, text editing, and vocabulary updates are performed at the same time by the person who is doing the dictation. Adaptation includes adaptation of acoustic models, language models, and background noise.

Although the system is being used by developers to create specialized dictation applications, the basic design of *DragonDictate* is as a turnkey speech-to-text dictation system that can be used immediately after it is installed. Speaker adaptation is done on-the-fly. Each discrete-word recognition event produces a ranked list of the words achieving the highest recognition scores. If the candidate with the best score is not the correct word, the speaker can select another word from the list by saying its number. If the word is not on the ranked list, it probably is not in *Dragon-Dictate's* sixty thousand word resident vocabulary. To add the word to the resident vocabulary, the speaker can verbally invoke a vocabulary-update function. The new entry can be typed using the computer keyboard or spelled verbally using the military alphabet in a hands-free mode. If the system locates the word in its backup dictionary, it will retrieve the dictionary's baseform model and add it to the application's resident vocabulary rather than adding the user's speaker-dependent model for the word. Other runtime editing activities and document navigation are available through the use of a small command-and-control vocabulary.

DragonDictate's language models are derived from statistical analysis of generic business documents. Customer organizations and application developers can adapt that language model by applying the system's optimization tools to large quantities of text representative of the documents the system will generate. The system is also capable of *personalizing* the language model through on-the-fly adaptation to the speaking style of a user.

2. The dictation application toolkit. Philips Dictation Systems

The object of the toolkit is to enable developers to create a range of speech processing applications. This accounts for the modular structure of the toolkit. Dictation applications can involve digital recording and playback only, or they can include speech recognition. The modular orientation is clearly present in the structure of speech recognition application design: speaker adaptation, dictation, recognition, and text editing tools are separate modules to facilitate integration into third-party software.

Although the system has speaker-independent models, users are encouraged to use the rapid enrollment procedure before using the recognition. Dictation is input via a continuous speech dictation system. The *SpeechNote* module stores the input as a high-fidelity digital recording. No runtime editing or other interaction with the system is needed. Later, when the *SpeechMagic* speech recognition module is invoked, it uses continuous speech recognition to convert the stored dictation into text. During the recognition process, *SpeechMagic* maintains a link between the recognized text and the original digitized recording. That link later facilitates editing of the recognized text by causing the computer cursor to move through the on-screen text in synchrony with playback of the dictation. The link is maintained after editing, enabling the application to identify words in the document that are not included in its vocabulary. The person editing the document marks the new words the application needs to add to its vocabulary.

The toolkit is designed for application developers and is not intended to be an end-user system. Developers use the *SpeechPro* module to build language models using large quantities of text that typify the documents the application will generate. Each language model is constructed from statistical analysis of the language patterns occurring in these documents. Application vocabularies contain a maximum of twenty-five thousand words taken from the training texts and from a three hundred thousand word backup dictionary.

8.3.5 Using the Telephone

The ability to use speech recognition over the telephone has been an industry goal for forty years, but it was not viable until the mid-1980's. Commercial success did not come until the beginning of the 1990's. Since then, the popularity of speech recognition over the telephone has continued to grow.

The popularity and success of telephone applications derives from several factors. Among these are the importance, familiarity, and ubiquity of the telephone as well as the existence of a long-established interaction paradigm: the prompt-and-response pattern. That paradigm was established for touch-tone interactive voice response (IVR) applications and has been imported to speech recognition applications. The prompt-and-response paradigm has achieved success, in part, because it is highly controlled. The level of control makes it easier to satisfy a caller's objective quickly and effectively.

The implementation of speech recognition over the telephone has assumed three basic configurations:

- *Network-level systems* Technology embedded in a public telephone network or residing in an *intelligent peripheral,* such as a minicomputer, linked to a public telephone network
- *PC systems* Software and/or firmware for PC's that can be used with private telephone networks; many of these systems are components of boards for PC's
- *Chip-level systems* Firmware on chips or chip sets

Telecommunications companies, like AT&T, Ameritech, and McCaw Cellular, first used speech recognition on their telephone networks for operator services and voice dialing. By 1994, network-level speech recognition was deployed as a fee-based service to businesses and residential customers (see chapter 9, section 9.2).

At the same time, PC-based applications were gaining a presence in business. One of the earliest applications was developed by InterVoice, an IVR provider. InterVoice's *Voice Dial* system was marketed to the banking industry as a method of extending telephone-banking services to customers with rotary-dial telephones. Soon other IVR companies began licensing speech recognition technology, integrating it into their IVR products, and embedding it in their PC boards. By 1992, more industries began integrating speech recognition into their private telephone networks (see chapter 9, section 9.6.3). Additional information on PC systems can be obtained from Foster & Schalk.

The use of chips and chip sets also began in the early 1990's and is part of the general hardware trend towards miniaturization. Chip-level systems allow the technology to be embedded into small telephone handsets and are still used primarily for voice dialing.

One of the most frequently cited reasons speech recognition is used by businesses is to extend service to customers with rotary dial telephones. Although touch-tone technology predominates in the United States, it is rarely used outside of North America. Typically, the customer service options that are extended resemble those already offered to customers with touch-tone technology. There are several situations which make the use of speech recognition for this purpose particularly beneficial:

- 24-hour and weekend service
- Service to overseas markets
- Backup service during peak calling hours

Customers with rotary dial telephones do not need to wait for business hours to access an organization only to find themselves waiting in a queue for service. Overflow calls can be handled automatically, even when a customer does not have a touch-tone telephone. Service levels of this sort represent a competitive advantage for businesses that have elected to use speech recognition. See chapter 9 (section 9.6.3) for examples of businesses using speech recognition for this purpose.

A second business reason for using speech recognition over the telephone is to reduce staffing costs for receptionists and answering services. It may be utilized, for example, by businesses interested in offering services to customers on a 24-hour basis without increasing staffing costs for evening and weekend service. An unusual example is the implementation of a speech system at K-Mart which allowed its employees access to information stored in corporate databases. Cost benefits accrued immediately.

Personal use of speech recognition over the telephone is largely centered around voice-activated dialing. It promotes safety in automobiles because it allows drivers to keep their eyes on the road and their hands on the steering wheel while dialing a car telephone. The use of speech recognition to dial car telephones may become a necessity in some states, notably California and Michigan, that have considered enacting laws requiring drivers to keep their hands on the steering wheel as they place calls.

8.3.5.1 Design issues of using the telephone.

1. Vocabulary size and selection

Until AT&T announced the incorporation of subword modeling in its *Conversant* system in 1993, commercial telephone applications were limited to very small vocabularies. Most had fewer than twenty words. The use of digits, "yes," "no," and a small selection of control words is still appropriate for some applications, but the introduction of subword modeling offers developers larger vocabulary options.

Subword modeling has liberated vocabulary development from labor-intensive sampling (see chapter 5, sections 5.3.1 and 5.3.2) and vocabulary development time is reduced from months to minutes. By 1994, subword modeling began to appear as a vocabulary design feature in other products.

Subword modeling also freed speech recognition from the touch-tone application model. The response options presented to callers can be much more meaningful. It is easier for callers to remember to say "clothing" to get the clothing department than "3" (see chapter 9, section 9.6.3), making the interaction simpler, faster, easier to understand, and more accurate.

By 1994, the *Conversant* system could be programmed to use a two thousand-word active vocabulary. An active vocabulary that large may be well beyond the needs of most prompt-and-response telephone applications, but it facilitates the creation of new types of applications. Even in the existing format, a larger active vocabulary makes it possible to include better coverage of synonyms and word variants (such as "yeah," "yep," "OK," "sure," and "alright."). It also expands the number of choices that can be presented in a list. Research at U S WEST has found that the number of options presented to a caller can be long if the caller can use barge-in (see section 8.2.2.1) when the desired option is mentioned. Longer lists are enhanced by subword modeling because the choices are more meaningful.

The use of subword modeling is double-edged. It increases the naturalness and flexibility of an application but recognition accuracy is poorer for vocabulary created using subword modeling than for vocabulary created by sampling. A developer, consequently, must be careful to maximize acoustic differences in the active vocabulary.

The English alphabet is an important vocabulary set for many telephone applications, but it is still rarely used. If alphabetic spelling is needed for an application, accurate recognition can be enhanced through careful design (see chapter 3, section 3.5.3). Implementation of the military alphabet is generally unsuitable for telephone applications because many applications expect one-time users and because virtually all telephone systems are designed to be used by an extremely demanding group of users: consumers.

2. Translation

Voice activated dialing is converted to touch-tone or pulse-tone signals. The translation of all other input depends entirely upon the nature and communication requirements of the application.

3. Language structure

The most commonly used language structure is the finite-state grammar (see chapter 4, section 4.2) or a comparable, highly structured technique. Developers specializing in telephone applications often call this structured approach *scripting*. Like other types of finite-state grammar development, scripting is concerned with the sequence of events that can occur in an application, but it places far greater emphasis on the design of good prompts (see chapter 4, introduction).

Another technique that is gaining popularity is word spotting (see chapter 4, section 4.5). Word spotting does not eliminate the need for scripting the application, but it removes the rigid language requirements placed upon the caller. One of the technologies that has contributed to the success of speech recognition over the telephone, it is particularly useful for diverse populations of speakers who will access an application once or rarely. Word spotting increases the probability that they will accomplish their goals, even if they do not restrict their utterances to the words or phrases requested in the prompts. Despite its increasing robustness, word spotting is not infallible and careful design of error correction and fallback procedures are needed to prevent recognition errors from taking a caller down a wrong path.

4. Speaker model

Some applications, such as voice dialing, can be speaker-dependent, but most telephone applications require speaker-independent recognition because they are designed for large populations of users.

A speaker-independent model should always be tested on a sample of the speakers who will use an application to make certain that their speech patterns are included in the model. Such testing is especially important when subword modeling has been used, because subwords may not be tuned to the specific speaker characteristics of the user population (see chapter 5, sections 5.5 and 5.8).

5. Speech flow

If the vocabulary is well defined but the behavior of the speaker population unpredictable, word spotting is a valid option. Applications that use word spotting expect the input to be continuous speech, but they scan the input for specific keywords.

Discrete-word and continuous speech recognition (not using word spotting) are also commonly used for digit-oriented input. Discrete-word systems may pace the input by inserting a tone or beep between words to enhance separation between words. It is slowly being supplanted by continuous speech input, which is faster and more natural.

8.3.5.2 Speaking environment of using the telephone.   Speech recognition systems for the telephone channel must be very robust. The bandwidth of the channel is narrow and the channel itself is noisy. Figure 8.2 displays the types of noise with which a speech recognition system must contend. The speech is uttered into a telephone surrounded by background noise that can

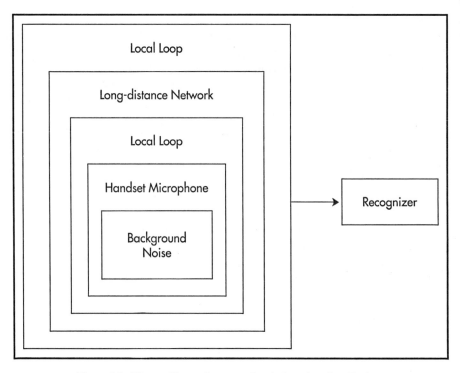

Figure 8.2   The speaking environment of a telephone-based application

range from virtual silence to a roar (see chapter 7, section 7.1.2). A recognition system has little preparation for the background noise surrounding the voice of a caller. The speech and background noise are transduced by a microphone with unknown attributes and quality. The microphone contributes its own noise as well as characteristic signal distortion patterns (see chapter 7, section 7.1.3). The transduced, modified signal is carried by a local *telephone loop* to the central office of the telephone company. The loop is part of the local telephone network. It introduces more noise into the signal. The impact of noise in the local loop varies from network to network and is influenced by the coding techniques employed, the age of the network components, maintenance, and other factors. If the call is placed to an outside calling area, it first traverses the local loop, then it enters the long distance network (or networks) where it confronts another set of noise and distortion characteristics, before it enters a second local telephone loop.

The situation is worse when the transmission is sent over a cellular telephone network. The transmission quality is generally poorer than for land-line telephones. In addition, the recognition system must contend with variable signal strength that may cause the voice to fade.

The best recognition is produced by chip-level systems that are embedded in telephone handsets. These systems are tuned to the microphone characteristics of the handset and do not experience added network noise because the recognition is performed in the telephone itself. Since chip-level, cellular telephone systems are often used in cars, they must be capable of handling the challenges of the automobile environment (see chapter 7, section 7.10), especially if they are left in their cradles and used like speaker-phones.

8.3.5.3 Human factors of using the telephone.

As with IVR using touch-tone input, the suitability of automated call processing must be compared with the needs of the callers. When call routing is complex, when callers frequently require more assistance than an automated system can offer, or when receptionists routinely provide information to callers, automation can create a perception of poorer customer service.

If the speaker population consists primarily of sophisticated telephone users, such as business professionals, they will be familiar with IVR applications that require touch-tone input. That paradigm makes human factors design simpler because it provides a basic prompt-and-response model that can guide the caller through a comparable speech recognition application. Conversely, any deviation from the established paradigm, including requests for word responses rather than numbers, can surprise and confuse the caller. The relatively poorer accuracy of speech recognition, compared with touch-tone input, may irritate callers who will not take into account such things as environmental noise.

Technologically unsophisticated callers may not have the IVR paradigm to guide them and they may become confused, intimidated by the technology, or angry about having to talk to a computer. These users are more likely to produce extraneous speech and respond slowly to prompting. Lack of a familiar paradigm can produce a great deal of extraneous speech. The use of word spotting, however, facilitates recognition without interfering with the natural speech patterns of such users.

Any type of user may express surprise at unexpectedly encountering a speech recognition system. Exclamations, such as "Hey, am I talking to a computer?" are not uncommon and generate recognition errors.

The touch-tone paradigm presents an obstacle when it tempts developers to model speech recognition applications on it. This strategy produces both good and bad design decisions. An example of a good decision is the basic structure of simple prompts. Experience with touch-tone system design has demonstrated that a caller's behavior is strongly influenced by the way a prompt or announcement is worded. The pattern

For sales, say "one"
For technical support, say "two"

will, for example, generate more consistently accurate responses than

Say "one" for sales
Say "two" for technical support

As with touch-tone applications

- The language of a prompt must be clear
- The response options must be simple and obvious
- Reprompts generally need to provide additional clarification
- The speed of the system's response to input must be acceptable
- Callers must feel they are progressing toward their goals
- There must be a failure fallback method

Using the touch-tone experience led to the practice of limiting the number of menu choices to three or four items. This assumption has been carried into speech recognition applications, but recent experiments by U S WEST suggest that when users can respond with topic-related words, like "sales" or "tech support," the list can be much longer. More research is needed to clarify situations where menu limits are suitable. The "common sense" belief that people will respond with the words specified as legitimate responses in a prompt was proven incorrect by AT&T Bell Laboratories in research that led to their utilization of word spotting. Disease State Management, Inc. (DSMI) encountered a similar phenomenon when they tested how callers responded to the prompt "Say the digit five."

> They said 'code five;' they spelled five; and they hit number 5 on the touch tone keypad (Leon Zak, Director of Systems, DSMI, personal communication, 1995).

With the expanded vocabulary options provided by subword modeling, it is likely that many new lessons will be learned through error and experience.

As speech recognition applications grow in vocabulary and flexibility, they depart from the established prompt-and-response paradigm. The human factors challenge is to define a new interaction paradigm that will be acceptable to people who use such systems.

8.3.5.4 Example of using the telephone.
Call management. Wildfire Communications

The *Wildfire Electronic Assistant* coordinates the call management activities performed by most business professionals. It seamlessly integrates a wide range of diverse call-management functions, including

- Placing (using voice-activated dialing) and returning calls
- Receiving and announcing incoming calls to the user
- Taking messages
- Playing voicemail messages
- Scheduling follow-up calls
- Scheduling reminders to the user

- Forwarding calls to pagers or other numbers
- Enabling users to assign priority levels to contacts for future call handling

The quality of *Wildfire* is not due to very advanced speech recognition technology: it uses discrete-word recognition and word spotting, speaker-independent and speaker-dependent speaker models, and its vocabulary is modest. Rather, it is the result of careful interleaving of disparate functions and a superior human interface. It replaces complex touch-tone key sequences with simple verbal commands, such as "call office" to place a call or "I'll take it" in response to being told that a specific person is calling. If an incoming call arrives while another call is in progress, *Wildfire's* announcement of the new caller's name is heard only by the user who can instruct *Wildfire* to take a message or to place the current call on hold while the new call is taken. Users initiate commands to *Wildfire* by calling it by name. The system responds with "Here I am!" or "What can I do for you?" spoken in a friendly, childlike voice. When given a command it might reply "OK" or "Got it!" A typical dialogue for scheduling a reminder might proceed as follows:

USER	WILDFIRE
Wildfire	*What can I do for you?*
Remind me	*What should I remind you about?*
<says topic. Silence when done>	*When?*
tomorrow	*At what time?*
8:30	*Morning or evening?*
In the morning	*Tomorrow at 8:30 AM. Is that correct?*
Yes	*I will remind you at that time*
Goodbye Wildfire	*Thank you, goodbye*

Wildfire is designed to be used by outbound and on-site company employees. It resides on a company's internal phone network and is connected to the public telephone network by a T-1 line so that it can be accessed by any telephone on the public network.

Other examples of telephone applications appear earlier in this chapter and in chapter 9. A command-and-control system performing operator services is described in section 8.3.1.4. Section 8.3.3.4 presents a telephone banking data access system.

8.4 SPEECH-ENABLED APPLICATIONS

A speech-enabled system (also called *speech aware*) binds the functions of an application to the spoken input. The speech is part of the application. This link fosters faster responses and greater consistency, while it reduces the likelihood that the speech interface will lose synchronization with the rest of the system. Navistar's *Worker's Compensation Reserving Advisor* [see section 8.3.2.4 and Markowitz (1987)], for example, embedded control of the speech interface into the expert-system rules. Figure 8.3 shows the contents of a rule that activates graphics and speech in tandem.

```
IF
    The INJURY-TYPE is FRACTURE and
    Injury SEVERITY is UNKNOWN
THEN
    ACTIVATE speech input for FRACTURE-SEVERITY
    DISPLAY SPEECH-INPUT instructions-display-screen
    ACTIVATE menu-popup screen for FRACTURE-SEVERITY
```

Figure 8.3   Rule activating speech and graphical interface

When it is done well, a speech-enabled system can enhance the naturalness of a system by structuring the application to expect input that conforms to normal speech patterns. Ultimately, this will include the ability to supersede a graphical interface just as GUI's have freed users from the command-line.

This is an important area where users will begin to achieve productivity and usability gains. Instead of providing a different way of navigating dialogues, speech can completely bypass the GUI interface and execute the user intent (Bruce Armstrong, Manager of the Novell Speech Technologies Group, WordPerfect, The Novell Applications Group, "Speech recognition application program interface committee," 1994, p. 23).

In short, the ultimate speech-enabled system is one capable of communicating with a human being in a natural, goal-oriented fashion. This type of system must await the integration of speech with intelligent computing software (see chapter 10, section 10.2), but speech-enabled systems of a simpler sort can be, and have been, developed already.

8.5 ASSESSMENT

Assessment is concerned with measuring the performance of a system. It can be applied to the evaluation of

- Algorithmic methods (used in research systems)
- Products for use in a specific application (called the *application-oriented* product assessment)
- The application itself

Assessment can require a great deal of time. Too often, it is viewed as secondary and separate from application design. In fact, the implementation of a good formal assessment program can be critical to the successful deployment of a system. Some of the primary functions of assessment are to:

1. Select an appropriate algorithm or product for a specific application
   Product assessment is often performed with this goal in mind. The number of good commercial speech recognition products is growing rapidly. Each product is designed for specific types of applications and possesses unique capabilities. Until industry standards for application programming interfaces (API) become fully established (see chapter 10), the price of selecting an inappropriate product can be high.
   API standards facilitate changing recognizers once an application has been created, but they cannot eliminate the need to account for feature differences between products. Nor can API standards guarantee that a given product will function properly in the target environment of an application or with the expected user population. Products will continue to differ in these areas and will need to be tested for the application.

> Typically, many vendors . . . cite performance of their technology at 98–99% accuracy without ever specifying the conditions under which testing was carried out. Without knowing something about the structure of the vocabulary used in testing, how many talkers and tokens of speech were used, how training was carried out, or what signal-to-noise ratio or microphone was used, it is literally impossible to determine what 99% correct recognition really means or how it compares to some other performance measure (David Pisoni, Howard Nusbaum & Subrata Das, "Automatic measurement of speech recognition performance," 1986, p. 4).

Consequently, it is imperative to evaluate products in the context of the application.

2. Assess an application's performance before deployment

> It is very important to understand how to measure the performance of speech recognition [technology]. This is a user interface technology and you will not get it perfect the first time—even if you are an organization, like AT&T, with a lot of experience. One reason is that every time you introduce a new technology to people you cannot predict their response (Judith Tschirgi, Direction of Services and Speech Technology, AT&T Network Systems, personal communication, 1994).

It is more cost- and time-effective to identify and correct design weaknesses during development than to modify a system after it has been deployed. If speech will be incorporated into a product, miscalculations can damage customer perception of the product and the company. This is true whether the speech technology was developed by the product manufacturer or by an external source. From the user's standpoint there is no such thing as "not invented here" for a component or feature of a product (see section 8.1).
   When the application developer is unfamiliar with speech recognition, the op-

portunities for error are immense. This is compounded by the fact that speech recognition is an emerging interface technology. Like all human interface technologies, speech recognition is sensitive to flaws in human factors design. As an emerging technology, it is characterized by technological change and by the lack of an easily accessible body of knowledge about human factors design.

If the project is a prototype designed to evaluate the benefit of incorporating speech recognition into an application, flaws in human-factors design and other facets of the application design can impair recognition accuracy. This is likely to be interpreted as evidence of flaws in speech recognition technology rather than as a specific example of a poor human-computer interface design. Such oversights can be fatal to acceptance of speech recognition by an organization and, more unfortunately, by users who encounter the failed system.

3. Define improvements to existing speech recognition applications

Formal, systematic assessment can be applied to an existing system or application that is not performing as well as expected. It is used to identify problems and can provide insights into the remediation of those problems.

> Without systematic measure of recognition performance under controlled conditions, it is almost impossible to determine whether changes in a recognition algorithm will result in reliable changes in recognition performance (David Pisoni, Howard Nusbaum & Subrata Das, "Automatic measurement of speech recognition performance," 1986, p. 4).

4. Determine the value of adding speech to an existing system

Speech recognition can be incorporated into existing systems to extend functionality or to improve productivity. This is likely to entail the redesign of the task or the system. As with the creation of new applications and products, it is critical to test plans for redesign prior to implementation. The results of incorporating speech should then be compared with the existing configuration. These comparisons will help determine whether to proceed with the addition of speech and, if so, how to accomplish it.

8.5.1 Formal vs. Informal Assessment

Formal assessment involves designing test protocols, creating databases of speech samples, and selecting testing equipment. Test protocols for application assessment examine the basic application design, especially human factors design features, and include evaluation of the application's performance with regard to

- Target speaker populations
- Target environment
- Vocabulary

- Application structure and scripts
- Application interfaces
- Human factors

Formal testing of this sort led AT&T Bell Laboratories to the discovery that one-time users of telephone-based systems are likely to add extraneous speech to their responses. That revelation and the realization that existing speech recognition technology could not be deployed for such applications, resulted in the selection of word spotting technology (see chapter 4, section 4.5).

Informal assessment requires no pre-recorded systematic testing design or equipment. Despite this, it can still be systematic, particularly if it is employed as a method of exploring the capabilities of one or more products.

One metric to use in selecting a formal or an informal approach is the cost of failure. If the cost of failure is low, then an informal assessment or minimal formal assessment is reasonable. Low-cost activities include assessment for

- Personal use of low-cost recognition products
- Gaining an initial familiarity with speech recognition technology
- Formulating the initial conceptualization of an application

If the cost is high, a thorough assessment should be developed. High-cost activities include assessment for

- Widespread use of a recognition system in an organization
- Development or enhancement of a product
- Customer service

The primary risk of applying informal assessment to high-cost activities is the failure of the application or product. Customers may label a product as poorly designed or useless; the organization may reject speech recognition technology as immature; and having learned nothing from the experience, a developer may persist in misconceptions about the technology.

8.5.2 Product Assessment

One of the lessons learned from the ARPA SUR project of the 1970's was that it is impossible to compare systems that differ in task, vocabulary, and structure. How could *Hearsay-II*, a blackboard system designed for document retrieval, be compared with *HWIM*, a system that combined a phonetic lattice with an augmented transition network in a travel-budget management task? It was clear that the only way to properly assess the performance of a group of systems was to insure that they had comparable vocabularies and performed equivalent functions on the same task. This is the spirit of application-oriented product assessment.

Application-oriented product assessment compares two or more recognition products on pre-selected features of the application:

- Target speaker populations
- Target environment
- Vocabulary
- Application perplexity
- Application interfaces

There are no universal standards for application-oriented product evaluation. The selection of a speech-recognition product is governed by the uses to which the speech recognition is to be put and the priorities associated with those tasks. The validity of the results depends upon the quality of the tools and methods used.

There is an interest in designing more generic product assessment tools. This has been one of the objectives of ESPRIT's *Speech Assessment Methodology (SAM)* project. *SAM* attempted to establish product performance evaluation methods that utilize standard equipment. Bellcore took another approach. It built a family of speaker-independent reference databases and standard test methodology for performance assessment of speech recognition technology running over telephone networks (see chapter 10, section 10.1). Vendors arrange to have Bellcore perform audits on their products and to provide detailed results to the vendor. The reference databases remain within Bellcore's Technical Audit Service. See Nortz, et al. for more information on Bellcore's system.

8.5.2.1 Reference databases/corpora.
A *reference database,* or *corpus,* is a basic tool of application-oriented product assessment. It contains speech samples that reflect the speaker, environment, vocabulary, perplexity, and other conditions of the application. The quality of the reference database is a major factor in determining the validity of the test results. Ordinarily, the data are recorded using high-quality equipment to minimize noise introduced by the recording equipment and microphones comparable to those that will be used for the application. Speakers are taken from the population of expected application users. All human errors, deviations from the script, and terms not in the system's vocabulary are annotated or removed from the data to prevent spurious recognition errors that will misrepresent product performance.

There are existing spoken language corpora that can be used as reference databases. If they accurately reflect the conditions of the application, the inclusion of such corpora in a testing program can be of great value. One problem with many, but not all, of these corpora is that their samples do not contain spontaneous speech. In many cases, the data have been read from a prepared text or elicited by having the data gathering system request repetition of specific words. The development of an in-house corpus is more time consuming but, if it is well done, it can provide a more accurate assessment of a product's ability to handle the conditions of a given application in a specified environment.

SPOKEN LANGUAGE CORPORA

The number of spoken language corpora is growing rapidly. One reason is that ARPA and NIST use them to perform annual benchmarking tests on large vocabulary recognition systems and spoken language understanding systems. To establish a level of task and vocabulary uniformity needed for comparative testing, ARPA often contacts for the construction of specific reference databases. These corpora are then used by ARPA contractors to build, as well as benchmark speech recognition systems. This use of corpora has fostered technological advances in research and commercial systems.

One of the first corpora of this sort was Texas Instruments' *TI Digits* corpus. It was completed in 1984 and was funded entirely by Texas Instruments. The corpus contained samples of connected digits spoken by 326 women, men, girls and boys. The *TI Digits* corpus has become a standard tool for development and testing of connected-digit systems.

The *TIMIT* corpus was developed under a DARPA contract to cover all the sound patterns and phonetic sequences in American English. *TIMIT* was a collaborative effort by Texas Instruments (TI), Massachusetts Institute of Technology (MIT), and Stanford Research Institute International (SRI). It contains speech samples from 630 people representing all dialect regions of the United States. *TIMIT* has been used in research on speech acoustics and for the initial development of statistical modeling techniques. It has also been used to evaluate phoneme-based recognition systems. The *DARPA Resource Management* corpus was completed in 1988. It contains 2,800 sentences spoken by one hundred native speakers of American English querying a naval database about military resources. The *Air Travel Information System (ATIS)* task has led to the creation of a number of corpora created under DARPA sponsorship. *ATIS* was designed for use in the development of speech understanding technology. It contains approximately 14,000 utterances for two-party dialogues.

Some of these corpora have been made available by Linguistic Data Consortium, a not-for-profit organization affiliated with the University of Pennsylvania.

Consult Mariani (1989) for additional information about the history of product performance assessment. Hirschman, et al. (1994) describes *ATIS*. Price, et al. (1988) describes the *Resource Management Database,* Pallett (1989) explains NIST's use of that database for benchmarking. Zue, et al. (1990) presents MIT's commitment to the development of spoken language corpora.

A few spoken language corpora which were designed to address specific types of application issues might be acceptable for product testing. Logica Cambridge Ltd. constructed both a corpus and a methodology for assessing product performance with regard to specific speaker variability parameters. The corpus contains samples spoken at various speaking rates by people with different vocal tract sizes and shapes using variable degrees of vocal effort. Another corpus, *NOISEX-92*, contains samples of spoken digits embedded in various types of noise. *NOISEX-92* was developed as part of the ESPRIT project 2589 (also called *SAM,* see section 8.5.2) to enable developers of both speech technology and applications to identify noise types and conditions that degrade recognizer performance.

Pallett, et al. (1993) describe ARPA benchmarking testing for 1992–1993.

Thomas, et al. (1989) describe the techniques used to construct the Logica database and Varga & Steeneken (1993) describe NOISEX-92. See the papers by Mariani (1989), Pallett (1985, 1987, and 1989), and Pisoni, et al. (1986) for additional information on product performance assessment.

8.5.2.2 Test protocols. The testing methodology needs to reflect the priorities of an application and its conditions of use. Vendor guidelines for equipment setup, enrollment, microphone selection, and other features of equipment operation need to be followed, or the equipment will not be able to perform at its optimum. Test protocols are designed to insure that the equipment is functioning properly during the testing.

Test protocols include specifications for the design and usage of a reference database or databases. This insures that a corpus developed internally will provide necessary testing data. If an existing corpus is to be used, specifications should guide the selection of the corpus, should ascertain whether products being tested are comparable to those for which the corpus was originally designed, and insure that the scoring procedures are identical to those used in the original tests.

8.5.2.3 Types of errors. There are three types of errors that are generally calculated in scoring the performance of a recognition product:

- *Deletion*   Dropping of words. For example, the system hears "124" when the speaker says "1234."
- *Substitution*   Replacing a spoken word with another, usually similar, word. For example, the system hears "9" when the speaker says "5."
- *Insertion*   Adding a word. For example, the system hears "12384" when the speaker says "1234."

In some cases, simple deletions are referred to as *no-hear* responses. No-hear errors can occur when the system is looking for a single response, such as a "yes" or "no" response. A no-hear occurs when the user's response is not heard by the system. Other types of errors that can be included in scoring are

- *False Acceptance*   Recognition of a word that is not in the vocabulary as a word that is in the vocabulary (called *out-of-vocabulary*).
- *Split*   A polysyllabic word is recognized as two or more shorter words. For example, "pandemonium" is recognized as "point and mention."
- *Merge*   Two words are recognized as a single word. For example, "lamp and," is recognized as "lampoon."

False acceptance data is important for applications whose users are likely to use out-of-vocabulary terminology. They are most often committed by people who have little or no prior experience with the application. Split and merge errors apply to continuous speech recognition systems and are most appropriate for large vocabulary systems using statistical language models.

Word spotting systems recast false acceptance and deletion errors into

- *False alarm*   The system incorrectly identifies a segment of the input as one of the keywords. For example, the system hears "Lending" when the speaker says "Please, let me have some information."
- *False Reject*   Failure to spot a valid keyword in the input.

8.5.2.4 Scoring.   Two simple approaches to scoring discrete-word systems are *percent correct* and *word accuracy*. Percent correct counts the total number of words in the input (total-words) and counts the number of words that were correctly identified (number-correct). It then divides the number-correct by the total-words. Word accuracy is better in that it examines performance using three error types: substitutions, insertions, and deletions. The number of errors of each type is tabulated. The sum of these errors is subtracted from the total-words to get the number-correct. Then a percent correct can be calculated. Percent correct and word accuracy are easy to obtain, but they can misrepresent the actual error count. By its nature, percent correct ignores insertion errors and thereby is likely to produce a low error rate. Systems that generate more insertion errors will wrongly appear to perform better than those that generate other types of errors. Because it does count insertion errors, the word accuracy approach can arrive at an apparent negative number-correct score corresponding to word error rates greater than 100 percent.

The use of a *dynamic programming (DP) symbol string alignment* method is more complex, but it can be used with discrete-word, connected, and continuous speech input. It uses dynamic programming techniques to align and then to compare the sequence of symbols representing the recognized words with the sequence of symbols containing the actual input. Penalties are assigned for substitution, insertion, and deletion errors. Results are reported in terms of percentage of word or sentence errors. DP string alignment was developed at a number of research sites. It was first implemented in large-scale tests by NIST for DARPA benchmark tests in 1987. DP string alignment, now one of the most widely used scoring methodologies, has been automated and now incorporates a range of statistical significance techniques.

For more information on DP string alignment consult Pallett (1987).

8.5.2.5 Beyond scoring.   There are many good speech recognition products capable of scoring well on the measures described in the previous section. It is dangerously misleading to obtain a single number that appears to embody the performance of a product. Such a number is sometimes called a *figure of merit*.

The convenience of being able to quote a single number is so great that one will inevitably be produced, whatever its shortcomings. Accepting this, we need to choose a good figure of merit, where "goodness" implies a measure that is easy to obtain, that accurately reflects the underlying performance that it purports to measure, and that produces a ranking that is reasonably close to what most users with specific applications would want (Melvyn Hunt, "Figures of merit for assessing connected-word recognisers," 1990, p. 329–330).

These are extremely difficult goals to meet. They point to the need for using application priorities to guide the interpretation of product performance scores.

Detailed analysis of error patterns can provide information of far greater value than a simple figure of merit. An unusually high error count can indicate that a product is malfunctioning in some way. A large number of deletion or substitution errors for a discrete-word recognizer may be a sign that the pacing of the spoken input is too rapid or that there is a poor connection to peripheral devices. Some errors signal an incompatibility between the recognizer and application priorities. A recognizer that needs a slower pace of input is inappropriate for tasks that depend upon speed or for which users are likely to speak rapidly. Other errors reflect problems in application design or implementation. The inclusion of sets of confusable words in an application, for example, can produce substitution errors by many products.

Steeneken (1993) and Steeneken, et al. (1989) provide additional information on evaluation tools and methods.

8.5.3 Application Testing

Application testing is concerned with evaluating the design of the application rather than on the ability of a recognition product to function within that design. Assessment begins as soon as an application is deemed acceptable, and it continues after the completed system has been deployed. A good basic approach is iterative design and testing using

- Wizard of Oz testing
- Prototype development
- Field testing of pilot systems
- Field testing of the complete system

Wizard of Oz testing (see sections 8.2.3 and 8.3.3.4) is useful for assessment of design concept alternatives. It helps determine whether the application will be accepted by users. It can help identify vocabulary and speech patterns needed in the application. Later use of Wizard of Oz testing with prototypes can locate places in the application where users become confused or make errors.

Demonstration and prototype systems offer a quick and relatively inexpensive method of evaluating many implementation features, including

- Specific design options that tested well in Wizard of Oz testing
- Different branching factors, or levels of perplexity

- Design tradeoffs, such as speed vs. accuracy
- Errors and error types associated with specific segments of the application
- Fallback techniques, such as reprompting or routing to a human being
- The overall design of the application

These evaluation methods can be used in Wizard of Oz testing or independently. Prototypes also facilitate testing of manipulable features of a recognition system, such as *rejection thresholds*. Most recognition systems have adjustable rejection thresholds.

8.5.3.1 What should be tested?

One of the first tests that is applied to an application is whether it will be acceptable to the population of expected users. The application must make sense to the users or they will not use it. If the application is to be a product or widely used service, one useful method of gathering such information about user acceptance is through market research.

> You can use a focus group approach to find out if people accept it or if they will think poorly of the company—especially if the system does not work well (Robert Perdue, Supervisor, AT&T Bell Laboratories, personal communication, 1994).

Once it has been determined that an application is worthwhile, the design and testing cycle begins and covers the facets of the application that have been discussed in chapters 3 through 8.

Chapter 3: Vocabulary

Some of the facets of vocabulary assessment are:

- Overall vocabulary size
- Need to add words
- Confusable words
- Perplexity
- Proper word choices

Users must understand the vocabulary selections.

> In one credit-card application there were the choices "lost card," "stolen card," or "associate." People did not know what "associate" meant (Robert Perdue, Supervisor, AT&T Bell Laboratories, personal communication, 1994).

This includes the language in auditory and visual *prompts*. The function of prompts is to direct the user towards appropriate responses.

Chapter 4: Structure

One objective of application assessment is to determine whether the users understand and can follow the structure of the application. As part of its work on several telephone-based applications, Ameritech monitored how well users understood what was required of them.

We kept records of what was said at the beginning of the interaction by both parties so that we were able to track the beginning of a call and look at the accuracy rates. There were a whole bunch of people who did not know that that's what the bong meant. They kept going to the operator and giving the numbers then (Eileen Schwab, Network services engineer, Ameritech, personal communication, 1994).

A second goal is to ascertain whether the system moves the users towards completion of the task quickly and efficiently. Assessment can tabulate points where user confusion and human errors occur and can calculate the time required to move between specific points in the application. These considerations need to be added to calculations of how many users actually made it to the goal.

Another objective of application testing is to determine whether the application structure matches the priorities of the task. A priority of many factory and loading dock applications is speed. Activities on a production line are paced and throughput is critical. In contrast, a priority of telephone applications is flexibility. These applications must be able to handle the unpredictable speech and behavior of people who are unfamiliar with the application.

Chapter 5: Speaker models

Speaker modeling assessment includes accuracy of the models and enrollment procedures (speaker-dependent systems). Testing with application prototypes during development can determine the adequacy of the speaker models in the application. Continuing this assessment after initial deployment of an application is useful for both speaker-dependent and speaker-independent systems. Users of speaker-dependent systems tend to speak differently as they become accustomed to a system. The result is that reference models generated by the initial enrollment will become less accurate. Continued monitoring will also determine the effectiveness of retraining or speaker adaptation procedures.

Once a system has been deployed, it may be determined that the people accessing a speaker-independent system are not limited to those whose speech was initially thought to match the models in the system. There may be greater variability in dialect, speed of speech, vocal stress, and other speaker characteristics than had been anticipated. This may require building new speaker models. The use of recordings from the field help identify the sources of recognition problems and will determine the kinds of adjustments needed.

If another task is being performed while a person is speaking to a recognition system, it should be determined whether and to what extent performance of the task affects speech. Tasks that require physical exertion, in particular, will alter speech patterns. If a protective mask or other equipment is worn on the face, products should be tested on speech produced while speakers are wearing the equipment. When the recognizer's microphone is placed within a mask, it can attenuate ambient noise rendering testing or enrollment based upon the background noise conditions less useful. If performance of the task produces noise, it needs to be included in the assessment as well.

Chapter 6: Speech flow

Speech flow assessment includes evaluation of accuracy, ease of use, and speed. Sometimes these objectives represent tradeoffs. Greater speed, for example, may entail a reduction in overall accuracy. Discrete-word entry may not be appropriate for an application requiring a great deal of speed, but continuous speech systems still require reasonably clear enunciation. If accuracy is more important than speed, discrete-word input can be paced using auditory tones or visual prompts.

Chapter 7: Speaking and task environment

An application should be tested to determine how well it has modeled features of the speaking environment. Among the features of the environment that are reflected in the input signal are

- Signal-to-noise ratio
- Noise power spectrum
- Noise variability

If a system is to be used in more than one speaking environment, the noise characteristics of all environments may not be properly represented.

Most recognition products have adjustable rejection thresholds. At least one matching score for a word candidate must exceed the rejection threshold for the system to report a recognition. Frequent deletion or substitution errors result when the voice of the speaker is too soft or the signal-to-noise ratio is too high. Adjustment of the rejection threshold will reduce these errors.

One of the benefits of using prototypes for testing is that they can determine whether the physical configuration of the recognition system is suitable for performance of the task or if, as in the Kodak example (section 8.3.2.4), adjustments must be made to the equipment.

Chapter 8: Human factors

> You cannot assume that you just put an application together and people will cooperate (Robert Perdue, Supervisor, AT&T Bell Laboratories, personal communication, 1994).

Since speech recognition is an interface technology, human factors testing is a constant that underlies assessment of all other facets of its performance in an application. It guides the design and evaluation of vocabulary, prompting, reprompting, and other backup subsystems. It examines the ways people will interact with the system, how well they understand what the system is doing, and how well the system moves them towards their goals. It separates facets of the application that are considered valuable from those that are annoying.

8.5.3.2 Scoring in application testing.   The scoring techniques often applied to applications are comparable to those used for product assessment. A figure of merit (sometimes called the *hit rate*) is often reported as the basis of accuracy.

That is misleading because all single number ratings, whether percent-correct or word accuracy, and scoring procedures based on the use of DP string alignment (see section 8.5.2.4), fail to account for inappropriate responses by the user and for no-hear errors (or false rejection errors in word spotting applications). The reason for the failure to capture no-hear responses is that the occurrence of these errors usually stimulates a reprompt followed by a new response. Failure to acknowledge the occurrence of such errors contributes to the rejection of an application by users who are annoyed when they are forced to repeat correct responses.

One enhancement to scoring is to count the number of times a person must repeat a correct response. In telephone-based applications, it is possible this will occur as often as 20 percent of the time. A false reject rate of that magnitude can be an indicator that the input voice is too soft or the rejection threshold is too high. Another scoring enhancement is to assign higher penalties to errors on selected, important vocabulary items. This will allow problems with those items to be noted and quickly corrected.

8.5.3.3 Beyond scoring in application testing.

Advanced researchers and systems developers recognize the fact that for any speech recognition application the standard tabulation methods do not accurately characterize how well a system is working. None of the simple approaches to tabulation, for example, considers the inherent complexity of the application and its impact on the user.

> If you have a complex application with several loops you may want to count the percentage of people who actually make it to their goal. You may want to look at each point to see how much time it took them to get there and compare it with the non-automated system (Judith Tschirgi, Direction of Services and Speech Technology, AT&T Network Systems, personal communication, 1994).

Analysis of tape recordings of field tests and prototypes can distinguish between true recognition errors and errors generated by the impact of the application on the user. Many telephone applications include *time-out windows* to stimulate a reprompt or termination of the application when no response is received from the caller. A substitution error can occur if the speaker does not speak until just prior to the time-out. Errors produced by such violations of the time-out window may indicate that users are confused by a prompt or that the prompt forces the user to pause and think. An error can also occur when the speaker starts to speak before the system begins listening. Other errors are produced by noise.

Substitution and insertion errors (and false alarms in word spotting) can cause the application to take improper action, and the system will not know that it made an error. These errors can be used to define points in the application where a confirmation of the response can be inserted, or where further analysis of the vocabulary can eliminate confusable words.

Some products generate a ranked list of word candidates for each recognition event. When the highest candidate is the correct word, it is helpful to compare its matching score with that of the word next on the list (the *nearest neighbor*). The proximity of these scores can indicate potential problems from confusable words. More training (for speaker-dependent systems) may improve the results or it may be necessary to change the words. If a substitution error has occurred, the list of alternatives can be used to determine whether the correct word ranks high on the list. If there is a pattern of substitution errors, a confusion matrix can be generated to reflect the patterns of acoustic confusions. Such a matrix can be used to provide error correction for highly confusable word sets, such as the English alphabet (see chapter 3, section 3.5.3) or to modify vocabulary design.

One of the most important features of assessment is user satisfaction. Every field test should include a way to contact people testing the system for comment and reactions. That score outweighs tabulations of any other type.

9

APPLICATIONS AT WORK

INTRODUCTION

Commercial speech recognition applications exist in a wide variety of industries. The number and diversity of these applications continue to expand as the technology gains credibility and acceptance.

This chapter shows the scope and variety of speech recognition applications. Specific products and applications have been highlighted to provide a sense of the ways in which the technology described in the preceding chapters can be applied.

The list of industries found in this chapter is meant to be representative rather than exhaustive. Similarly, the systems selected for description within each industry do not constitute the entire set of products or applications found in an industry. Consequently, the examples found in this chapter have been selected because they

- Were the first of their kind
- Are creative
- Illustrate a class of applications/products

and the use of a commercial product as an example should not be construed as a recommendation by the author.

9.1 COMPUTER SYSTEM INTERFACES

Many of the applications described in the following sections use speech recognition as an interface for a computer application. This section examines products designed specifically to navigate through operating system interfaces and off-the-shelf products running under them. The wide distribution of Microsoft's *Voice Pilot* interface for *Windows* is largely responsible for consumer awareness of these products.

Commercial voice-driven interfaces have been developed for the Macintosh, PC, and UNIX workstation environments. The number of voice-activated interfaces available for a platform reflects the popularity of that platform among consumers. Thus, it is not surprising that most products have been designed for Microsoft *Windows 3.1* while Interactive Products' *SimplyVoice for DOS* is one of the few interfaces for DOS.

Articulate Systems' *Voice Navigator* was the first speech recognition product developed for the Macintosh and first successful voice-driven interface designed for the graphical user interface (GUI) of a personal computer. To create the *Voice Navigator,* Articulate Systems ported the discrete-word technology of Dragon Systems to the Macintosh and adapted it to satisfy the requirements of controlling a GUI. Named by *MacUser* as the best input device of 1990, the product contained commands for menus, windows, dialogue boxes, palettes, and other components of the Macintosh interface. It also had tools for adding vocabulary, customizing an interface, and creating new ones.

Command Corp.'s IN^3 *Voice Command* system is one of the few commercial interfaces designed for the GUI of a UNIX workstation. The product runs on Sun Microsystems' workstations and offers continuous-speech voice control of the GUI interface as well as of commonly-used applications, such as the *AutoCAD* computer-aided design system. In 1995, Command Corp. began shipping a comparable interface for *Windows NT* called *IN CUBE Pro*. It is one of the few voice-activated interfaces for *Windows NT*.

Most GUI interfaces are designed to control Microsoft *Windows* and *Windows* applications. Like the *Voice Navigator,* they possess built-in vocabulary for the menus and other components of the interface and offer vocabulary development and interface customization. Many of the products include or sell interfaces for widely-used applications, such as *Lotus 123*. Some require discrete-word input while others offer continuous speech input. Most allow users to intersperse spoken commands with mouse clicks and keyboard input. Some products include a proprietary board that performs preprocessing functions. Other products are software-only systems that rely on the signal processing capabilities of commercial audio boards.

Verbex Voice Systems' *Listen for Windows* product uses continuous speech and both speaker-dependent and speaker-independent recognition. In many other

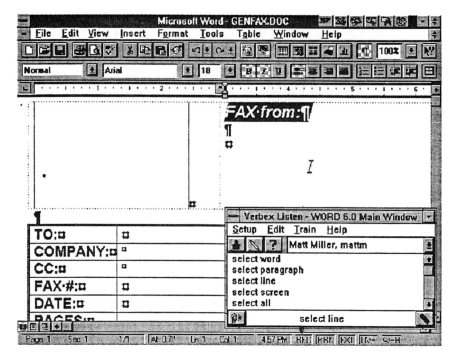

Figure 9.1 *Listen for Windows* interface for Microsoft *Word* (provided by Verbex Voice Systems)

ways, it is typical of existing commercial *Windows* interface products. A typical *Listen for Windows* screen is shown in figure 9.1. The phrase window at the lower right contains the items in the active vocabulary ("select word," "select paragraph," etc.). The small box below the phrase window displays the word or phrase that has just been recognized by the system ("select line"). Since the function of these two boxes is to assist the user, either or both of them can be removed from the screen if they are not needed.

Consult Avant's (1992) article for a description the Command Corp. products and Ito's (1993) article for information about the *Voice Navigator*. Markowitz (1994d) reviews *Listen for Windows 1.1*.

9.2 TELECOMMUNICATIONS

When speech recognition is placed on a telephone network rather than in a telephone handset, the potential size of the user population increases dramatically. Instead of limiting the input instrument to specific telephones, the possibility of accessing speech from any telephone on the public telephone network is realized. Network-level solutions can be done within individual companies by attaching PC's or other peripherals to PBX's or other internal systems. Speech recognition can also be embedded in, or attached to, the public telephone network of a telecommunications provider.

Telecommunications companies have been leading the development of network-based speech recognition, particularly for land-line (as opposed to cellular) networks. Many of the services being used in business and banking (see sections 9.6.3 and 9.7.2) are provided as network-based solutions by telecommunications companies as well as by speech recognition vendors working with regional, local, and cellular telecommunications carriers.

Network-level speech recognition can be embedded in the switches of the telephone network or can reside on *intelligent peripherals* linked to network switches. An intelligent peripheral is a workstation or more powerful platform capable of communicating with network switches. Switches are faster and more powerful, but the use of intelligent peripherals hastens the deployment of new technologies and adds less complexity to the switching device. Depending upon how it is connected to the network, an intelligent peripheral may need to comply with standards and regulations of the telecommunications industry with regard to their operation and reliability. This is called Network Equipment Building Specification (NEBS) compliance. AT&T opted to embed speech in all 120 digital switches of its domestic long-distance network. This work was completed in January, 1993. Most other telecommunications companies have elected to provide speech recognition and other advanced technologies/services through intelligent peripherals.

Network-level speech recognition applications of interest to telecommunications companies fall into two classes: operator services and subscriber services.

9.2.1 Operator Services

The use of speech recognition for operator services addresses two functions. It extends automated services to customers who otherwise would not have access to them (primarily people with rotary dial telephones) and it saves the carrier money by reducing staffing requirements. In order to accomplish these two goals, the systems must be easy to use and extremely reliable. They are generally subjected to extensive reliability and human factors testing before being fielded.

AT&T and Bell-Northern Research were among the earliest to develop operator services applications. Ameritech, the regional telephone company for the north central United States, was the first to implement Bell-Northern Research's *Automated Alternate Billing Services (AABS)* system. *AABS* obtains verbal acceptance or denial of collect telephone calls. After extensive testing and modification, Ameritech deployed *AABS* in 1989. *AABS* has improved service levels and produced substantial cost savings for Ameritech.

In 1992, AT&T began deploying its *Voice Recognition Call Processing (VRCP)* system to handle collect-calls in rural areas of the United States where rotary telephones are still common (also see chapter 8, section 8.3.1). As figure 9.2 shows, it has an extremely simple interface with a fallback to a human operator. The purpose of using such a simple interface was to maximize the success of callers us-

This is AT&T. Please say
collect
calling card
third number
person-to-person
or   *operator*   now

Figure 9.2 The prompt for AT&T's *Voice Recognition Call Processing* system

ing the system. Despite its apparent simplicity, AT&T subjected *VRCP* to extensive field testing and found that a sizeable percentage of callers failed to follow the specified protocol. As a result, AT&T designed a keyword spotting system (see chapter 4, section 4.5; chapter 8, section 8.3.1.4) robust enough to operate over long-distance, public-telephone lines. By the end of 1993, nearly fifty million calls per month were being handled by the system, representing a significant cost savings for the company. *VRCP* is still in nationwide operation.

Also in 1993, Bell-Northern Research and Bell Canada began to field test Bell-Northern's bilingual directory assistance system for the 65,000 Bell Canada telephone subscribers in northern Quebec province. In 1994, Bell-Northern began a second field test with US West. Bellcore began testing its own directory assistance system in 1993. It is a word spotting system designed to accept 1,200 locality names in French and English as well as 500 additional synonyms for these names.

For more information on AT&T's *VRCP* system consult Haszto, et al. (1994). Sharp & Lennig (1994) discuss Bell-Northern's directory assistance and other Bell-Northern speech recognition systems. Additional information on network-based telecommunication applications can be found in Markowitz (1994e).

9.2.2 Subscriber Services

Subscriber services represent a more varied and lucrative arena for network-based applications. These services include voice dialing, call routing, calling-card calls, and a range of other fee-based services. For such services to be attractive they must offer the subscriber obvious benefit and they must be easy to use.

One of the most popular of these services is voice-activated dialing. It is being offered by long-distance carriers, regional Bell operating companies (RBOC's), other local land-line service providers, and cellular service providers. Its most popular form is the personal dialing directory service. These are data-access systems that maintain a speaker-dependent dialing database for each subscribing household. They can be accessed by subscribers using any telephone in the household that is on the provider's network.

One of the most well-known systems is Sprint's *Voice FONCARD* (also see chapter 8, section 8.3.3), which uses Texas Instruments' speech recognition and speaker verification technology. Callers using the *Voice FONCARD* can dial Sprint's toll-free number from any telephone and say their personal identification number.

Using speaker-independent recognition, the system interprets the identification number and uses it to access the voice print for that authorized user. The voice print is compared with the spoken input to verify that the caller is the person who is authorized to use the system. Once verification is complete, the caller can dial the desired number or, if that party's telephone number is stored in the caller's personal telephone directory, the caller simply says the speed dial words for that number (such as "call Mom").

McCaw Cellular was one of the first to implement voice-activated dialing on a cellular telephone network. In 1993, they deployed a system developed by Voice Control Systems (VCS). Within two years, voice-activated dialing had become a popular feature of cellular telephones and was being offered by a growing number of service providers.

AT&T was the first long-distance carrier to offer speech recognition to business customers with toll-free 800-numbers. This service was created to support businesses with large numbers of domestic and international customers. By the end of 1993, AT&T had extended the voice-activated toll-free service to calls emanating from sixty-two of the sixty-seven countries served by AT&T's international 800 network.

In 1995, Northern Telecom began offering a unique variant of voice-dialing to its customers: telecommunications service providers. The service, called *Voice-Activated Premier Dialing (VAPD)*, allows businesses to include their business names, products, and promotion names in a speaker-independent, voice-dialed directory residing on the service provider's telephone network. Potential customers of those businesses can dial a *VAPD* access code, such as "*00," say the name of a company or its product, and obtain information. Systems like *VAPD* have opened the door to development of ambitious business applications, such as verbal searching of yellow-pages listings that would enable, for example, a caller seeking a Chinese restaurant located in a specific geographical area to select a restaurant and then use speaker-independent, voice-activated dialing to call the selected restaurant directly from the voice directory.

Some telecommunications companies offer information services to their business customers. Bell Northern's *Stock Talk* system (see section 9.7) is an example of a service of this type. The data for these services are in specially prepared files on intelligent peripherals that are linked to the network. To get information, subscribers call the access number and say the name of a stock.

Markowitz (1994c and 1994e), Cerf, et al. (1994), and Haszto, et al. (1994) provide additional information on applications for subscriber services.

9.3 EDUCATION AND TRAINING

One of the problems facing developers of training systems is that existing speech recognition technology is not capable of engaging in a human-like dialogue with a student. As a result, the implementation of a system needs to be highly controlled and focused on learning activities with structured and well-defined responses.

International Trading Institute (ITI) developed a creative technique for training futures and options traders. ITI is a Chicago-based training institution for the global derivative securities industry. Realizing that brokerages and trading companies experience a great deal of lost revenue from on-the-floor learning errors and missed opportunities, ITI created a trading floor simulation system. The system, *Trade$tar,* teaches students how to respond quickly to market conditions through simulations of typical trading-floor scenarios, such as

Trader1: Ask 40 combo at 3/8
Student: Buy 5
Trader1: You got 'em

Trader2: Ask 45 puts
Student: 1/8, 3/8
Trader2: Buy 1
Student: Sold. Sold one put at 2 3/8

By using speech synthesis and recognition it acclimates students to the conditions of the trading floor and to the verbal patterns needed to succeed there. Students compete with fifteen simulated traders who, like real competitors, maneuver and trade around slow and indecisive opponents. Depending upon the level of the student, *Trade$tar* can deliver trade requests as slowly as every twenty-five seconds or as quickly as every five seconds and can adjust the aggressiveness of the simulated traders. The system tracks student performance so that instructors can identify and correct problems.

Several simulation systems have been developed to train air-traffic controllers in a realistic, but safe, environment. BBN's *HARK* technology is embedded into one commercially available system that is configured to represent air traffic approach control for Boston's Logan International Airport. The operator verbally enters clearances to simulated pilots and the system adjusts the aircraft speed, altitude, and direction to prepare for landing. Emulating actual air-traffic control conditions, the system allows multiple clearances to be entered in sequence without pausing.

The *Say&See* system of Natural Speech Technologies allows students to see graphic representations of how they are pronouncing specific phonemes. It is designed to assist in the training of adults and children undergoing speech therapy. Using speaker-independent techniques, *Say&See* analyzes spoken input in real time and displays a split screen graphical representation comparing the incoming sound to the ideal. As figure 9.3 illustrates, the left side of the *Say&See* display contains a cross-section of the student's vocal tract showing how the student is producing the phoneme. It is derived from the acoustic parameters of the input. The right side contains an idealized representation of how the sound should be produced. In figure 9.3, the student's pronunciation of SH positions the tongue too far forward. Stu-

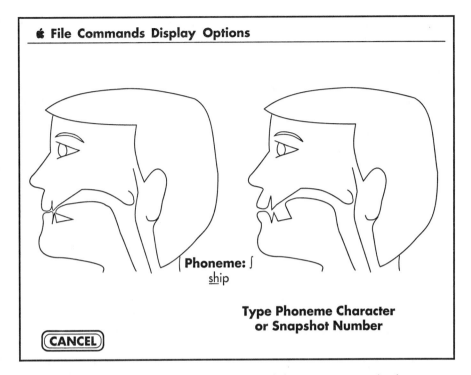

Figure 9.3   Graphical display of the *Say&See* speech therapy system comparing the student's pronunciation of the phoneme *sh* with the correct vocal tract configuration (provided by Natural Speech Technologies)

dents can use the real-time feedback from the images to help them modify the way they produce a sound.

For more information on the ITI system consult the Markowitz (1993c) and Michaels (1991) papers. Rosenblum (1991) describes the *Say&See* system.

9.4 PEOPLE WITH DISABILITIES

People with disabilities are using speech recognition to perform work-related tasks and to become more independent in their personal lives. One of the primary challenges of designing applications for people with disabilities is that each group has unique requirements and concerns. Motor impaired individuals, for example, range from quadriplegics to people with repetitive stress syndrome (RSI). Furthermore, the population of individuals within each group is not at all uniform in its needs. Despite their diversity, these people share one characteristic: a desire for greater personal independence. Speech recognition is seen as a tool to effect that goal. The groups who have been the primary focus of speech recognition application development are people with motor and visual impairments. Research systems have also been designed for people with mild cognitive impairments and individuals with speech and hearing impairments. IBM's Special Needs Systems Group offers a line of products designed specifically for individuals with disabilities. Among these products is IBM's *VoiceType* speech recognition.

For additional information on speech recognition for people with disabilities consult articles by Harkins (1989), Markowitz (1994a), Marshall (1991), Rothapel (1990), and Scott (1994).

9.4.1 Computer Use

Dictation systems represent a widely used form of speech recognition for both professional and personal use. Most vendors of dictation systems have structured their products to allow the totally hands-free operation needed by people with motor impairments. There are also systems for people with visual impairments. *Keystone,* a product of ApTech Limited, is one such application. It links speech synthesis to the recognized dictation so that visually impaired users can verify the recognized input.

Smaller vocabulary, computer applications interfaces (see section 9.1) enable people to navigate an application and do data entry tasks. The *Speech Secretary* system of Applications Express is an example of a system that is used by children and adults with severely impaired speech. Like some dictation systems, it uses an N-gram model capable of adapting to the word sequencing patterns of the user (see chapter 4, section 4.3.1). This personalization of the language model enhances the accuracy of the system and makes it easier to use.

Some organizations and educational institutions that provide services to people with disabilities are using speech recognition with their clients and students. The Easter Seal Society, for example, has used computer program interface systems to increase the job skills of some of its clients.

9.4.2 Environment Command-and-Control

Environment control systems are used to operate wheelchairs, hospital beds, lights, and other items in the personal environment of the individual. Several vendors have systems to control wheelchairs. One of the earliest of these systems was *SAVR (Stand Alone Voice Recognizer)* by Mimic. It uses speaker-dependent recognition with a small, specialized, command-and-control vocabulary. Hill-Rom's *Enhancemate* is a fairly elaborate system that was designed for individuals with severe physical disabilities. It enables them to control specially equipped hospital beds and other objects in their immediate environment. Figure 9.4 contains a schematic representation of *Enhancemate*. The bottom portion of the figure displays the *Enhancemate* control panel showing the range of environmental control commands available. The top half of the figure illustrates how the system is used.

Systems like *SAVR* and *Enhancemate* can provide significant benefits to peo-

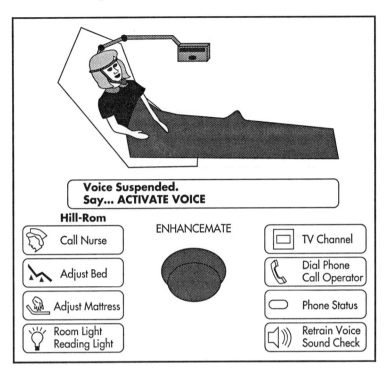

Figure 9.4   Schematic of Hill-Rom's *Enhancemate* product (provided by Verbex Voice Systems)

ple with motor disabilities. Although they are essentially turnkey products, they still need to be tuned to the individual needs and capabilities of their users.

9.5 MANUFACTURING

Any company which pursues excellence in its products has a place to put voice recognition to work in the service of process control (Martin Klaver, Project engineer, Lenox China, "Making voice recognition work for process control," 1988, p. 144).

Manufacturing was one of the earliest industries to use speech recognition technology. It has been implemented primarily on production lines and loading docks. It is part of quality control inspections, process control, inventory control, and product design. A typical manufacturing application is an eyes-busy/hands-busy, data entry task performed by a mobile speaker working in a high-noise environment.

DuPont developed a speech recognition interface for an internal manufacturing design system. The system calculates the materials needed for an engineering design construction drawing. Voice makes it a hands-free system because it allows

```
                              To enter a valve
          user says:          ECHO 1 3 ZULU SIZE 6 INCH
          computer says:      E 1 3 Z SIZE 6 QUANTITY 1

                            To add 3 to the quantity
          user says:        ADJUST QUANTITY
          computer asks:    ADJUST QUANTITY BY?
          user responds:    3
          computer responds: 3, NEW QUANTITY IS 4
```

Figure 9.5   Typical interaction for DuPont materials application (Paul Immediato, All-states Design and Development Company, "Material take-off utilizing voice recognition," 1991, p. 90)

designers to verbally describe valves and other needed materials while they are drawing. The application contains a vocabulary of 76 words in 13 utterances. Vocabulary includes digits, military-alphabet correlates for alphabet letter names (e.g., "alpha" for "a," "zulu" for "z"), command words, and phrases such as "adjust quantity." Figure 9.5 is a typical interaction.

In 1987, Delco Electronics developed a speech-driven, statistical process control application for their manufacturing production line (also see chapter 8, section 8.3). The purpose of the application is to collect detailed production information in real time as a means of eliminating manufacturing defects. Prior attempts to assemble handwritten or keyboard entry documentation resulted in lost data and interfered with the basic eyes-busy/hands-busy tasks of the statistical process control operators. The format was a highly-structured, prompt-and-response pattern that enabled operators to report defect data to the system while repairing flawed units. The system provided detailed data on manufacturing processes to the plant management in real time.

> Using older technologies, such as paper and pencil or keyboard entry, an operator only had time to tally how many of each defect type were discovered in a lot and how many boards were inspected. Now, with voice systems, inspectors can indicate what defect was found and on which part the defect occurred. This is valuable information (Lee Pfarrer, Project Engineer, Delco Electronics, "Using voice recognition for data collection in a factory environment," 1989, p. 154).

Computer Products and Services Incorporated (CPSI) has developed a creative speech recognition product called the *Mobile Assistant*. It is a patented system designed primarily for equipment maintenance, inspection, and computer data collection. Housed in a portable 486 computer worn on a technician's belt, the *Mobile Assistant* affords hands-free access to maintenance manuals and other computerized resources. Hands-free operation is achieved through a combination of speech input and output to a video display visor that provides a display equivalent to that of a standard PC monitor. Technicians needing to consult manuals simply raise their eyes to view the screen and then enter verbal commands to select the manuals and pages required.

The paper by Pfarrer (1989) discusses the Delco application, and Immediato's (1991) article describes the DuPont system. Good examples of other manufacturing applications are provided by Klaver (1988), Markowitz (1994a), and Olson (1987).

9.6 BUSINESS AND PROFESSIONAL

This group of industries is populated by well-trained and educated individuals. The language they use is characterized by highly technical, industry-specific vocabulary. The primary focus of speech recognition in these industries has been on structured dictation, especially report generation systems. The number of large-vocabulary data entry systems being developed is also beginning to increase.

Human factors issues vary with the status of the expected users of a system. High-status users of dictation systems (notably, physicians, attorneys, and executives in upper management) expect that dictation with speech recognition will parallel using a human transcriptionist or secretary. Users accustomed to secretarial support often chafe at having to adjust to discrete-word recognition systems that require them to verify the accuracy of the recognized text and to perform the editing functions normally provided by others. Some users resist spending the time needed to complete the rapid enrollment process required by some dictation systems. This is not necessarily true of professionals who do not have administrative support staffs.

9.6.1 Healthcare

The federally mandated standards for automating patient records [called the *computer-based patient record* (CBPR)], the drive to reduce costs, and the need to shorten the delay between service and billing have all stimulated interest in speech recognition for dictation and data entry. The healthcare industry is also experiencing a number of pressures for greater quantity, quality, accountability, and speed of delivery of documentation. Medicare, Medicaid, and insurers are increasing demands for accountability and the industry as a whole is moving towards more standardization in reporting. In 1992, the federal government established the year 2000 as its deadline for creating a nationwide standard for computer-based patient records. This mandate was motivated by a need for greater consistency and more efficient communication regarding healthcare services and their outcomes. Once these standards are set they will become part of the accreditation criteria for hospitals. Speech recognition, particularly dictation of medical reports, is seen by the healthcare industry as a means of satisfying these demands.

Kurzweil AI introduced the first medical dictation system, *VoiceRAD*, in 1986. By 1992 it had evolved into a family of turnkey dictation systems, called *VoiceMed*. Other vendors and application developers followed suit with turnkey dictation systems for medical sub-specialties, such as radiology, pathology, and emergency medicine.

The operation of many medical dictation systems is exemplified by Kurzweil AI's *VoiceRAD* system. It has three report-generation formats: free-form dictation, structured dictation, and report-generation via *trigger words* (see chapter 8, section 8.3.4). Trigger words are macros that allow the rapid generation of large blocks of pre-defined text. By speaking command words to shift between free-form and structured dictation, users can employ all three techniques in a single report. Free-form dictation allows large vocabulary, discrete-word dictation to a system using a statistical language model (see chapter 4, section 4.3).

The structured dictation interface is shown in figure 9.6. It follows the pre-defined report structure for a specific exam and employs a fill-in-the-blank approach to report generation. Figure 9.6 displays the start of a report for a set of aneurysm X-rays. The current word, "aneurysm," was correctly recognized at the top right along with several alternatives. If the recognition system had selected the wrong word as its best candidate, the user could select one of the alternatives by saying its number. Since "aneurysm" is a trigger word, it generated the paragraph of text at the bottom of the screen. The bold segment within the paragraph identifies

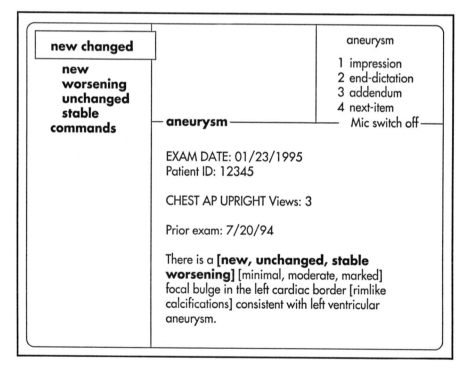

Figure 9.6 Main screen format of Kurzweil AI's *VoiceRAD* medical dictation system (provided by Kurzweil Applied Intelligence Inc.)

the next expected utterance and the choices for it are displayed in the column on the left.

Trigger words can be used within structured report generation or, as figure 9.7 illustrates, for rapid generation of routine reports. Since the trigger-word vocabulary is limited and very familiar, only the recognized text is displayed.

The healthcare industry's need for detailed documentation has spawned portable and networked data entry systems as well. The *ChartWell Patient Tracking System* (also see chapter 8, section 8.3.2) being developed by KorTeam International is one example. It is a portable charting system that uses speech recognition to facilitate hands-free data entry during bedside patient care-giving. Its form-creation tools allow hospital information systems staff to define and describe the forms associated with each type of procedure. This information is used to structure the input and to create displays that emulate the forms being completed. The *ChartWell* system is designed to be integrated with the central computing system of the hospital.

Dr. Monroe Harris, a New York physician, developed a unique data entry application that allows his patients to schedule appointments. When a patient calls to schedule an appointment, the system requests the patient's number. The number is used to access the patient's name and data from the office database. Using numeric

USER INPUT	SYSTEM DISPLAY
"Today" "Mammography" "Bilateral"	1/10/95 Mammography (bilateral)
"Routine"	A low dose film technique was used. Cephalocaudal and modified lateral views were obtained.
"Diffuse nodularity"	Both breasts show a very prominent duct pattern with diffuse nodularity throughout. Such diffuse nodularity makes the breasts difficult to evaluate.
"No focal lesions"	There are no dominant masses or clustered calcifications on either side.
"Obtain outside study"	The patient gives a history of previous mammography elsewhere. If these could be obtained for comparison it would be helpful to exclude any interval change.
"Signature"	Mary L. Jones, M.D. 9:18:32 1/10/95

Figure 9.7   Generation of a complete routine mammography report using trigger words (provided by Kurzweil Applied Intelligence Inc.)

input, the patient selects the office location and type of appointment required. Once the system has determined how long the appointment must be, the patient is asked to specify a desired month, day, and time for the appointment. The system negotiates with the patient and an appointment is set. Each spoken selection is verified by the system before the next step is initiated. Virtually all patient input is spoken numbers. Since numeric information must be said as single digits, the system is also programmed to handle other numeric input, such as "first" and "half past," as errors.

HealthTech Services Corporation has a prototype voice-activated *Home Assisted Nursing Care (HANC)* robot. *HANC* resides with the patient but is electronically linked to a central healthcare services station. The robot is programmed to prolong independent living of patients by assisting them with healthcare needs, such as scheduling and delivery of medication, and transmission of emergency alerts to healthcare providers at the central services station. *HANC* responds to highly-structured command-and-control input by patients.

Additional information on applications in medicine can be found in papers by Cipriani (1991), Einstein (1994), and Kurzweil (1989).

9.6.2 Law

In the legal profession, computer-based document creation systems (called *document assembly*) using keyboard and mouse input have existed for several years. They are recognized as an easy, efficient method of generating standard documents, such as wills and certain types of contracts. In 1994, speech recognition vendors began offering voice-activated document assembly systems comparable to those used in medicine.

Legal research utilizing on-line database systems, such as *WESTLAW* (West Publishing) and *Lexis* (Mead Data), is a critical component of case development. In 1993, West Publishing and Kolvox Communications adapted *LawTalk,* Kolvox's dictation product, to serve as a speech interface for *WESTLAW.* The *LawTalk* speech interface allows free-form dictation to *WordPerfect,* structured dictation comparable to that used for medical dictation, and complete voice control of the *WESTLAW* system. *LawTalk for WESTLAW* is designed to be used with *WESTLAW is Natural (WIN)*, West's natural language query mode. *WIN* provides the ability to use natural language queries to access information on *WESTLAW.* For example it can process queries like:

What is the government's obligation to warn military personnel of the dangers of past exposure to radiation?

LawTalk can also be used to generate standard SQL database queries, such as

(government or military) w/50 warn ** w/50 (soldier or sailor or service member or service-man or serviceman) w/50 radiation

The information retrieved from *WESTLAW* can be integrated into a *WordPerfect* document.

> You can do an entire research session in *WESTLAW*—from start to finish—using speech and without touching a keyboard (Vance Opperman, President, West Publishing, personal communication, 1994).

Additional information about the use of speech recognition in law can be found in Markowitz (1994f).

9.6.3 Business

Free-form dictation is attractive to business professionals as well. There are generic systems that can be used by business professionals, but intra- and inter-industry diversity has limited the number of industry-specific turnkey dictation products.

Despite the allure of free-form dictation, smaller-vocabulary applications for business are growing at a much faster rate. Speech recognition has begun to appear in personal digital assistants (PDA's). The first PDA with speech was the *Voice Organizer* of Voice Powered Technology. A palm-size, speaker-dependent, data entry and access device, the *Voice Organizer* is designed for storage of telephone numbers, recorded speech, gentle reminders, and appointments.

Technological improvements, such as word spotting and barge-in (also called *cut-through*) have made telephone-based applications more attractive to business. Barge-in enables callers to interrupt system prompts with their response. Subword vocabulary development makes it possible to replace responses that mimic former touch-tone input:

> say *1* for sales
> say *2* for technical support

with requests for more natural responses:

> say *sales* for sales
> say *technical support* for technical support

The use of speech recognition over the telephone has been centered around customer service, sales support, and staffing cost reductions. The technology is being applied to reducing staff needed to handle large call volumes and as a way of extending business hours without adding staff. More often, it is perceived as a source of competitive advantage for businesses serving customers with rotary-dial telephones. For businesses with existing international operations, it offers better support for overseas clients and staff who are more likely to use rotary-dial telephones than touch-tone telephones. For businesses planning international activity, it is an avenue to new markets across the world.

This perception of speech recognition as a viable technology for business has been enhanced by Sprint's well-publicized use of speech recognition in its *Voice FONCARD* and the growing media coverage of speech recognition technology. Kalmbach Publishers, a Wisconsin-based publisher of hobby and leisure literature and videos, implemented speech recognition for call-routing as a way to improve handling of calls made to their 800-number sales line after business hours and on weekends. Their previous system was costly and forced rotary-telephone customers to wait in a queue for service. Since they estimate that 35 percent of their customers have rotary telephones, Kalmbach wanted a system that would serve all their customers. The speech recognition feature enabled Kalmbach to route calls more efficiently and cut Kalmbach's answering-service costs. It ran so smoothly from the start that a Kalmbach representative observed, "There wasn't even a hiccough."

Speech recognition applications for business can be deployed on a telecommunications network (see section 9.2) or attached to the private PBX or internal telephone system of an organization. Data access applications can be linked to company databases. An application developed by the Art Research and Trading Cooperative of Santa Fe, New Mexico, allows art dealers to check the latest trading price of a piece of artwork or to receive a list of the available titles by a specific artist. The information is contained in a FoxPro database on the Cooperative's PC network.

The recent development of digital signal processing technology capable of emulating telephones, facsimile machines, and other telecommunications devices has made telephone-computer integration a reality. This type of unified communication system is extremely attractive to business professionals who want to navigate all systems using a single interface. It is also attractive to outbound professionals who seek easy access to home-office systems. One of the first voice-controlled integrated systems is the *InterActive Communicator* of InterActive Inc. It provides voice-controlled access to incoming calls, voice messages, FAX transmissions, and e-mail from a PC. To accomplish these complex links, the Communicator uses IBM's *Windsurfer* telephony and sound card along with *Windows*-based software that allows customization of the system. The *Windsurfer* sound card has DSP technology capable of emulating a telephone, telephone answering system, FAX machine, and modem. The speech input device is a proprietary telephone handset (called the *SoundXchange*). It can be held like a telephone or used from a distance for hands-free operation.

> When you conceptualize a business person using a system like ours you have to consider privacy and convenience. They must have the ability to go hands-free when they access e-mail, for example. They must also have privacy when they are issuing commands. Basically, the business user must be as comfortable and relaxed as possible using the system. That is why we offer a telephone handset rather than a headset and have hands-free operation, too (Michael Pulizzi, Vice President of Marketing, InterActive Inc., personal communication, 1994).

The newest version of the system allows access to e-mail from a public telephone and offers Verbex Voice Systems' speaker-independent and speaker-dependent technology (also see chapter 7, section 7.3). Systems like the *InterActive Communicator* are expected to grow increasingly popular.

The *Wildfire Electronic Assistant* (Wildfire Communications) is a voice-controlled call management system for mobile professionals. It contains advanced call-management features and consolidates a user's home, office, and car telephone numbers into a single personal-access telephone number. The system functions at a corporate level and is connected to the public telephone network by a T-1 line at a corporation site. Using Voice Processing Corporation's continuous speech technology, the *Wildfire Electronic Assistant* includes voice-activated dialing, as well as commands to filter incoming calls and manage telephone messages. A similar system with multi-lingual speech recognition was recently introduced in Germany by MOSCOM/Votan.

Very little has been published on the use of speech recognition by business professionals. For a product review of the *InterActive Communicator* consult the paper by Luhmann (1994). Markowitz (1994b) covers some of the other topics.

9.7 FINANCIAL INDUSTRY

Applications used in brokerage houses, for banking, and with credit cards are discussed in the following sections.

9.7.1 Brokerages

In the brokerage industry the speed with which traders can capitalize on market information determines whether or not they will profit from rapidly changing market conditions. Differences of seconds in a trader's ability to respond to breaking market news translate into increased profits or losses. Any technology capable of reducing the time it takes for a broker to access information or to generate a transaction constitutes a strategic competitive advantage.

> Voice is ten times faster than a trader writing a ticket and five times faster than using a keyboard. The traders talked a deal into the system faster than they wrote a ticket or typed the order into the system (Steven Gott, Executive Vice President, Shearson Lehman Hutton, "Verbex *Voice Trader* named one of 1989's outstanding products in financial and banking markets," Verbex Voice Systems press announcement, 1990).

Trading rooms offer a significant challenge for speech recognition. Noise levels can be as high as 88 to 90 dB, requiring robust recognition. Traders speak rapidly, requiring continuous speech recognition, and their voices exhibit stress, fatigue, the Lombard effect, and strong emotion.

In 1989, Verbex Voice Systems introduced the *Voice Trader*. It was the first voice-controlled trading system in the financial industry and was identified by *Banker's Monthly* as one of 1989's outstanding products serving the financial and banking industries. The *Voice Trader* accepts orders like

> I buy 100 million long bonds from Dillion at seven and a half percent
> One year T-bills one thousand at fifty-five for Greenwich
> Sell 10,000 IBM at fifty and an eighth

It then waits for the trader to correct the input or to place the order by saying "done" or "go." Several other trading systems have been developed since the introduction of *Voice Trader*. Some have been developed as collaborative efforts between speech recognition providers and trading-industry companies, such as Quotron Systems and Shark Information Services.

StockTalk by Bell-Northern Research represents a different type of trading system. It provides real-time quotations over the telephone. Callers say a company's name and get the current quote for its stock. The speaker-independent system uses Bell-Northern's subword technology. Subword vocabulary development enables system developers to add companies as they appear on one of the exchanges the system supports. *StockTalk* handles between 2,000 and 2,500 calls per day for more than six thousand companies listed on the New York Stock Exchange (NYSE), the Toronto Stock Exchange, and the National Association of Securities Dealers Automated Quotations (NASDAQ).

Consult Marion (1989) for more information on Shearson's use of the *Voice Trader*. Sharp & Lennig (1994) discuss Bell-Northern's *StockTalk* system. Markowitz (1993c) contains an overview of speech recognition in the financial industry and Yraslorza (1989) describes two early trading applications.

9.7.2 Banking and Credit Cards

The use of speech recognition for banking and credit cards has focused on banking by telephone. In contrast with its use in brokerage houses, speech recognition in the banking and credit card industries is viewed as a component of customer service. The addition of speech to home banking is seen as a competitive advantage because it allows the financial institution to offer the same 24-hour, home banking services to rotary telephone customers that it provides to customers with touch-tone telephones. Customers can move funds between accounts, check account balances, apply for credit, and request information. The use of speech for home banking represents a marked competitive advantage overseas where virtually all telephone systems rely on rotary technology.

The telephone channel is noisy and limited in the frequencies it processes (see chapter 7, section 7.1.3). As with most telephone applications, the likelihood of extraneous speech requires the use of word spotting. Customer diversity and the expectation that customers will access the system infrequently demand clearly defined and thoroughly tested application scripts. One metric used to evaluate these systems is the percentage of customers able to complete a telephone transaction without requiring assistance from a human being. Banks with an international presence and those serving multi-cultural communities need multi-lingual prompts and recognition. Vendors have responded by developing word models for basic vocabulary items in British English, Spanish, French, German, Japanese, and other languages.

The use of speech recognition in the credit card industry is just beginning. Because of the concern with credit card fraud, the voice technology used has generally been for speaker verification rather than for speech recognition. JC Penney has adapted the home banking concept for its credit card holders to get information about their credit card limits, account balances, and payment dates. Several companies, including AT&T, are working on speech recognition and speaker verification for ATM machines.

Markowitz (1993c) contains an overview of speech recognition in the financial industry.

9.8 CONSUMER PRODUCTS AND SERVICES

The consumer market is one of the newest and most dynamic arenas of speech recognition product/application development. It is broadbased and diverse, making it difficult to describe its overall characteristics or requirements. Potential applications and platforms are more varied than for any other market. Platforms are expected to range in size from specialized chips for handheld devices to network servers. Applications already deployed or under development include

• *Entertainment*	interactive toys, interactive kiosks, computer games, drive-thru food ordering
• *Travel*	hand-held translation systems, cameras, information kiosks, car navigation
• *Home appliances*	refrigerators, washers and dryers, ovens, and dishwashers
• *Home electronics*	VCR's, PDA's, and televisions
• *Consumer services*	kiosks, drive-up banking

Among the areas of greatest development activity are drive-up services, primarily for fast-food restaurants and banks. Another potential growth area is in kiosks. The success of AT&T's *Alice's Interactive Wonderland* (see chapter 7, section 7.6.4) in Disney World bodes well for comparable kiosk applications, but should not be used to argue that the problems facing public-access kiosks and other far-field microphone settings have been solved.

For many consumer products, success depends upon the perceived benefit derived from speech recognition. Consumers expect voice control of VCR's, for example, to eliminate the need to learn how to program the equipment. The speech recognition in these systems must be very robust because many of them are likely to be used in at least one adverse speaking environment, including surviving outdoors (see chapter 7).

Voice Powered Technology is one of the active developers of voice-controlled consumer products. Their first product, *VCR Voice* (see section 9.6.3), was a voice-driven remote control device for VCR's. *VCR Voice* does speaker-dependent, discrete-word recognition and has a vocabulary of thirty-one words for basic commands and VCR programming instructions. To instruct the VCR to record a program on channel 2 between 7:00 and 9:00 P.M., for example, a user would need to load their personal voice file and say

Two, Monday, 7PM, 9PM

Voice Powered Technology is rapidly expanding its product line to include systems as diverse as the *Voice Organizer* PDA (see section 9.6.3), a voice-activated telephone dialing system, and a voice-interactive doll.

Amerigon Inc. recently introduced *AudioNav,* a voice-interactive vehicle navigation system designed to reduce the frustration and confusion associated with finding locations in an unfamiliar city. Unlike most automobile navigation systems, *AudioNav* is a hands-free, voice-activated product that does not require the driver to consult a screen display. It is programmed to obtain the speaker's current location and destination. It then provides detailed directions for getting to the destination. The system contains software for calculating routes, a simple dialogue manager, and discrete-word speech recognition. It uses these tools to access a database of the streets and highways of a metropolitan area on a compact disc and to interact with the user. Figure 9.8 displays a typical interaction.

As figure 9.8 indicates, alphabetic spelling is critical for the operation of this system. Discrete-word spelling is paced through the use of tones. Spelling recognition accuracy is accomplished through the use of a confusability matrix (see chapter 3, section 3.5.3). To facilitate recall of directions, they are administered in chunks when the speaker says "Next." Misrecognitions from the noisy automobile environment are minimized by automatically turning recognition off after each direction. To continue an interaction with the system the motorist simply says "Navigator." Each CD contains several major metropolitan areas, grouped geographically.

Speech recognition in toys has been used to increase their entertainment value. In 1987, Playmates Toys introduced *Julie,* a doll capable of responding to eight words/phrases:

yes, no, OK, Julie, pretend, hungry, melody, be quiet

Julie was not a commercial success and was removed from the market, but the concept of using speech in toys was established. In 1993, Toy Biz and Buddy L introduced speech-controlled mechanical toys for boys. Buddy L has a line of voice-

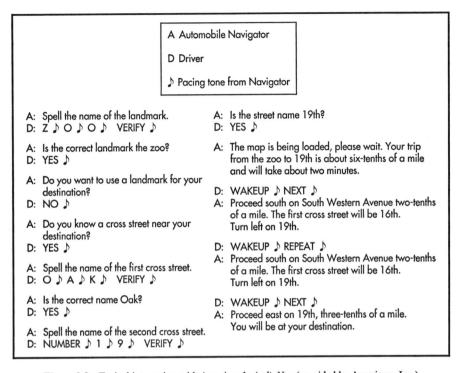

A Automobile Navigator

D Driver

♪ Pacing tone from Navigator

A: Spell the name of the landmark.
D: Z ♪ O ♪ O ♪ VERIFY ♪

A: Is the correct landmark the zoo?
D: YES ♪

A: Do you want to use a landmark for your
    destination?
D: NO ♪

A: Do you know a cross street near your
    destination?
D: YES ♪

A: Spell the name of the first cross street.
D: O ♪ A ♪ K ♪ VERIFY ♪

A: Is the correct name Oak?
D: YES ♪

A: Spell the name of the second cross street.
D: NUMBER ♪ 1 ♪ 9 ♪ VERIFY ♪

A: Is the street name 19th?
D: YES ♪

A: The map is being loaded, please wait. Your trip
    from the zoo to 19th is about six-tenths of a mile
    and will take about two minutes.

D: WAKEUP ♪ NEXT ♪
A: Proceed south on South Western Avenue two-tenths
    of a mile. The first cross street will be 16th.
    Turn left on 19th.

D: WAKEUP ♪ REPEAT ♪
A: Proceed south on South Western Avenue two-tenths
    of a mile. The first cross street will be 16th.
    Turn left on 19th.

D: WAKEUP ♪ NEXT ♪
A: Proceed east on 19th, three-tenths of a mile.
    You will be at your destination.

Figure 9.8   Typical interaction with Amerigon's *AudioNav* (provided by Amerigon, Inc.)

controlled vehicles, including a tank, a fire hook and ladder, and a stock car. Toy Biz' *VOICE-BOT* is a transforming robot capable of changing its shape and moving in response to eight distinct commands, including

COMMAND	RESPONSE
Start engines	Vehicle starts. Drive engines turn over and idle. *VOICE-BOT* says "Ready for command." and both headlights and eyes flash.
Begin transform and attack	Transformation into robot occurs. *VOICE-BOT* says "I am *VOICE-BOT*." Headlights and eyes pulse.

In 1995, TYCO introduced a similar toy, called *Gorzak*. In addition to several predefined commands, *Gorzak* can learn up to twenty new commands created by its owner.

    Computer games represent another area of significant commercial opportunity. Speech recognition is a natural adjunct to games that rely heavily upon digitized speech and sound output. InterPlay Production was one of the first to incorporate recognition technology into a computer game. Their *Star Trek: 25th Anniversary* game contains a small, speaker-independent vocabulary designed to enable players to replace manual control with voice commands. Computer and video game manufacturers have been moving slowly to incorporate speech recognition into their products because the music and noise associated with many games present a significant challenge for accurate recognition. As with many types of consumer products, improvements in the accuracy of recognition algorithms, better microphone technology, and the declining cost of adding speech recognition is encouraging more experimentation in this area.

The number of educational toys and games is also growing. Although they may not need to operate under the high noise conditions of entertainment systems, educational products often require larger vocabularies. The *Busytown Talker,* introduced in 1995 by Tomy, incorporates characters and style created by Richard Scarry for his *Busytown* educational books and videos. It is a portable toy shaped like a laptop computer with a handle, display screen, speaker, and external microphone. It contains more than thirty-five words and several modes of operation, including functioning as an interactive learning game. In that mode, the *Busytown Talker* asks the child questions about pictures on a card inserted into the system. The use of graphics helps reduce some of the variability in the child's response. Intertainment's CD-ROM *Robby Rabbit Rhyme Reason-n-Remember* is modeled after television game shows. The child selects a category and responds to questions from the host, Robby Rabbit. As with the *Busytown Talker,* the use of visual prompts controls the size of the vocabulary and enhances accuracy.

10

WHAT LIES AHEAD?

INTRODUCTION

The ultimate goal of the speech recognition industry is to create systems that are capable of communicating with human beings in a natural, effective manner. The preceding chapters have shown that, although this goal for verbal interaction has not yet been achieved, speech recognition has moved significantly closer to it.

The forces that are driving the industry towards that goal can be divided into two complementary and interactive groups: technological advances and application-related needs. The business-related need for affordable, continuous speech, free-form dictation systems, for example, is both a motivator and a benefactor of technological advances in continuous speech recognition.

In addition to the advances generated from within the speech recognition industry, progress is being stimulated by technological advances in computer hardware and software, particularly by the design of increasingly powerful microprocessors, by extensive miniaturization, and by the growth of global business (see chapter 1, section 1.1.3).

The Technology Focus will discuss four active areas of research and development:

- Continuous speech dictation
- Spoken language understanding
- Speech-to-speech translation
- Chip-level technology

Each is described in terms of its motivating forces, challenges, and its focus of research activity.

The Application Focus examines speech recognition in its usual role as a component of larger, multi-functional systems. It is divided into three sections:

- Industry standards
- Application directions
- Outlook for the future of the industry

The first of these sections considers standards for application programming interfaces, product evaluation, and human interface design. It examines why creation of standards is vital to the commercial success of speech recognition and describes what is being done to define them. The second section describes two new application areas that will offer enormous opportunities for speech recognition: computer-telephone integration and multimedia. The last section is a brief summary and forecast.

10.1 CONTINUOUS SPEECH DICTATION

A long-standing goal of the speech recognition industry has been to create a *listening typewriter*. The first steps towards realization of that goal were taken with the commercialization of very large vocabulary, discrete-word recognition technology at the end of the 1980's. A second step was taken in 1994, when Philips Dictation Systems introduced the first commercial, large vocabulary, continuous speech dictation product.

One of the issues impeding the widespread commercialization of large vocabulary, continuous speech dictation systems has been computational complexity (see chapter 6, section 6.3). Unlike discrete-word recognition systems, continuous speech must process both intra-word and cross-word coarticulation as well as locate word boundaries. To be commercially viable, continuous speech dictation systems must be able to accomplish these tasks with free-form input containing very large vocabularies. Furthermore, they must complete their work very rapidly and exhibit a high level of accuracy. The Philips Dictation Systems' product sidestepped the speed requirement by performing recognition after the dictation was completed. Recognizers that are prepared to operate in real time do not have that option.

Assistance has been coming from the new generations of microprocessor chips that are capable of running more sophisticated algorithms and larger vocabularies at a rate that is fast enough to satisfy users. This hardware is enabling other vendors to join Philips Dictation Systems in offering continuous speech dictation systems and allowing Philips to design a real-time version of its software.

The drive to miniaturize is playing a role in the commercialization of continuous speech dictation as well. Palmtop and other hand-held devices are accruing more functionality for both business and personal use. Standard input devices, such as the keyboard and mouse, are cumbersome and inefficient, placing greater emphasis on new forms of input, particularly speech and handwriting. These forms of input must be easy to learn, easy to use, and capable of performing all the functions users wish to perform on small devices. As a result, the ability to deploy large vocabulary, continuous speech dictation on PDA's, hand-held telecommunication systems, and other portable devices will be a critical component of the success of speech recognition in the future.

10.2 SPOKEN LANGUAGE UNDERSTANDING

> One of the reasons that speech is appealing to people is because in everybody's mind computers are hard to deal with and if we could speak to those systems we think it would be better . . . People's expectations are higher for speech. They want a bit of intelligence. They want the system to make more of an effort to reach out to them (Jeff Hill, Vice President of New Product Development, Voice Processing Corporation, personal communication, 1993).

Unfortunately,

> There is still a big difference in errors between a recognition system and a human—even for good recognizers. Speech is a psychological experience and we don't understand enough about that to work as well as a human. This argues for natural language processing and cognitive systems—systems that can recognize larger vocabularies and know the context of the situation (Robert Perdue, Supervisor, AT&T Bell Laboratories, personal communication, 1994).

This realization has stimulated renewed research on linguistic and cognitive models. The focus so far has been on developing systems capable of participating in dialogues with human beings (called *discourse processing;* see chapter 4, section 4.4). Techniques of statistical language processing, pattern matching, natural language processing, and neural networks are being combined into the field of *spoken language understanding.*

As with continuous speech dictation, the computational complexity resulting from combining speech recognition with language analysis is enormous. There are several promising areas of research designed to increase accuracy and speed for these systems. One is the development of sophisticated searching algorithms, such as N-best, that

> use the results of a simple and fast speech recognition technique to constrain the search space of a following more accurate but slower running technique. This may be done iteratively—each progressive search pass uses a previous pass' constraints to run more efficiently and faster without significant loss in accuracy (Hy Murveit, John Butzberger, Vassilios Digalakis, Mitch Weintraub, SRI International, "Progressive-search algorithms for large-vocabulary speech recognition," 1993, p. 1).

Gisting (see chapter 4, section 4.5.2) represents another type of useful approach. Currently, gisting prototypes extract information from idiomatic but highly structured dialogues between humans in situations that do not allow active participation by an interactive speech recognition device. Prototypes that have been developed for air-traffic control communication could easily be extended to interactions between taxicab drivers or mobile police officers and dispatchers. Extensions of gisting to less structured communication include applications requiring rapid, automatic summarization of large quantities of spoken language. Such systems will become a valuable resource for incorporating verbal data into online database research systems, such as *Westlaw*.

An important area of research that has received little attention from the speech recognition industry is *prosody*. Prosody refers to the patterns of emphasis placed upon words and phrases and on the pitch and rhythm we impose upon sentences. Prosody can be used to improve the accuracy of continuous speech recognition systems by helping to differentiate similar sounding patterns, such as "Ann Jones" from "and Jones." It is also useful for identifying the communicative intent of the speaker. Statements of fact, questions, and exclamations, for example, possess distinct intonation patterns. Figure 10.1 provides examples of how prosodic patterns can assist spoken language understanding for English.

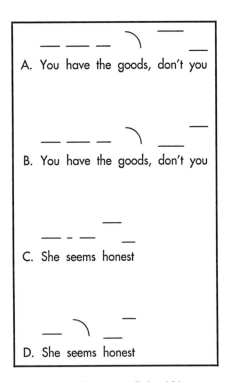

Figure 10.1 Prosodic patterns distinguishing utterances

The lines above each utterance indicate changes in pitch and emphasis. The pattern in 10.1a is a question, but 10.1b is a statement (or even a threat). The utterance in 10.1c is a simple statement, but 10.1d is clearly communicating doubt. Prosody can also be used to remove the ambiguity in an utterance. When the utterance

Does the train run on Saturday or Sunday?

is meant to ask whether the train runs on either day, it will have a standard question intonation with pitch rising at the end. When the questioner knows the train runs on one of those days but wants to know which, the word "Saturday" will have a rising pitch, but the pitch on "Sunday" will fall.

One of the most active centers of research on prosody for language understanding is at SRI International. Interest is growing among other speech researchers, but it lags behind development in other facets of spoken language understanding. More work is being done to enhance the quality of speech synthesis and for speech recognition of tone languages, like Mandarin.

10.3 SPEECH-TO-SPEECH TRANSLATION

Effective translation requires extensive knowledge about the semantics, word structure, and culture of each language. The operational challenges include all those facing continuous-speech dictation and spoken language understanding. In addition, development is arduous, frustrating, and filled with linguistic traps. Despite such hurdles, research on speech-to-speech and speech-to-text translation is active. Existing prototypes and systems are still confined to clearly-specified tasks with straightforward vocabulary.

Multi-national collaborative efforts are moving the research forward at a rapid pace. One of the most successful multi-national efforts is the Consortium for Speech Translation Research (C-STAR). C-STAR is a collaborative effort involving U.S., German, and Japanese organizations (originally ATR, CMU, Siemens AG, and Karlsruhe University). The aim of C-STAR is to develop English-German-Japanese speech-to-speech translation technology for use over public telephone networks. C-STAR has fostered the development of several prototypes capable of translating structured speech over the telephone. A limited test of the capabilities of the C-STAR systems was publicly demonstrated in January, 1993, in several trans-oceanic telephone calls.

The rise of global business, activity on the information superhighway, increasing linguistic diversity within nations, and international travel are driving research on spoken language translation, particularly in Japan and Europe. The Advanced Telecommunications Research Institute (ATR) in Kyoto, Japan has Interpreting Telecommunications Research Laboratories working on multi-modal and speech-only systems. Their research is directed at translating the speech of a single speaker and interpreting dialogues involving two or more speakers. NEC Corporation has an experimental English-Japanese system capable of handling several types of structured queries, such as purchasing concert tickets. The NEC system can also translate either of these languages into French or Spanish. Siemens AG has created its own machine translation company that is working on both spoken language and text translations. In the United States, most work on speech-to-speech and speech-to-text translation resides in research laboratories of universities (e.g., MIT, SRI, and CMU) and federally funded contractors, including Language Systems Inc. and BBN.

Additional information about some of these systems can be obtained from Montgomery, et al. (1993), Osterholtz, et al. (1992), Sagayama, et al. (1993), and Woszczyna, et al. (1993). Boitet & Loken-Kim (1993) describe work at ATR and examine human factors issues in the design of systems capable of interpreting multi-speaker dialogues.

10.4 CHIP-LEVEL SYSTEMS

The push to embed speech recognition in chips is being driven by market pressure to develop multi-functional consumer products. These include portable communication systems and consumer products from educational toys to PDA's.

> We wanted to put the speech on a single chip so that in applications like cellular telephones you can put it into a very thin package. This would allow it to be used in other packages [or products] where it could not be used before (Joe Baranowski, Vice President of Sales and Marketing, OKI Semiconductor, personal communication, 1994).

The effort to create chip-level systems is being supported by continued leaps in the power and performance of chip technology. In 1994, Digital Equipment Corporation, for example, built a commercially available microprocessor capable of performing more than a billion instructions per second. The following year International Meta Systems filed a patent for hardware emulation technology that enables its *META 3250* to functionally duplicate the characteristics of other microprocessors, such as the Power PC (IBM) and Digital's Alpha chip (also see chapter 1, sections 1.1.3 and 1.2; chapter 8, section 8.3.5).

The potential market in consumer products is accelerating the trend to increase the size of the speech recognition vocabulary on chips. Chip manufacturers, like AT&T and Oki Semiconductor, are moving from small vocabulary systems suitable for voice-activated telephone dialing to chip-based systems with one hundred or more words. Meanwhile, other companies, like International Meta Systems, are developing large vocabulary systems for dictation. Consult Zakai (1994) for more information about the Oki Semiconductor chip.

10.5 STANDARDS

The more we commit to industry-standard interfaces, standard components and standard protocols, the easier we'll make it for developers to create more innovative and more useful applications (Pat Russo, President, AT&T Global Business Communication Systems, Keynote speech at *Advanced Speech Applications and Technologies Conference '94*).

The creation of standards is a critical element of the utilization of speech recognition by application developers and the general public. It serves a number of functions:

- Facilitates the integration of speech with other technologies
- Enhances widespread acceptance of the technology
- Supports the design of speech-enabled systems

There are three primary types of standards that will move the industry in these directions:

- Application programming interface (API)
- Product evaluation
- Human-interface

All of these are still works in progress.

10.5.1 Application Programming Interface

Speech technology has reached the stage where it can become a broad based productivity tool, instead of a niche product. However, two barriers must be overcome for this potential to be realized:

- Speech Recognition must be robustly integrated into applications to maximize gains in productivity and significantly enhance ease of use.
- Speech enabled applications must be able to write to one API for integration across a variety of speech recognition technologies.
  (Bruce Armstrong, Chair, SRAPI committee and Manager, Novell Speech Technology Group, "Speech recognition application program interface committee, 1994," p. 20)

Both of these require the creation of API standards. The absence of such standards forces developers to design their applications and products for specific recognition products. This amplifies the work required to ensure that the product will function properly with the rest of the application and it increases concern about the potential need to change to another recognition product. In short,

Now, every project is a headache because there are no standards for multiple-technology . . . applications (Terry Henry, Marketing manager, Dialogic Corporation, personal communication, 1993).

To address these problems Dialogic, WordPerfect, and Microsoft all organized API standards efforts. The standards efforts of these three companies attracted broad-based support from within the speech recognition industry, as well as from large and small software and hardware manufacturers.

Dialogic Corporation, one of the world leaders in interactive voice response (IVR) equipment, began its standards effort in 1993. The effort involved two groups: a five-person Speech Recognition Standards Workgroup and an eighty-company Standards Advisory Group. The workgroup focused on establishing standards for call-processing systems operating over public telephone networks by defining a vendor-independent API for Dialogic's Signal Computing System Architecture (SCSA) call-processing specifications. By early 1994, the recommendations of the workgroup were distributed among the eighty software and hardware companies comprising the Standards Advisory Group. The final standards were published as part of Dialogic's 1994 SCSA manual and have become the basis of a white paper on speech recognition standards written by the members of the workgroup.

In 1994, both Novell/WordPerfect and Microsoft organized API standards efforts directed at desktop systems. The Novell/WordPerfect Speech Recognition API workgroup (called SRAPI) consisted of developers and value-added resellers from within the speech industry and non-industry organizations interested in applying speech recognition. SRAPI distributed the first draft of recommendations for *Windows 3.1* in October, 1994. By the second quarter of 1995 it had published *version 0.5* of its API specifications for *Windows 3.1* and *Windows 95* and had begun to extend those standards to UNIX, Macintosh OS, and other platforms.

Microsoft's internal standards group focused on designing specifications for *Windows 95*. These standards cover speech recognition, text-to-speech synthesis, and multimedia audio objects. A detailed Beta version of the Microsoft specifications appeared in April, 1995.

The success of these standards efforts depends heavily upon the participation of speech recognition technology vendors, value-added resellers, and application developers. Many vendors have agreed to design to the three sets of standards, but the overall industry trend to move between platforms strongly suggests that differences among the three sets of specifications will ultimately need to be resolved into a more global standard.

For more information on the SCSA standard effort consult Markowitz (1993d). Microsoft's (1995) standard can be obtained via Internet from msspeech@microsoft.com and the SRAPI (1995) standard can be obtained from the Speech Recognition Application Program Interface Committee at SRAPI@novell.com.

10.5.2 Product Evaluation

There are no standards for product evaluation, but there are techniques and tools that can be applied to the evaluation of products (see chapter 8, section 8.5). Bellcore's Technical Audit program (also see chapter 8, section 8.5) provides one solution for technology designed to operate over telephone networks. Their reference databases and evaluation methods assess the *accuracy* of speech recognition technology under specific telephone network conditions, but their Technical Audit does not attempt to validate or test any other product features.

> The primary purpose of the technical analysis is to determine whether a supplier's VIT [voice input technology] product does not meet, meets, or exceeds the accuracy requirements for a particular VIT application. The conditions of the technical analysis will be as close as possible to the conditions experienced in a real network VIT application (Doug Nortz & Candace Kamm of Bellcore, Rob Bossemeyer of Ameritech, Harry Chang of NYNEX Science & Technology, Mike Boyden of Pacific Bell, Jeff Scruggs & George Velius of SBC Technology Resources, and Frank Wu of US West Advanced Technologies, "Bellcore/BCC voice input technologies technical analysis specification," 1992, p. 333).

Product testing using the Bellcore program began in 1994.

Carefully designed evaluation programs like Bellcore's Technical Audit are sorely needed. They make it easier for technology developers to obtain an objective performance assessment without having to develop assessment tools themselves. Furthermore, if a representative sampling of vendors agrees to subject their technology to such testing, the process will serve to advance speech technology and to establish *de facto* performance standards for specific speaking environments.

10.5.3 Human Factors

Speech is a basic, universal mode of human communication. The human model, combined with images of communication devices in science fiction, defines the *naturalness* standard that is often applied to speech recognition. Human-quality performance is a goal that will not be achieved for many years, but response to the *Wildfire Electronic Assistant* (chapter 8, section 8.3.5.4; chapter 9, section 9.6.3) demonstrates that it is not a necessary prerequisite for the perception of naturalness. Furthermore, the popularity of voice-activated dialing systems demonstrates that naturalness is not a prerequisite for acceptance. Most voice-activated dialing and messaging systems exploit user familiarity with the unnatural prompt-and-response paradigm for touch-tone interaction. There is no model for interaction with other devices (e.g., PC's, workstations, hand-held devices, and most consumer products) that can be as readily applied to speech recognition.

> The mass market will be waiting for that paradigm to advance to the point where when you walk up to your PC or workstation and there is a microphone there you say "I know

how to use this. I know how it works with this new application. Even though I have never used this application before." (Michael Krasner, President, Speech Group, BBN, Industry leaders panel *Advanced Speech Applications and Technologies Conference '94*).

Technologies like word spotting (chapter 4, section 4.5), subword vocabulary development (Chapter 3, section 3.1.5), and techniques of object-oriented and artificial intelligence (chapter 4, sections 4.5.2 and 4.10) are important tools that are moving the industry towards Krasner's needed paradigm. They are simply the means to implement natural human-computer interfaces.

The human component of naturalness for spoken interaction is still poorly understood and appears to vary from task to task. The definition of human-factors standards for speech remains one of the greatest challenges facing speech recognition today.

10.6 APPLICATION DIRECTIONS

As the earlier chapters of this book have demonstrated, the range of speech recognition applications under development is impressive. This section highlights two arenas of enormous commercial potential for speech.

10.6.1 Computer Telephone Integration (CTI)

Computer telephony unites the two most essential business instruments—PC's and telephones—and it can't come a moment too soon (Jon Udell, Senior Technical Editor, *Byte*, "Computer Telephony," 1994, p. 81)

The late 1980's saw the emergence of a simple form of voice-controlled CTI to access bank accounts and comparable telephone-based tasks. InterVoice was among the first to successfully offer systems of this sort. A more sophisticated example is the first version of Wildfire Communications' *Wildfire Electronic Assistant*. In these applications, the nature and extent of the data access is entirely under the control of businesses providing the services and the caller is generally not aware of the participation of the computer.

By the end of 1994, there had been a revolution in the concept of CTI. Its technological roots consisted of advances in telecommunications and computing technology, teleconferencing, multimedia, and the drive to miniaturize communication devices. At the same time, demands on the telecommunications industry for faster local and global communication, greater diversity in personal wireless communication services, and more telephone numbers created a business need for advanced telecommunications systems.

In January [1994], the Personal Communications Industry Association (PCIA) projected that by 2003 there could be nearly 31 million domestic PCS [personal communication systems] subscribers . . . Motorola Inc . . . a manufacturer of PCS equipment, envisions more than 150 million domestic wireless users in the long run. Two other pioneer PCS companies, American Personal Communications (APC) . . . and California Microwave Inc . . . estimate that PCS will become an international industry worth US $195 billion by the end of the decade (Narses Colmenares, Consultant, AT&T Services Company, "The FCC on personal wireless," 1994, p. 39.).

In the United States, this activity was fostered by moves of the FCC and Congress to modify regulations on mobile communications and other telecommunications services, and by increased FCC licensing for narrow band and electro-magnetic spectrum frequencies to providers of advanced personal communication service systems and emerging technologies. Similar actions were taken by the European Telecommunications Standards Institute and by the Japanese telecommunications industry.

CTI systems are multi-faceted and can emphasize the role of the computer or the telephone. Computer-oriented CTI systems often contain features that can be controlled by an individual user. Some products link computers with FAXes, telephone answering machines, and other equipment. The utility of speech recognition for these systems has been identified, but one of the few products using speech recognition is InterActive's *InterActive Communicator* (chapter 9, section 9.6).

The telephone has been undergoing changes that make telephone-centered CTI more viable. Telephones with display screens that are based upon the Analog Display Services Industry Standard (ADSI) are beginning to appear. The ADSI standard supports the use of text and voice, including speech recognition, over public telephone lines without modification to the local telephone loop.

The value of speech recognition for CTI is recognized, but its integration into CTI has been slow. One reason is the need for standards within the speech recognition industry (see section 10.5) complicated by the lack of a single CTI standard. There are a number of CTI standards for different functions. The two vying for dominance in call control involving workstations are:

- *TAPI* (Microsoft & Intel)
- *TSAPI* (AT&T & Novell)

TAPI is designed for workstation-based CTI where there is a direct link between the telephone and computer. *TSAPI* is oriented towards telephone networks and is applicable to environments where there is no direct link between the telephone and the computer. Proponents of each design are working towards establishing it as a standard. Since they address different environments *TAPI* and *TSAPI* may not need to be in conflict. Northern Telecom wrote a superset of *TAPI* and *TSAPI* specifications that exploits the strengths of each. The product, *Tmap,* was developed in cooperation with Microsoft and Novell. It translates *TAPI* programming requests into *TSAPI* requests, allowing developers to use the specifications with which they are more familiar.

CTI is an important facet of a joint effort by AT&T, IBM, Siemens, and Apple Computer to delineate product specifications designed to eliminate problems of "interoperability" between products of those companies. The specification effort, called *Versit,* includes the creation of a new form of *TSAPI,* called *Versit TSAPI,* that will be employed by all of those companies.

The *Orbitor* project of Bell-Northern Research exemplifies CTI development of personal communication systems. *Orbitor* is the concept for a pocket-size, wireless device combining speech-recognition, touch-screen, handwriting understanding, animated graphical display, telephone operation, and computer storage. The concept of the *Orbitor* was generated by focus group studies exploring the communication needs of different groups of telecommunications users.

> The user groups helped the Corporate Design team identify five key user values—mobility, ease of use, controlled accessibility, personalization and call closure (Michael Brown, Nancy Carboni, Neal Cowan, Jeff Fairless, Marilyn French-St. George, Donald Lindsay, Tracy Roberts & Desmond Ryan, Corporate Design Group, Bell-Northern Research, "*Orbitor:* A new personal communications concept," 1994, p. 4).

The *Orbitor* represents a vision of the future but not necessarily of the twenty-third century. The continued trends towards miniaturization, increased power at the chip level, and portable communications are likely to make mobile, integrated communications devices, like the *Orbitor,* a reality within the next few years.

10.6.2 Multimedia

Multimedia refers to a broad spectrum of products and systems with human interface elements that combine two or more non-text modalities. CTI applications represent one form of multimedia because they combine graphics with speech. Other types of multimedia systems integrate graphics, video, and sound for computing applications. The quality of these systems has improved markedly after 1990, and declining costs caused the market for multimedia systems to skyrocket. Between 1992 and 1993, sales leaped from approximately 300,000 to almost two million units sold and this trend continued as multimedia CD-ROM drives became standard equipment on desktop computers.

As with CTI, the value of speech recognition in multimedia was recognized in the early 1990's, but its integration into multimedia systems has been slow. Early use was by universities and laboratories, in multimedia research systems, such as CMU's prototype reading coach *LISTEN* and the *VOYAGER* system for getting directions developed in MIT's Media Laboratory.

Commercial use of speech recognition with multimedia began to grow in the mid 1990's but has been slow. It is being used as an element of educational software, notably Natural Speech Technologies' *Say&See* (see chapter 9, section 9.3). Multimedia edutainment has also begun to use speech (see chapter 9, section 9.8). Compton's NewMedia announced plans to incorporate speech recognition into its *Interactive Encyclopedia* and *Sporting News Pro Football* guide in 1993. The same year, Interplay Productions added small vocabulary, speaker independent recognition to its *Star Trek: 25th Anniversary* computer game.

Realization of the potential of speech recognition for multimedia edutainment is being delayed by several considerations. The lack of API standards makes the integration of speech recognition more difficult and risky. Another question voiced by multimedia software developers is whether speech recognition can overcome the blaring music, noise, and digitized speech that typify computer games and other multimedia systems. Finally, the absence of a well-defined human-interface for speech is likely to perpetuate the still-daunting expectation that it will perform as a human.

In the long run, speech recognition will become a standard component of multimedia systems. It is likely to occur in stages as the technology becomes more robust and versatile, and as the API and human-interaction standards evolve. As these problems are resolved we will witness the evolution of voice-activated multimedia from command-and-control to spoken interaction with intelligent multimedia agents and, finally, as intelligent virtual reality participants or holographic assistants.

10.7 OUTLOOK FOR THE FUTURE

The fuel that is driving the progress described in this book is the growing market for products and services that utilize speech recognition. Global business communication, entertainment, portability, competitive advantage, and better customer service all represent sources of existing and future markets, and all of them are transforming speech recognition from an interesting novelty into a fundamental and familiar feature of machines we encounter every day.

Much of the research described in this book has been funded by government agencies in the United States and overseas. Awareness of the commercial value of speech recognition is encouraging private industry to increase its contribution to these research and development efforts, but governments around the world recognize their continuing role. The *technology transfer* programs recently instituted by the United States government foster growing participation by private industry through an economic partnership among government, private industry, and academia. The object of these programs is to speed the commercialization of existing research systems and, hopefully, stimulate private funding for new research as well.

The rapid commercialization of speech recognition that began in the early

1990's has demonstrated the maturity of the technology. Examples provided throughout this book demonstrate the range of innovative and exciting applications that exist already. Many of the challenges that remain are symptomatic of an industry that is evolving towards its goals, but the economic and technological forces described in chapters 1, 9, and 10 promise to continue to move the industry forward at a rapid pace.

BIBLIOGRAPHY

ALLEVA, FIL, XUEDONG HUANG, and MEI-YUH HWANG. "An Improved Search Algorithm Using Incremental Knowledge for Continuous Speech Recognition." *Proceedings of the International Conference on Acoustics, Speech, and Signal Processing* 2 (1993): 30.

ANGLADE, YOLANDE, DOMINIQUE FOHR, and JEAN-CLAUDE JUNQUA. "Speech Discrimination in Adverse Conditions Using Acoustic Knowledge and Selectively Trained Neural Networks." *Proceedings of the International Conference on Acoustics, Speech, and Signal Processing* 2 (1993): 279–282.

ARMSTRONG, BRUCE. "Speech Recognition Application Program Interface Committee." *AVIOS '94 Proceedings* (1994): 19–26.

ASADI, AYMAN, RICHARD SCHWARTZ, and JOHN MAKHOUL. "Automatic Modeling for Adding New Words to a Large Vocabulary Continuous Speech Recognition System." *Proceedings of the International Conference on Acoustics, Speech, and Signal Processing* (1991): 305–308.

ASR NEWS 6(1). "Contel Cellular Signs Contract with Enhanced Speech Systems to Provide Voice Activated Dialing Systems." (January 1995): 1–2.

AVANT, HARRY. "Why Not Talk to Your Computer?" *UNIXWorld* (September 1992): 81–82.

BAHL, LALIT, PETER BROWN, PETER DESOUZA, and ROBERT MERCER. "A Tree-based Statistical Language Model for Natural Language Speech Recognition." *Transactions on Acoustics, Speech, and Signal Processing* 37(7) (1989): 1001–1008.

BAHL, LALIT, PETER BROWN, PETER DESOUZA, ROBERT MERCER, and MICHAEL PICHENY. "Acoustic Markov Models Used in the *Tangora* Speech Recognition System." *Proceedings of the International Conference on Acoustics, Speech, and Signal Processing* (1988): 497–500.

BAHL, LALIT, FREDERICK JELINEK, and ROBERT MERCER. "A Maximum Likelihood Approach to Continuous Speech Recognition." *IEEE Transactions on Pattern Analysis and Machine Intelligence* 5(2) (1983): 179–190. Reprinted in *Readings in Speech Recognition*, edited by Alex Waibel and Kai-Fu Lee (1990).

BAKER, JAMES. "Stochastic Modeling for Automatic Speech Understanding." *Speech Recognition*, edited by Raj Reddy. London: Academic Press, (1975a): 521–541. Reprinted in *Readings in Speech Recognition*, edited by Alex Waibel and Kai-Fu Lee (1990).

———. "The *DRAGON* System—An Overview." *IEEE Transactions on Acoustics, Speech, and Signal Processing* ASSP-23(1) (1975b): 24–29.

BAKER, JANET. "Dictation, Directories, and Data Bases: Emerging PC Applications for Large Vocabulary Speech Recognition." *Advanced Speech Applications and Technology Conference '94:* section 1 (1994).

BALENTINE, BRUCE. *Goodlistener Cookbook.* Denton, TX: Scott Instruments Corporation, 1992.

BATES, MADELEINE, ROBERT BOBROW, PASCALE FUNG, ROBERT INGRIA, FRANCIS KUBALA, JOHN MAKHOUL, LONG NGUYEN, RICHARD SCHWARTZ, and DAVID STALLARD. "The BBN/*HARC* Spoken Language Understanding System." *Proceedings of the International Conference on Acoustics, Speech, and Signal Processing* 2 (1993): 111–114.

BAUM, L. "An Inequality and Associated Maximization Technique in Statistical Estimation of Probabilistic Functions of a Markov Process." *Inequalities* 3 (1972): 1–8.

BIDDLE, J. "An Efficient Elastic-Template Method for Detecting Given Words in Running Speech." *Proceedings of the British Acoustic Society Meeting* (1973): 1–4.

BOITET, CHRISTIAN and KYUNG-HO LOKEN-KIM. "Human-Machine-Human Interactions in Interpreting Telecommunications." *International Symposium on Spoken Dialogues* (1993): 247–250.

BORDEN, GLORIA, KATHERINE HARRIS, and LAWRENCE RAPHAEL. *Speech Science Primer: Physiology, Acoustics, and Perception of Speech.* Baltimore, Maryland: Williams & Wilkins, 1994.

BOU-GHAZALE, SAHAR and JOHN H. L. HANSEN. "Duration and Spectral Based Stress Token Generation for HMM Speech Recognition Under Stress." *Proceedings of the International Conference on Acoustics, Speech, and Signal Processing* 1 (1994): 413–416.

BOURLARD, HERVÉ and NELSON MORGAN. *Connectionist Speech Recognition: A Hybrid Approach.* Dordrecht, The Netherlands: Kluwer Academic Publishers, 1994.

BROWN, MICHAEL, NANCY CARBONI, NEAL COWAN, JEFF FAIRLESS, MARILYN FRENCH-ST. GEORGE, DONALD LINDSAY, TRACY ROBERTS, and DESMOND RYAN. "*Orbitor:* A New Personal Communications Concept." Internal document, Bell-Northern Research, 1994.

CARLSON, BETH and MARK CLEMENTS. "Speech Recognition in Noise Using a Projection-based Likelihood Measure for Mixture Density HMMs." *Proceedings of the International Conference on Acoustics, Speech, and Signal Processing* 1 (1992): 237–240.

CARRELL, THOMAS. "Acoustical Cues to Auditory Object Formation in Sentences." (Forthcoming) *Theories in Spoken Language: Perception, Production, and Development,* edited by J. Charles-Luce, P. Luce, and J. Sawusch. Norwood, NJ: Ablex Press, 1992.

CARRELL, THOMAS and JANE OPIE. "The Effect of Amplitude Comodulation on Auditory Object Formation in Sentence Perception." *Perception & Psychophysics* 52(4) (1992): 437–445.

CATER, JOHN. *Electronically Hearing: Computer Speech Recognition.* Indianapolis, IN: Howard W. Sams, & Co, Inc., 1984.

CAUDILL, MAURINE and C. BUTLER. *Understanding Neural Networks: Computer Explorations, Vols 1 and 2.* Cambridge, MA: MIT Press, 1992.

CERF, G., F. GRAY, S. MEHTA, G. VYSOTSKY, and L. ZREIK. "The NYNEX *VoiceDialing* Service." In *AVIOS '94 Proceedings* (1994): 147–153.

CHENG, YAN MING and DOUGLAS O'SHAUGHNESSY. "Speech Enhancement Based Conceptually on Auditory Evidence." *Transactions on Signal Processing* 39(9) (1991): 1943–1946.

CIPRIANI, MICHAEL. "Voice Recognition in Pathology from and [sic] 'End Users' Perspective." *Speech Tech '91* (1991): 320–323.

COLE, RONALD. "Performing Fine Phonetic Distinctions: Templates vs. Features." *Variability and Invariance in Speech Processes,* edited by J. S. Perkell and D. Klatt. Hillsdale, NJ: Lawrence Erlebaum, 1986.

COLMENARES, NARSES. "The FCC on Personal Wireless." *IEEE Spectrum* 31(5) (1994): 39–46.

COOK, RICK. "Voice Recognition: Time for Another Look?" *Managing Automation* (November 1990).

COOLEY, JAMES. "How the FFT Gained Acceptance." *IEEE Speech Processing Magazine* (1992): 10–13.

DAMPER, BOB and GRAHAM LEEDHAM. "Human Factors." *Speech Processing,* edited by Chris Rowden. New York: McGraw-Hill Book Company: 360–393, 1992.

DARWIN, C. "Perceptual Grouping of Speech Components Differing in Fundamental Frequency and Onset Time." *Quarterly Journal of Experimental Psychology* 33A (1981): 185–208.

DAS, SUBRATA, RAIMO BAKIS, ARTHUR NÁDAS, DAVID NAHAMOO, and MICHAEL PICHENY. "Influence of Background Noise and Microphone on the Performance of the IBM *Tangora* Speech Recognition System." *Proceedings of the International Conference on Acoustics, Speech, and Signal Processing* 2 (1993): 71–74.

DAVIS, K., R. BIDDULPH, and S. BALASHEK. "Automatic Recognition of Spoken Digits." *The Journal of the Acoustic Society of America* 24(6) (1952): 637–642.

DEFFNER, GERHARD, LINDA JO BLACK, and MARK OLLMANN. "*Wizard of Oz* Market Testing of Spoken Command Interface Style." *AVIOS '94 Proceedings* (1994): 123–128.

DE MORI, RENATO. "Extraction of Acoustic Cues Using a Grammar of Frames." *Speech Communication* 2 (1983): 223–225.

DE MORI, RENATO, YOSHUA BENGIO, and PIERO COSI. "On the Generalization Capability of Multi-Layered Networks in the Extraction of Speech Properties." *Proceedings of the Eleventh International Joint Conference on Artificial Intelligence* 2 (1989): 1531–1535.

DENG, LI, MATTHEW LENNIG, PHILIP SEITZ, and PAUL MERMELSTEIN. "Large Vocabulary Word Recognition Using Context-Dependent Allophonic Hidden Markov Models." *Computer Speech and Language* 4(4) (1990): 345–357.

DENNEBERG, L., H. GISH, MARIE METEER, T. MILLER, JON ROHLICEK, W. SADKIN, and M. SIU. "Gisting Conversational Speech in Real Time." *Proceedings of the International Conference on Acoustics, Speech, and Signal Processing* 2 (1993): 131–135.

DESIMIO, MARTIN and TIMOTHY ANDERSON. "Phoneme Recognition with Binaural Cochlear Models and the Stereausis Representation." *Proceedings of the International Conference on Acoustics, Speech, and Signal Processing* 1 (1993): 521–524.

EINSTEIN, DAVID. "Computer Age Enters its Final Frontier." *The San Francisco Chronicle*, 26 September 1994, B1 and B12.

ENGLISH, THOMAS and LOIS BOGGESS. "Back-Propagation Training of a Neural Network for Word Spotting." *Proceedings of the International Conference on Acoustics, Speech, and Signal Processing* 2 (1992): 357–360.

ERMAN, LEE, FREDERICK HAYES-ROTH, VICTOR LESSER, and D. RAJ REDDY. "The *Hearsay-II* Speech-understanding System: Integrating Knowledge to Resolve Uncertainty." *Computing Surveys* 12(2) (1980): 213–251.

EVENS, MARTHA, BONNIE LITOWITZ, JUDITH MARKOWITZ, RAOUL SMITH, and OSWALD WERNER. *Lexical-Semantic Relations: A Comparative Survey*. Champaign, IL: Linguistic Research, Inc., 1980.

FANTY, MARK, RONALD COLE, and KRIST ROGINSKI. "English Alphabet Recognition with Telephone Speech." *Advances in Neural Information Processing Systems 4*, edited by John Moody, Steven Hanson, and Richard Lippmann. San Mateo, CA: Morgan Kaufmann Publishers (1992): 199–206.

FISSORE, L., P. LAFACE, G. MICCA, and R. PIERACCINI. "A Word Hypothesizer for a Large Vocabulary Continuous Speech Understanding System." *Proceedings of the International Conference on Acoustics, Speech, and Signal Processing* (1989). Reprinted in *Readings in Speech Recognition*, edited by Alex Waibel and Kai-Fu Lee (1990).

FLANAGAN, JAMES, MANFRED SCHROEDER, BISHNU ATAL, RONALD CROCHIERE, NUGGEHALLY JAYANT, and JOSE TRIBOLET. "Speech Coding." *IEEE Transactions on Communications* COM-27(4) (1979): 710–737.

FOSTER, PETER and THOMAS SCHALK. *Speech Recognition*. New York, NY: Telecom Library, Inc., 1993.

FUKUZAWA, KEIJI, YASUHIRO KOMORI, HIDEFUMI SAWAI, and MASAHIDE SUGIYAMA. "A Segment-Based Speaker Adaptation Neural Network Applied to Continuous Speech Recognition." *Proceedings of the International Conference on Acoustics, Speech, and Signal Processing* 1 (1992): 433–436.

GARDNER, M.B. "Effect of Noise System Gain and Assigned Task on Talking Levels in Loudspeaker Communication." *Journal of the Acoustic Society of America* 40 (1966): 955–965.

GHITZA, ODED. "Temporal Non-place Information in the Auditory-nerve Firing Patterns as a Front-end for Speech Recognition in a Noisy Environment." *Journal of Phonetics* 16 (1988): 109–123.

———. "Auditory Models and Human Performance in Tasks Related to Speech Coding and Speech Recognition." *IEEE Transactions on Speech and Audio Processing* 2(1) (1994): 115–132.

GIACHIN, EGIDIO, AARON ROSENBERG, and CHIN-HUI LEE. "Word Juncture Modeling Using Phonological Rules for HMM-based Continuous Speech Recognition." *Proceedings of the International Conference on Acoustics, Speech, and Signal Processing* 2 (1990): 737–739.

GORIN, ALLEN, L. MILLER, and STEPHEN LEVINSON. "Some Experiments in Spoken Language Acquisition." *Proceedings of the International Conference on Acoustics, Speech, and Signal Processing* 1 (1993): 505–508.

GRAY, ROBERT. "Vector Quantization." *IEEE ASSP Magazine* 1(2) (1984): 4–29.

GRISHMAN, RALPH and JOHN STERLING. "Smoothing of Automatically Generated Selectional Constraints." *Proceedings of the ARPA Human Language Technology Workshop, Section 8* (1993).

HACKENBERG, ROBERT. "Intelligent Voice Control of Cameras and Robots." *AVIOS '87 Proceedings* (1987): 325–334.

HAFFNER, PATRICK, MICHAEL FRANZINI, and ALEX WAIBEL. "Integrating Time Alignment and Neural Networks for High Performance Continuous Speech Recognition." *Proceedings of the International Conference on Acoustics, Speech, and Signal Processing* (1991): 105–108.

HAFFNER, PATRICK and ALEX WAIBEL. "Multi-state Time Delay Neural Networks for Continuous Speech Recognition." *Advances in Neural Information Processing Systems 4,* edited by John Moody, Steven Hanson, and Richard Lippmann. San Mateo, CA: Morgan Kaufmann Publishers (1992): 135–143.

HAMMOND, GEOFF. "Deploying Speech Technology in Telephone Banking Services." *Speech Technology* 5(2) (1990): 30–33.

HAMPSHIRE, JOHN II and ALEX WAIBEL. "The *Meta-Pi* Network: Connectionist Rapid Adaptation for High-performance Multi-speaker Phoneme Recognition." *Proceedings of the International Conference on Acoustics, Speech, and Signal Processing* (1990): 165–168.

HANSEN, JOHN H.L. "Adaptive Source Generator Compensation and Enhancement for Speech Recognition in Noisy Stressful Environments." *Proceedings of the International Conference on Acoustics, Speech, and Signal Processing* 2 (1993): 95–98.

HANSEN, JOHN H.L. and LEVENT M. ARSLAN. "Robust Feature-estimation and Objective Quality Assessment for Noisy Speech Recognition Using the *Credit Card Corpus.*" *IEEE Transactions on Speech and Audio Processing* 3(3) (1995): 169–184.

HANSEN, JOHN H.L. and OSCAR BRIA. "Improved Automatic Recognition of Speech in Noise and Lombard Effect." *EUSIPCO '92* (1992): SP3P-13.1 and 13.4.

———. "Lombard Effect Compensation for Robust Automatic Speech Recognition in Noise." *1990 International Conference on Spoken Language Processing* (1990): 1125–1128.

HANSON, BRIAN and TED APPLEBAUM. "Subband or Cepstral Domain Filtering for Recognition of Lombard and Channel-distorted Speech." *Proceedings of the International Conference on Acoustics, Speech, and Signal Processing* 2 (1993): 79–82.

————. "Robust Speaker-independent Word Recognition Using Static, Dynamic and Acceleration Features: Experiments with Lombard and Noisy Speech." *Proceedings of the International Conference on Acoustics, Speech, and Signal Processing* (1990): 857–860.

HARKINS, JUDITH. "Voice Processing and Disabled People: A Symbiotic Relationship." *International Voice Systems Review* 1(1) (1989): 10.

HASZTO, EDWARD, WILLIAM LONGENBAKER, and JAMES SCHERER. "Talking to the Network." *AT&T Technology* 9(1) (1994): 22–27.

HAUPTMANN, ALEX, JACK MOSTOW, STEVEN ROTH, MATTHEW KANE, and ADAM SWIFT. "A Prototype Reading Coach that Listens: Summary of Project *LISTEN.*" *Proceedings of the ARPA Workshop on Human Language Technology* (1994).

HERMANSKY, HYNEK, NELSON MORGAN, and HANS-GUNTER HIRSCH. "Recognition of Speech in Additive and Convolutional Noise Based on *RASTA* Spectral Processing." *Proceedings of the International Conference on Acoustics, Speech, and Signal Processing* 2 (1993): 83–86.

HIRSHMAN, LYNETTE, MADELEINE BATES, DEBORAH DAHL, WILLIAM FISHER, JOHN GAROFOLO, DAVID PALLETT, K. HUNICKE-SMITH, PATTI PRICE, ALEXANDER RUDNICKY, and E. TZOUKER-MANN. "Multi-site Data Collection and Evaluation in Spoken Language Understanding." *ARPA Human Language Technology Workshop:* Section 1 (1994).

HO, JANET and GABRIEL GRONER. "Speech Recognition in a Hospital Bedside Charting System." *AVIOS '94 Proceedings* (1994): 37–48.

HON, HSIAO-WUEN and KAI-FU LEE. "On Vocabulary-independent Speech Modelling." *Proceedings of the International Conference on Acoustics, Speech, and Signal Processing* 2 (1990): 725–728.

HUANG, XUEDONG and KAI-FU LEE. "On Speaker-independent, Speaker-dependent, and Speaker-adaptive Speech Recognition." *IEEE Transactions on Speech and Audio Processing* 1(2) (1993): 150–157.

HUNT, MELVYN. "Figures of Merit for Assessing Connected-word Recognisers." *Speech Communication* 9 (1990): 329–336.

IMMEDIATO, PAUL. "Material Take-off Utilizing Voice Recognition." *Speech Tech '91* (1991): 88–90.

ISO, KEN-ICHI and TAKAO WANATABE. "Speaker-independent Word Recognition Using a Neural Prediction Model." *Proceedings of the International Conference on Acoustics, Speech, and Signal Processing.* Reprinted in *Readings in Speech Recognition,* edited by Alex Waibel and Kai-Fu Lee (1990).

ITO, RUSSELL. "Plain TALK." *MacUser* (October 1993): 95–98.

JELINEK, FREDERICK. *Probabilistic Information Theory.* New York, NY: McGraw-Hill, 1968.

————. "Continuous Speech Recognition by Statistical Methods." *Proceedings of the IEEE* 64 (1976): 532–556.

————. "The Development of an Experimental Discrete Dictation Recognizer." *Proceedings of the IEEE* 73(11) (1985): 1616–1624. Reprinted in *Readings in Speech Recognition,* edited by Alex Waibel and Kai-Fu Lee (1990).

————. "Self-organized Language Modeling for Speech Recognition." *Readings in Speech Recognition,* edited by Alex Waibel and Kai-Fu Lee (1990).

JELINEK, FREDERICK, LALIT BAHL, and ROBERT MERCER. "Design of a Linguistic Statistical Decoder for the Recognition of Continuous Speech." *IEEE Transactions on Information Theory* TI-21(3) (1975): 250–256.

JELINEK, FREDERICK, ROBERT MERCER, and SALIM ROUKOS. "Classifying Words for Improved Statistical Language Models." *Proceedings of the International Conference on Acoustics, Speech, and Signal Processing* 2 (1990): 621–624.

JUNQUA, JEAN-CLAUDE and YOLANDE ANGLADE. "Acoustic and Perceptual Studies of Lombard Speech: Application to Isolated-words [sic] Automatic Speech Recognition." *Proceedings of the International Conference on Acoustics, Speech, and Signal Processing* (1990): 841–844.

KAISSE, ELLEN. *Connected Speech: The Interaction of Syntax and Phonology.* Orlando, FL: Academic Press, 1985.

KLATT, DENNIS. "Review of the ARPA Speech Understanding Project." *Journal of the Acoustic Society of America* 62 (1977): 1345–1366.

———. A Digital Bank Filter for Spectral Matching. *Proceedings of the International Conference on Acoustics, Speech, and Signal Processing* (1976): 573–576.

KLAVER, MARTIN. "Making Voice Recognition Work for Process Control." *Official Proceedings of the Telephone Revolution & Military Speech Tech '88 and Talking Shop & Speech Recognition* (1988): 144–149.

KOHONEN, TEUVO. "The 'Neural' Phonetic Typewriter." *IEEE Computer* 21(3) (1988): 11–22.

KONIG, YOCHAI and NELSON MORGAN. "Supervised and Unsupervised Clustering of the Speaker Space for Connectionist Speech Recognition." *Proceedings of the International Conference on Acoustics, Speech, and Signal Processing* 1 (1993): 545–548.

KUBALA, FRANCIS and RICHARD SCHWARTZ. "A New Paradigm for Speaker-independent Training." *Proceedings of the International Conference on Acoustics, Speech, and Signal Processing* 2 (1991): 883–886.

KURZWEIL, RAYMOND. "The Application of Large Vocabulary Speech Recognition and Knowledge Engineering to the Creation of Written Documents." *Speech Tech '89* (1989): 39–44.

LADEFOGED, PETER. *Elements of Acoustic Phonetics.* Chicago, IL: The University of Chicago Press, 1962.

LAWRENCE, JEANNETTE. *Introduction to Neural Networks: Design, Theory, and Applications.* Nevada City, CA: California Scientific Software Press, 1993.

LEDERER, RICHARD. *More Anguished English.* New York: Dell, 1994.

LEE, CHIN-HUI, JEAN-LUC GAUVAIN, ROBERTO PIERACCINI, and LAWRENCE RABINER. "Subword-based Large-vocabulary Speech Recognition." *AT&T Technical Journal* 72(5) (1993): 25–35.

LEE, KAI-FU. *Automatic Speech Recognition—The Development of the SPHINX System.* Boston, MA: Kluwer Academic Publishers, 1989.

LEE, KAI-FU, HSIAO-WUEN HON, MEI-YUH HWANG, and SANJOY MAHAJAN. "Recent Progress and Future Outlook of the *SPHINX* Speech Recognition System." *Computer Speech and Language* 4 (1990a): 57–69.

LEE, KAI-FU, HSIAO-WUEN HON, and RAJ REDDY. "An Overview of the *SPHINX* Speech Recognition System." *IEEE Transactions on Acoustics, Speech, and Signal Processing* 38(1) (1990b): 35–45.

LEEDHAM, GRAHAM. "Pattern Recognition and its Application to Speech." *Speech Processing*, edited by Chris Rowden. New York, NY: McGraw-Hill Book Company, (1992): 256–286.

LENNIG, MATTHEW. "Using Speech Recognition in the Telephone Network to Automate Collect and Third-number Billed Calls." *Speech Tech '89* (1989): 124–125.

LEVIN, ESTHER. "Word Recognition Using Hidden Control Neural Architecture." *Speech Tech '90* (1990): 20–25.

LIANG, MARC and KRISHNA NARAYANAN. "The Application of Voice Recognition to Robotic Positioning of a Hospital Bed." *Speech Technology* 5(1) (1989): 30–33.

LIEBERMAN, PHILIP and SHEILA BLUMSTEIN. *Speech Physiology, Speech Perception and Acoustic Phonetics.* New York, NY: Cambridge University Press, 1988.

LINDEMAN, MARTHA. "How to Design 'caller friendly' applications." *Voice Processing Magazine* 5(10) (1993): 16–20.

LIPPMANN, RICHARD. "Review of Neural Networks for Speech Recognition." *Neural Computing* 1 (1989): 1–38. Reprinted in *Readings in Speech Recognition,* edited by Alex Waibel and Kai-Fu Lee (1990).

LJOLJE, ANDREJ and STEPHEN LEVINSON. "Development of an Acoustic-phonetic Hidden Markov Model for Continuous Speech Recognition." *IEEE Transactions on Signal Processing* 39(1) (1991): 29–39.

LOMBARD, E. "Le signe de l'elevation de la voix." *Ann. Maladies Oreille, larynx, Nez, Pharynx* 37 (1911): 101–119.

LUHMANN, RICK. "Telecomputing Commuting." *Computer Telephony* (July/August 1994): 74–79.

MALTESE, G. and F. MANCINI. "An Automatic Technique to Include Grammatical and Morphological Information in a Trigram-based Statistical Language Model." *Proceedings of the International Conference on Acoustics, Speech, and Signal Processing* 1 (1992): 157–160.

MARIANI, J. "Recent Advances in Speech Recognition." *Proceedings of the International Conference on Acoustics, Speech, and Signal Processing* (1989): 429–440.

———. "Automated Voice Dictation in French." *Speech Communication* 13 (1993): 171–185.

MARION, LARRY. "Shearson Launches Voice-activated Trading System." *Wall Street Letter* 21(31) (1989): 1, 9.

MARKOWITZ, JUDITH. "An Expert System with Speech Recognition." *AVIOS '87 Proceedings* (1987): 319–324.

———. "Next Steps: Navistar's *Compensation Reserve Expert System Advisor.*" *Proceedings of COMPSAC '89* (1989): 781–782.

———. "Sound Advice." *International Voice Systems Review* 1(3) (1990): 12, 26.

———. "A Look at Speaker Independent Recognition." *Intelligent Systems Report* 10(4) (1993a): 10–11.

———. "Listening with Intelligence." *AI Expert* 8(6) (1993b): 38–45.

———. "Money Listens: Speech Recognition in the Financial Industry." *PC AI* 7(6) (1993c): 28–35.

———. "Standards Effort Underway for Speech Recognition." *Intelligent Systems Report* 10(12) (1993d): 10–11.

———. "Listening with Intelligence, Part II." *AI Expert* 8(10) (1993e): 28–35.

———. "Automatic Speech Recognition: Fundamentals, Facts and Fallacies." *PC AI* 8(1) (1994a): 16–22.

———. "Neural Networks for Speech." *PC AI* 8(3) (1994b): 31–34.

———. "Number Please: Speech Recognition Over the Telephone." *PC AI* 8(2) (1994c): 23–26.

———. "Product Review: Verbex *Listen for Windows 1.1.*" *PC AI* 8(4) (1994d): 14–15, 50.

———. "Speech Recognition on the Telephone Network." *Intelligent Systems Report* 11(1) (1994e): 13–14.

————. "Speech Recognition System for Lawyers Debuts." *Intelligent Systems Report* 11(6) (1994f): 11.

MARKOWITZ, JUDITH, THOMAS AHLSWEDE, and MARTHA EVENS. "Semantically Significant Patterns in Dictionary Definitions." *Proceedings of the 24th Annual Meeting of the Association for Computational Linguistics* (1986): 112–119.

MARKOWITZ, JUDITH, J. TERRY NUTTER, and MARTHA EVENS. "Beyond IS-A and PART-WHOLE: More Semantic Network Links." *Semantic Networks in Artificial Intelligence* edited by Fritz Lehmann (1992): 377–390.

MARSHALL, SHARON. "Hands Off Approach that Speaks for Itself." *The Guardian* 18 April 1991.

MARTIN, JAMES. *Telecommunications and the Computer.* Englewood Cliffs, NJ: Prentice Hall, 1990.

MARX, MATT and CHRIS SCHMANDT. "Reliable Spelling Despite Poor Spoken Letter Recognition." *AVIOS '94 Proceedings* (1994): 169–178.

MATEER, MARIE and JON ROBIN ROHLICEK. "Statistical Language Modeling Combining N-gram and Context-free Grammars." *Proceedings of the International Conference on Acoustics, Speech, and Signal Processing* 2 (1993): 37–40.

MCDERMOTT, ERIK and SHIGERU KATAGIRI. "Prototype-based MCE/GPD Training for Word Spotting and Connected Word Recognition." *Proceedings of the International Conference on Acoustics, Speech, and Signal Processing* 2 (1993): 291–294.

MEISEL, WILLIAM, M. ANIKST, S. PIRZADEH, J. SCHUMACHER, M. SOARES, and D. TRAWICK. "The SSI Large-vocabulary Speaker-independent Continuous Speech Recognition System." *Proceedings of the International Conference on Acoustics, Speech, and Signal Processing* 1 (1991): 337–340.

MERCIER, G., D. BIGORGNE, L. MICLET, L. LE GUENNEC, and M. QUERRE. "Recognition of Speaker-dependent Continuous Speech with *KEAL.*" *Proceedings of the IEEE* 136(2) (1989): 145–154.

MICHAELS, JENNA. "Talk First, Trade Later." *Wall Street Computer Review* 1(9) (1991): 54–55.

MICROSOFT CORPORATION. *Speech API Developer's Guide: Microsoft Speech API, Version 1.0-Beta, Windows 95.* Redmond, WA: Microsoft Corporation, 1995.

MILLER, L. and STEPHEN LEVINSON. "Syntactic Analysis for Large Vocabulary Speech Recognition Using a Context-free Covering Grammar." *Proceedings of the International Conference on Acoustics, Speech, and Signal Processing* 1 (1988): 270–274.

MONTGOMERY, CHRISTINE, BONNIE GLOVER STALLS, ROBERT STUMBERGER, NAICONG LI, S. WALTER, ROBERT BELVIN, and ALFREDO ARNAIZ. "Machine-aided Voice Translation." *IEEE Information Management Collection Processing & Distribution, Dual-Use Technologies & Applications Conference* (1993): 96–101.

MOON, SEOKYONG and JENQ-NENG HWANG. "Coordinated Training of Noise Removing Networks." *Proceedings of the International Conference on Acoustics, Speech, and Signal Processing* 1 (1993): 573–576.

MOORE, ROGER K. "Systems for Isolated and Connected Word Recognition." *New Systems and Architectures for Automatic Speech Recognition and Synthesis,* edited by Renato De Mori and Ching Suen. Berlin: Springer-Verlag (1984): 73–144.

MOORE, ROGER. "Recognition—The Stochastic Modelling Approach." *Speech Processing,* edited by Chris Rowden. New York, NY: McGraw-Hill Book Company (1992): 223–255.

MORGAN, NELSON and HERVÉ BOURLARD. "Continuous Speech Recognition." *IEEE Signal Processing Magazine* 12(3) (1995): 25–42.

MURVEIT, HY and ROBERT MOORE. "Integrating Natural Language Constraints into HMM-based Speech Recognition." *Proceedings of the International Conference on Acoustics, Speech, and Signal Processing* 2 (1990): 573–576.

MURVEIT, HY, JOHN BUTZBERGER, VASSILIOS DIGALAKIS, and MITCH WEINTRAUB. "Progressive-search Algorithms for Large-vocabulary Speech Recognition." *ARPA Human Language Technology Workshop*, Section 3 (1993).

MYERS, C.S. and LAWRENCE RABINER. A Level Building Dynamic Time Warping Algorithm for Connected Word Recognition. *IEEE Transactions on Acoustics, Speech, and Signal Processing* ASSP-29(3) (1981): 284–297.

NAKAMURA, SATOSHI and TOSHIO AKABENE. "A Neural Speaker Model for Speaker Clustering." *Proceedings of the International Conference on Acoustics, Speech, and Signal Processing* 2 (1991): 853–856.

NAKAMURA, SOTORU, HIDEFUMI SAWAI, and MASAHIDE SUGIYAMA. "Speaker-independent Phoneme Recognition Using Large-scale Neural Networks." *Proceedings of the International Conference on Acoustics, Speech, and Signal Processing* 1 (1992): 409–412.

NANDKUMAR, S. and JOHN H.L. HANSEN. "Dual-channel Speech Enhancement with Auditory Spectrum Based Constraints." *Proceedings of the International Conference on Acoustics, Speech, and Signal Processing* 1 (1992): 297–300.

NEY, HERMANN. "The Use of a One-stage Dynamic Programming Algorithm for Connected Word Recognition." *IEEE Transactions on Acoustics, Speech, and Signal Processing* ASSP-32(2) (1984): 263–271.

———. "Dynamic Programming Parsing for Context-free Grammars in Continuous Speech Recognition." *IEEE Transactions on Signal Processing* 39(2) (1991): 336–340.

NEY, HERMANN, R. HAEB-UMBACH, B-H TRAN, and MARTIN OERDER. "Improvements in Beam Search for 10000-word Continuous Speech Recognition." *Proceedings of the International Conference on Acoustics, Speech, and Signal Processing* 1 (1992): 9–12.

NEY, HERMANN and ANDREAS NOLL. "Acoustic-phonetic Modeling in the *SPICOS* System." *IEEE Transactions on Speech and Audio Processing* 2(2) (1994): 312–319.

NORTZ, DOUG, CANDACE KAMM, ROB BOSSEMEYER, HARRY CHANG, MIKE BOYDEN, JEFF SCRUGGS, GEORGE VELIUS, and FRANK WU. "Bellcore/BCC Voice Input Technologies Technical Analysis Specification." *AVIOS '92 Proceedings* (1992): 331–337.

OHKURA, KAZUMI, DAVID RAINTON, and MASAHIDE SUGIYAMA. "Noise-robust HMMs Based on Minimum Error Classification." *Proceedings of the International Conference on Acoustics, Speech, and Signal Processing* 2 (1993): 75–78.

OHKURA, KAZUMI and MASAHIDE SUGIYAMA. "Speech Recognition in a Noisy Environment Using a Noise Reduction Neural Network and a Codebook Mapping Technique." *Proceedings of the International Conference on Acoustics, Speech, and Signal Processing* (1991): 929–932.

OLSON, ERIC. "Voice Recognition for 100% Parts Audit." *Speech Tech '87* (1987): 95–96.

OSHIKA, BEATRICE, VICTOR ZUE, ROLLIN WEEKS, HELENE NEU, and JOSEPH AURBACH. "The Role of Phonological Rules in Speech Understanding Research." *IEEE Transactions on Acoustics, Speech, and Signal Processing* ASSP-23(1) (1975): 104–112.

OSTERHOLTZ, LOUISE, CHARLES AUGUSTINE, ARTHUR MCNAIR, IVICA ROGINA, HIROAKI SAITO, TILO SLOBODA, JOE TEBELSKIS, and ALEX WAIBEL. "Testing Generality in *JANUS:* A Multilingual Speech Translation System." *Proceedings of the International Conference on Acoustics, Speech, and Signal Processing* 1 (1992): 209–212.

PALLETT, DAVID. "Performance Assessment of Automatic Speech Recognizers." *Journal of Research of the National Bureau of Standards* 90(5) (1985): 371–387.

———. "Test Procedures for the March 1987 DARPA Benchmark Tests." *Proceedings of the DARPA Speech Recognition Workshop* (1987).

———. "Benchmark Tests for DARPA *Resource Management Database* Performance Evaluations." *Proceedings of the International Conference on Acoustics, Speech, and Signal Processing* (1989): 536–539.

PALLETT, DAVID, JONATHAN FISCUS, WILLIAM FISHER, and JOHN GAROFOLO. "Benchmark Tests for the DARPA Spoken Language Program." *ARPA Human Language Technology Workshop:* Section 1 (1993).

PAUL, DOUGLAS. "Speech Recognition Using Hidden Markov Models." *The Lincoln Laboratory Journal* 3(1) (1990): 41–61.

———. "The Lincoln Tied-mixture HMM Continuous Speech Recognizer." *Proceedings of the International Conference on Acoustics, Speech, and Signal Processing* (1991): 329–332.

———. "An Efficient A* Stack Decoder Algorithm for Continuous Speech Recognition With a Stochastic Language Model." *Proceedings of the International Conference on Acoustics, Speech, and Signal Processing* 1 (1992): 25–32.

PETEK, BOJAN and JOE TEBELSKIS. "Context-dependent Hidden Control Neural Network Architecture for Continuous Speech Recognition." *Proceedings of the International Conference on Acoustics, Speech, and Signal Processing* 1 (1992): 397–400.

PFARRER, LEE. "Using Voice Recognition for Data Collection in a Factory Environment." *Speech Tech '89* (1989): 153–155.

PICKETT, J. "Effects of Vocal Force on the Intelligibility of Speech Sounds." *Journal of the Acoustics Society of America* 28(5) (1956): 902–905.

PIERACCINI, ROBERTO, CHIN-HUI LEE, EGIDIO GIACHIN, and LAWRENCE RABINER. "Complexity Reduction in a Large Vocabulary Speech Recognizer." *Proceedings of the International Conference on Acoustics, Speech, and Signal Processing* (1991): 729–732.

PIERACCINI, ROBERTO and ESTHER LEVIN. "Stochastic Representation of Semantic Structure for Speech Understanding." *Speech Communication* 11 (1992): 283–288.

PISONI, DAVID, HOWARD NUSBAUM, and SUBRATA DAS. "Automatic Measurement of Speech Recognition Performance: A Comparison of Six Speaker-dependent Recognition Devices." Final Report IBM Corporation Contracts No. 435114 and No. 562010 (1986).

PLACEWAY, PAUL, RICHARD SCHWARTZ, PASCALE FUNG, and LONG NGUYEN. "The Estimation of Powerful Language Models from Small and Large Corpora." *Proceedings of the International Conference on Acoustics, Speech, and Signal Processing* 2 (1993): 33–36.

POTTER, RALPH, GEORGE KOPP, and HARRIET GREEN. *Visible Speech.* New York: D. Van Nostrand, 1947.

PRICE, PATTI, WILLIAM FISHER, JARED BERNSTEIN, and DAVID PALLETT. "The DARPA 1000-word *Resource Management Database* for Continuous Speech Recognition." *Proceedings of the International Conference on Acoustics, Speech, and Signal Processing* (1988): 651–655.

RABINER, LAWRENCE and BIING-HWANG JUANG. *Fundamentals of Speech Recognition.* Englewood Cliffs, NJ: Prentice Hall, 1993.

———. "An Introduction to Hidden Markov Models." *IEEE Acoustics Speech, and Signal Processing Magazine* 3(1) (1986): 4–16.

RIGOLL, GERHARD. "Information Theory-based Supervised Learning Methods for Self-organizing Maps in Combination with Hidden Markov Modeling." *Proceedings of the International Conference on Acoustics, Speech, and Signal Processing* (1991): 65–68.

ROOD, LONNIE and JOHN LEWIS. "Integrated Voice Data System for Central Steam Trap Maintenance." *Speech Tech '91* (1991): 91–101.

ROSE, GEORGE. "Speech Recognition/IVR Combo a Hit with Agency Members." *Voice Processing Magazine* (October 1991): 49.

ROSE, RICHARD and DOUGLAS PAUL. "A Hidden Markov Model Based Keyword Recognition System." *Proceedings of the International Conference on Acoustics, Speech, and Signal Processing* 2 (1990): 129–132.

ROSENBLUM, MARILYN. "The Value of Real Time Feedback in Improving the Articulation of the Speech Impaired." *Speech Tech '91* (1991): 312–316.

ROSTOLLAND, D. and C. PARANT. "Distorsion [sic] and Intelligibility of Shouted Voice." *Symposium: Speech Intelligibility* (1973): 293–304.

ROTHAPEL, GERRY. "The Write Stuff." *Newcastle Evening Chronicle,* 12 March 1990.

ROWDEN, CHRIS. "Analysis." *Speech Processing,* edited by Chris Rowden. New York, NY: McGraw-Hill Book Company, (1992): 35–96.

SAFFARI, BOBBY. "Putting DSPs to Work." *Byte* 9(13) (1989): 259–270.

SAGAYAMA, SHIGEKI, JUN-ICHI TAKAMI, AKITO NAGAI, HARALD SINGER, KOUICHI YAMAGUCHI, KAZUMI OHKURA, KENJI KITA, and AKIRA KUREMATSU. "*ATREUS:* A Speech Recognition Front-end for a Speech Translation System." *EuroSpeech '93* (1993): 1287–1294.

SAKOE, HIROAKI. "Two Level DP Matching—A Dynamic Programming Based Pattern Matching Algorithm for Connected Word Recognition." *IEEE Transactions on Acoustics, Speech, and Signal Processing* ASSP-27(6) (1979): 588–595.

SALAZAR, GEORGE and MARC SOMMERS. "Space Shuttle Voice Recognition Flight Experiment." *Speech Tech '91* (1991): 12–17.

SCHAFER, RONALD and LAWRENCE RABINER. "Digital Representations of Speech Signals." *Proceedings of the IEEE* 63(4) (1975): 662–667.

SCHWAB, EILEEN, C.A. BALL, and BARRY LIVELY. "Human Factors Contributions to the Development of a Speech Recognition Cellular Telephone." *Applied Speech Technology,* edited by A. Syrdal, R. Bennett, and S. Greenspan. Boca Raton, FL: CRC Press, 1995.

SCHWARTZ, RICHARD, STEVE AUSTIN, FRANCIS KUBALA, JOHN MAKHOUL, LONG NGUYEN, PAUL PLACEWAY, and GEORGE ZAVALIAGKOS. "New Uses for the *N-best* Sentence Hypotheses Within the *BYBLOS* Speech Recognition System." *Proceedings of the International Conference on Acoustics, Speech, and Signal Processing* 1 (1992): 1–4.

SCHWARTZ, RICHARD, YEN-LU CHOW, O. KIMBALL, S. ROUCOS, MICHAEL KRASNER, and JOHN MAKHOUL. "Context-dependent Modeling for Acoustic-phonetic Recognition of Continuous Speech." *IEEE International Conference on Acoustics, Speech, and Signal Processing* (1985): 1205–1208.

SCHWARTZ, RICHARD, YEN-LU CHOW, and FRANCIS KUBALA. "Rapid Speaker Adaptation Using a Probabilistic Spectral Mapping." *Proceedings of the International Conference on Acoustics, Speech, and Signal Processing* 1 (1987): 633–636.

SCOTT, NEIL. "Speech Recognition for Individuals with Disabilities." *Advanced Speech Applications and Technologies Conference '94:* Section 1 (1994).

SEITZ, PHILIP, VISHWA GUPTA, MATTHEW LENNIG, PATRICK KENNY, LI DENG, DOUGLAS O'SHAUGHNESSY, and PAUL MERMELSTEIN. "A Dictionary for a Very Large Vocabulary Word Recognition System." *Computer Speech and Language* (1990): 193–202.

SENEFF, STEPHANIE. "*TINA:* A Natural Language System for Spoken Language Applications." *Computational Linguistics* 18(1) (1992): 61–86.

SHARP, DOUGLAS and MATTHEW LENNIG. "Flexible Vocabulary Recognition—Unleashing the Power of the Phoneme." *Proceedings of AVIOS '94* (1994): 108–112.

SMITH, L., BRIAN SCOTT, L. LIN, and J. NEWELL. "Template Adaptation in a Hypersphere

Word Classifier." *Proceedings of the International Conference on Acoustics, Speech, and Signal Processing* 1 (1990): 565–568.

SORENSEN, HELGE. "A Cepstral Noise Reduction Multi-layer Neural Network." *Proceedings of the International Conference on Acoustics, Speech, and Signal Processing* (1991): 933–936.

SPEECH RECOGNITION APPLICATION PROGRAM INTERFACE COMMITTEE (SRAPI). *Speech Recognition Application Program Interface Specification: A Standardized Method for Applications to Integrate with Speech Recognition Systems. Version 0.5 for Windows 3.1 and Windows 95.* Orem, UT: SRAPI Committee, 1995.

STANTON, BILL, LEAH JAMIESON, and GEORGE ALLEN. "Robust Recognition of Loud and Lombard Speech in the Fighter Cockpit Environment." *Proceedings of the International Conference on Acoustics, Speech, and Signal Processing* (1989): 675–678.

STEENEKEN, HERMAN J.M. "Quality Evaluation of Speech Processing Systems." *Digital Speech Processing: Speech Coding, Synthesis and Recognition,* edited by A. Nejat Ince. Dordrecht, The Netherlands: Kluwer Academic Publishers, Chapter 6, 1993.

STEENEKEN, HERMAN J.M., M. TOMLINSON, and J.L. GAUVAIN. "Assessment of Two Commercial Recognizers with the *SAM* Workstation and *EUROM 0.*" *Proceedings of the ESCA Workshop.* Noordwijkerhout, The Netherlands (1989).

SUNDHEIM, BETH. "Plans for a Task-oriented Evaluation of Natural Language Understanding Systems." *Proceedings of the Speech and Natural Language Workshop* (February 1989): 301–305.

————. "Survey of the Message Understanding Conferences." *ARPA Human Language Technology Workshop* (March 21–24, 1993). Plainsboro, NJ. Section 2, 1993.

TEBELSKIS, JOE, ALEX WAIBEL, BOJAN PETEK, and OTTO SCHMIDBAUER. "Continuous Speech Recognition by Linked Predictive Neural Networks." *Advances in Neural Information Processing, Vol 3,* edited by Richard Lippmann, John Moody, and David Touretzky. San Mateo, CA: Morgan Kaufmann Publishers Inc., (1991): 199–205.

THOMAS, TREVOR, JEREMY PECKHAM, and E. FRANGOULIS. "A Determination of the Sensitivity of Speech Recognisers to Speaker Variability." *Proceedings of the International Conference on Acoustics, Speech, and Signal Processing* (1989): 544–547.

UDELL, JON. "Computer Telephony." *Byte* 19(7) (1994): 80–96.

VARGA, ANDREW and HERMAN J.M. STEENEKEN. "Assessment for Automatic Speech Recognition: II. *NOISEX-92:* A Database and an Experiment to Study the Effects of Additive Noise on Speech Recognition Systems." *Speech Communication* 12 (1993): 247–251.

WAIBEL, ALEX and JOHN HAMPSHIRE II. "Building Blocks for Speech." *Byte* 14(8) (1989): 235–242.

————. "Neural Network Applications to Speech." *Neural Networks: Concepts, Applications, and Implementations, Vol I,* edited by Paolo Antognetti and Veljko Milutinović. Englewood Cliff, NJ: Prentice Hall, (1991): 54–77.

WAIBEL, ALEX and KAI-FU LEE (EDS). *Readings in Speech Recognition.* San Mateo, CA: Morgan Kaufmann Publishers, 1990.

WARD, WAYNE. "Understanding Spontaneous Speech: The *PHOENIX* System." *Proceedings of the International Conference on Acoustics, Speech, and Signal Processing* (1991): 365–367.

WARD, WAYNE and SHERYL YOUNG. "Flexible Use of Semantic Constraints in Speech Recognition." *Proceedings of the International Conference on Acoustics, Speech, and Signal Processing* 2 (1993): 49–50.

WASSERMAN, PHILIP. *Neural Computing: Theory and Practice.* New York, NY: Van Nostrand Reinhold, 1989.

WEINTRAUB, MITCHEL. "Keyword-spotting Using SRI'S *DECIPHER* Large-vocabulary Speech-recognition System." *Proceedings of the International Conference on Acoustics, Speech, and Signal Processing* 2 (1993): 463–466.

WILPON, JAY and LAWRENCE RABINER. "A Modified K-means Clustering Algorithm for Use in Isolated Work [sic] Recognition." *IEEE Transactions on Acoustics, Speech, and Signal Processing* ASSP 33(3) (1985): 587–594.

WILPON, JAY, LAWRENCE RABINER, CHIN-HUI LEE, and E. GOLDMAN. "Automatic Recognition of Keywords in Unconstrained Speech Using Hidden Markov Models." *IEEE Transactions on Acoustics, Speech, and Signal Processing* 38(11) (1990): 1870–1878.

WINOGRAD, TERRY. *Language as a Cognitive Process, Volume I Syntax.* Reading, MA: Addison-Wesley Publishing Company, 1983.

WITTEN, I.H. *Principles of Computer Speech.* London: Academic Press, Inc., 1982.

WOODS, WILLIAM. "Language Processing for Speech Understanding." *Computer Speech Processing*, edited by Frank Fallside and William Woods. Englewood Cliffs, NJ: Prentice Hall (1983): 305–333. Reprinted in *Readings in Speech Recognition*, edited by Alex Waibel and Kai-Fu Lee (1990).

WOSZCZYNA, M., N. COCCARO, A. EISELE, A. LAVIE, ARTHUR MCNAIR, T. POLZIN, IVICA ROGINA. C.P. ROSE, TILO SLOBODA, M. TOMITA, J. TSUTSUMI, N. AOKI-WAIBEL, ALEX WAIBEL, and WAYNE WARD. "Recent Advances in *JANUS:* A Speech Translation System." *ARPA Human Language Technology Workshop*, Section 6 (1993).

YOUNG, SHERYL, ALEXANDER HAUPTMANN, WAYNE WARD, EDWARD SMITH, and PHILIP WERNER. "High Level Knowledge Sources in Usable Speech Recognition Systems." *Communications of the ACM* 32(2), 1989. Reprinted in *Readings in Speech Recognition*, edited by Alex Waibel and Kai-Fu Lee (1990).

YRASLORZA, TERESA. "Special Supplement: Voice Recognition." *Wall Street Letter* (June 1993): 1, 8–9.

ZAKAI, AVI. "Single-chip Speech Recognition Solutions for Multimedia Applications." *AVIOS '94 Proceedings* (1994): 215–220.

ZEPPENFELD, TORSTEN, RICK HOUGHTON, and ALEX WAIBEL. "Improving the *MS-TDNN* for Word Spotting." *Proceedings of the International Conference on Acoustics, Speech, and Signal Processing* 2 (1993): 475–478.

ZUE, VICTOR. "The use of Speech Knowledge in Automatic Speech Recognition." *Proceedings of the IEEE* 73(11) (1985): 1602–1615. Reprinted in *Readings in Speech Recognition*, edited by Alex Waibel and Kai-Fu Lee. (1990).

ZUE, VICTOR, JAMES GLASS, DAVID GOODINE, LYNETTE HIRSCHMAN, HONG LEUNG, MICHAEL PHILLIPS, JOSEPH POLIFRONI, and STEPHANIE SENEFF. "From Speech Recognition to Spoken Language Understanding: The Development of the MIT *SUMMIT* and *VOYAGER* Systems." *Advances in Neural Information Processing Systems 3*, edited by Richard Lippmann, John Moody, and David Touretzky. San Mateo, CA: Morgan Kaufmann Publishers (1991): 255–261.

ZUE, VICTOR, STEPHANIE SENEFF, and JAMES GLASS. "Speech Database Development at MIT: *TIMIT* and Beyond." *Speech Communication* 9(4) (1990): 351–356.

INDEX

A

accuracy
    in application testing, 226
    in commercial applications, 143
    as component of recognition, 49
    in data entry applications, 191
    in dictation applications, 204
    in discrete-word and connected-word
        speech, 140–41
    and erratic noise, 161
    and the Lombard effect, 156–57
    in multi-speaker models, 106, 119
    and noise levels, 50
    in product assessment, 221
    in small vocabulary systems, 65
    and SNR (signal-to-noise ratio), 149,
        152
    in speaker adaptation, 123
    and speaker models, 117–18, 119
    and structuring, 80
acoustic-phonetic analysis
    and articulation analysis, 31
    in commercial systems, 51
    in continuous speech systems,
        134–35

overview of, 37–38
    and phonemes, 58–59
acoustics
    definition of, 23
    and speech sounds, 26–32
active vocabulary
    definition of, 72
    and dictation applications, 202
    and perplexity reduction, 79
additive noise. *See also* ambient noise
    definition of, 149
    reduction filtering algorithms, 157
    in telephone applications, 153–54
Advanced Research Projects Agency. *See*
    ARPA
AI. *See* artificial intelligence
air-traffic control systems, 178
alphabet
    phonemic, 23–24
    as vocabulary issue, 73–74
ambient noise. *See also* additive noise
    definition of, 149
    and robustness, 163
Amerigon
    AudioNav, 196, 198
    spelling algorithm of, 73